G000081311

MAY DAY
MAYHEM

CHRISTOPHER JOHN REASON

Paperback edition first published in the United Kingdom in
2020 by aSys Publishing

eBook edition first published in the United Kingdom in
2020 by aSys Publishing

A CIP catalogue record for this book is available from
the British Library.

ISBN: 978-1-913438-32-6

aSys Publishing 2020

http://www.asys-publishing.co.uk

MAY DAY
MAYHEM

This book is dedicated partially to all those in peril upon the sea, and partially to the wonderfully understanding people of Padstow on the rugged and often dangerous northern coast of Cornwall.

"I will go down with this ship,
and I won't put my hands up and surrender.
There will be no white flag above my door,
I'm in love, and always will be!" (Dido)

To the very best of my recollection, the contents of this book are entirely, accurate, honest and true.

1

PROLOGUE

"Ahoy there dear friends," I shouted above the din in the back bar of the Shakespeare Tavern, "who's up for yet another long weekend of madness and misadventure then?"

It was a typically normal Sunday night in the back bar of the Shaky. Shabby and Lorna were being run ragged behind the bar, whilst countless seafaring and live-aboard buddies of ours kept them on their toes by attempting to drink the entire cellar dry of ale. To say there was standing room only would've been an understatement, and having fought one's way across the crowded flagstone floor to reach the bar, only to find that the draft Bass had expired, was inevitably just a tad frustrating. Nigel, the landlord, and all-round top host, was immediately on the case however, and whilst Anna, his delectable young wife, kept the few customers in the front bar happy, the supply of Bass was quickly and efficiently restored, with hardly a soul even noticing. It was a rather damp and chilly 4th of April evening in the early spring of 1999, so what better place to while away the hours singing along to a half-decent repertoire of traditional old sea shanties, whilst crammed around a roaring open log fire, with plenty of atmosphere, real ale, great company, and an endless cacophony of cheer and laughter emanating from the hearts and souls of our close circle of nautical amigos.

"What ya got in mind exactly, ya young scallywag?" chirped up Jamer from the centre of the crowded bench shoved up against the back wall. "Thinking of taking the Marovonne off out on yet another one of your infamous pirate misadventures again, eh?"

Old Jamer, sadly no longer with us, bless him, was the main instigator of the Sunday night singalongs, mainly on account of the fact that firstly, he knew all the words to all the songs, and secondly, he'd previously been a member of Winterbourne Amateur Operatic Society, and consequently had an excellent voice. To his credit, he was also the very first British tank commander to carry straight on through Berlin, in April 1945, in order to successfully liberate the sixty thousand prisoners holed up in Bergen-Belsen concentration camp on his way back towards Holland. *'Tankman Jamer'* we all used to know him as, and a nicer gentleman you could never wish to meet. Nothing ever phased old Jamer, that being just one of the reasons why he made an excellent crew mate aboard Raymondo's sturdy, seaworthy, 75ft ex-survey vessel, the good ship Roehampton. Before I had the chance to answer, Jamer started the whole bar off again on yet another loud and bawdy sing-song. I looked across at Ray, and he gave me a quick, knowing wink.

I turned to Ron, who happened to be sat at the same table as Helen and myself, and asked him if he was up for it, knowing full well that he'd already understood exactly where I was coming from. Ronnie kept his little ship, the Courageous 2, in Bristol City Docks, just like the rest of us. Although the Courageous 2 was a beautifully converted little MFV, she was only 50ft long, just a little too small to make for a permanent live-aboard by Ron's standards, so he didn't. But he loved that little ship to pieces, and spent many a week just steadily plodding around the shores of Wales and England's south-west coastline at her maximum speed of just seven knots.

"Chris, me boy, I've already got her booked in," replied Ronnie cheerfully. "Johnnie and me, we'll never ever miss one single May Day in Padstow, not for love nor money, *not never!* And specially seeing as how Johnnie's managed to get himself a new fancy-girl down there again, and what with him doin' most of me navigation stuff 'n' all that, yeah, we wouldn't be missin' it for the world. Fact is, subject to the weather of course, we plans to be leavin' Saturday the 24th, then shortly after Padstow I 'spect we'll hop on round to Falmouth for a coupla weeks, if the weather's good to us that is."

Cool, so Ron and Johnnie were definitely sailing the Courageous 2 down to Padstow for May Day. I wondered who else might be up for it too. I couldn't get across the room to ask Ray, there were far too many people in the way, but good old Rick was stood up at the bar ordering more drinks from Shabbs for himself and Kim, and as Helen and I had both finished our own drinks, I fought my way through the throng and joined him, glasses held at the ready for whoever might happen to find the time to refill them for me.

"What's reckon then Skipper?" I asked Rick, just as Shabby handed him a full glass of ale and a large G&T. "Fancy running the Joseph down to Padstow for yet another May Day celebration?"

The Joseph was effectively a sister ship to the Marovonne, a 65ft ex-navy MFV, heavily larch planked over massive oak frames, and powered by a single 152hp eight cylinder Gardner engine that gave her a comfortable cruising speed of eight knots. Unlike the Marovonne that Helen and I lived aboard, the Joseph had never been fully converted, but she was still more than roomy and comfortable enough for Rick to live aboard, which indeed he had done for just a little longer than Helen and myself had. We'd sailed together on several previous occasions, taking both ships, and more, often in convoy, into various little harbours, the likes of Ilfracombe, Appledore, and of course, the beautiful little Cornish town of Padstow.

"I'm already on the case matey-boy," replied Rick with a grin. "Lloyd said he's up for it, Kim's coming along too, and the three of us can set off from Bristol anytime we like. However, we thought it'd make a nice change to take a bit of a party on down with us this time, have ourselves a laugh along the way, and an even bigger one when we get there. So I'm just waiting on some feedback from a few friends, and then I'll start putting a passage plan together. When are you thinking of sailing down exactly?"

"I'm leaving Bristol on the morning of Tuesday the 27th, come hell or high water!" I stated boldly, whilst looking somewhat nervously back over at Helen. "Nik and Kev, my usual crew, they're already sorted, so that's Roger The Cabin Boy and Seaman Staines that'll both be coming along. And I think my old buddy Alf, the chap that taught me most of what I know about navigation, if he's feeling up to it following a fairly recent hip replacement, he said he'd like to come along too."

"I see," said Rick knowingly, "so the Marovonne's gonna be sailing down there as a proper old pirate ship once again then?"

"Yep!" I replied positively. "The three most infamous '*Harbour Bastards*' in the whole of Bristol. Watch out Padstow, here we come, *again!* Only problem I have is with Helen; she can't get the time off work. And not only that, but she knows I won't be sailing straight back to Bristol again afterwards, so there's yet another issue with her work. But hey, she's taken the Friday off, so she's going to drive down and meet up with us, then drive back on the Monday bank holiday morning. As you know, the actual *Obby Oss* celebrations always take place on the 1st of May, which happens to fall on a Saturday this year, so the Sunday is officially hangover day, and the May Day bank holiday Monday is when the town is just full of '*emmets*', the perfect day for Helen to make her escape, whilst the three of us cause a little more mayhem in and around the town."

"Where's Helen gonna stay whilst the Marovonne's out of town then Chris?" Rick asked inquisitively.

"Good point buddy," I replied, whilst handing Lorna a ten pound note for the drinks she'd just poured for Helen and myself. "However, seeing as her Mum's will went through probate towards the end of last year, she's managed to put a fairly decent sized deposit down on a nice little 3-bed terraced house in St George, and since she took possession of it back in January we've been doing it up bit by bit. The plan is to let it out at some point, but right now it's reasonably well furnished, so it's habitable, and that's where she'll be staying until I get back. I might even go stay there myself if I decide to leave the Marovonne down in Padstow for the whole summer. After all, we do have a once-in-a-lifetime total solar eclipse coming up in August. But for now I'll just play it by ear, see how the land lies after the first inevitably messy long weekend, so to speak."

Lorna handed me my change, and I took our drinks back across to the table that Helen was sat at, spilling just a little of mine whilst jostling for my seat. Ron asked me if Rick was thinking of sailing the Joseph down to Padstow, and I said yes, most definitely, although he couldn't put a day to it just yet. Brian was sat at the table next to ours, and overheard our conversation, despite the noise in the background.

"Best ee not leaves it too late me old mucker," Brian scowled, "you'm knows perzactly 'ow busy it d' get down by there that 'ticular weekend, innit. Speshly when all them snotty yotties 'eads on over from that there Welsh place them calls Swansea!"

"Indeed I do my dear friend," I replied understandingly. "That's precisely why we're leaving on the Tuesday beforehand, so we can moor up in a decent location before all the chaos starts. Yes, I know exactly how crazy it gets, especially on the Friday before, when there's over a hundred yachts all jostling for position in one very small lock-in tidal harbour. Add to that the Bristol pirate contingent, plus the usual Royal Navy's courtesy visit, yeah, it sure as hell gets pretty manic!"

As the evening wore on the singing grew increasingly louder, the sea shanties grew steadily bawdier, and the barrels of dafty Bass grew ever lighter. Like I said, nothing but a typical Sunday evening in the Shaky. Ray had managed to prise himself out of the crush at the back and was fighting his way gradually towards the bar for yet another round. Before reaching it, he sidled up to Helen and me, leant an arm on Ronnie's shoulder, and asked me if I was referring to the forthcoming May Day weekend.

"Yep, damned right Raymondo," I replied loudly above the din. "Me, Nik, Kev, maybe Alf, we're heading on down to Padstow on the 27th. Gonna try and get a mooring in a good spot against a quay wall somewhere for a change, instead of having to clamber across half a dozen other ships just to reach the quayside. You fancy bringing the Roehampton down then?"

"Oh, we'll be there alright my son, don't you worry about that," Ray replied enthusiastically. "Had to check with Jean first of course, but luckily she's well up for it, so yeah, we're taking the old girl out on a bit of a jaunt."

"That's no way to refer to your beautiful wife, my good sir!" I admonished him sternly.

"Not Jean, you daft sod, the bloody Roehampton!" he quipped back at me, whilst giving me an extra-soft slap around the back of the head. "Anyway, what about your kids Chris? I see you out and about with them so very often, all playing happily together around the harbour, all of them staying over aboard the Marovonne some weekends. Will that not be your weekend to have them then?"

"Nope!" I replied with a smug grin. "Purely by chance, I'm totally kid-free that particular weekend. Tori and Alex, my two younger ones, it's their mum's turn to have them. I've got them with me the weekend before, which is why I'm not sailing until the Tuesday, and we've not yet decided on the weekend after, that depends on whether I actually make it back to Bristol or not. As for Michelle, she has to work, although I shall ask her if she fancies taking the Friday off and coming down by car with Helen."

"I see," said Ray with a twinkle in his eye. "In that case, what could possibly go wrong, eh? Anyway, I'm taking my usual gang along with me; Jamer, Dave, Arthur and Sheila. Jean's really excited about it, but we're not stoppin' in Padstow for too long mind, we'll be running back out again on the early tide on the Monday morning. Providing the hangovers have all disappeared, we're gonna take a trip across to St Mary's. Neither Jean nor Sheila have ever been to the Scillies before, so I thought we'd go drop anchor in the bay for a few days, see how the weather's looking, maybe take a few trips ashore, if ever we can avoid the Scillonian that is, so we can tie up against her section of quayside whenever the tide's up and she's back in Penzance."

"Sounds fabulous! You never know, we might even come and join you at some point," I said, knowing full well that we wouldn't. "When are you planning on locking out of Bristol then?"

"We'll sail across to Penarth on the Wednesday, then lock in to Padstow on the following evening's tide, avoiding the mad rush across from Wales on the Friday," replied Ray sensibly. "If you get the chance, see if you can save us a half-decent space somewhere, like alongside the Marovonne for example, that'd do us just fine."

"I'll do better than that buddy," I said with a grin, "I'll give the Harbourmaster a call and let him know in advance to expect the Marovonne, the Roehampton, *and* the Joseph, all entering port on different days. That should keep the old bugger on his toes! I know he'll just tell me the usual mind; *'First come, first moored',* but in view of the amount of space that the three of us take up, maybe he could consider rafting us all up together. Ron's already booked the Courageous 2 in anyway, but being that bit smaller I expect they'll shuffle him off into a nice little corner somewhere. Anyway, leave it with me matey, I'll see what the Commissionaire's office has to say about it."

"Well that answers that question then!" I said excitedly to Helen. "We're *ALL* going! *Yee Ha!*"

Just then, not too long before closing, as the singalong slowly began to rise to a crescendo, Nik walked into the back bar accompanied by Rue and Alan. The three of them looked ever so slightly the worse for wear, and as they stood at the bar, each supporting the other on rather unsteady legs, they ordered a pint of beer each to the tune of Anna's voice screaming, as loud as she could possibly manage; *'Last orders at the bar please ladies and gents!'* Having successfully persuaded Shabby to pour them one final pint, Nik turned to me and drunkenly slurred the words;

"Hey Skip, look who I've managed to find. Big Al and the Rooster! I've told 'em 'tis fine if they both comes along with us down to Padstow in a coupla weeks. That's okay, innit Boss?"

Nik's eyes began to glaze over ever so slightly. He worked for me at that particular time in his sadly all too short a lifespan, and he also happened to live aboard the Marovonne with us too. Helen and I had an extremely comfortable double en-suite cabin down and for'ard from the wheelhouse, and Nik had somehow managed to invade the other double en-suite at the very stern of the ship, aft of the engine room. Which basically meant, wherever I went, he went too. Not that I had any kind of problem with that; he was a good worker, great company, and had a proper twisted sense of humour. A completely untrustworthy pirate in the truest sense of the meaning, and simply as naughty as it was possible to be, without actually getting caught out by the law and banged up for anything *too* serious. We were extremely close, were Nik and I, God rest his wicked little soul.

"What have you done with Kevin?" I asked Nik suspiciously, whilst Nigel passed across mine and Helen's final drinks of the night.

"Ee's gone got one o' them cabs 'ome Skip, ee's gotta go work 'n mornin'!" Nik managed to dribble the words out whilst sloshing more ale down his neck at the same time. Now that I'd taken a little more notice, it had become apparent to me that Rue and Alan were simply holding Nik up, rather than all three of them supporting each other. The rest of the pub gave them a cheer as soon as they saw them, and then burst into laughter at the typically irresponsible condition that Nik had managed to get himself into.

"Alan, Rue, good to see you guys," I greeted them. "Yes, of course, I'd be delighted to have you both come sail with us for May Day, let's all go down the Cornish way and do some *Merry Obby Ossin'* together, and the more of us the merrier. As for you, young Nikolas, you're coming to work with me first thing tomorrow morning young lad. You've got a full day booked in, working on site in Clifton with Tony and Roland, so I strongly suggest you make that your very last pint, get your young ass back aboard the Marovonne *asap*, and get your head down. I need you up, alive and kicking, come eight o'clock tomorrow morning please."

"Aye aye Skipper," Nik replied sullenly, still clinging securely to Alan and Rue's shoulders.

And with that, Anna loudly rang the final bell, the singing gradually died down, and everyone, including young Nik, obediently finished up their drinks and began to wish one another fond farewells until the next time. Helen and I took over from Al and Rue, bid a cheerful goodnight to one and all, and carefully escorted Nik back to his cabin aboard ship, taking great care to mind the gap between the Marovonne's port-side walkway and the quay wall. As the three of us were virtually the first to leave the Shakespeare that night, so we had no knowledge whatsoever as to the carnage that had occurred shortly afterwards on the pavement at the bottom of the steep set of worn stone steps just outside the pub's main front entrance. Just as well really, although to the best of my knowledge there were no hospitalisations as a result of the mass drunken tumble. *God I loved that place!*

And so the seeds were sown. Four ships from the Bristol contingent, possibly even more that I wasn't aware of as yet, all having made positive plans for yet another raucously long weekend of *Obby Ossin' in the Merry Morning of May!* I just couldn't wait, I knew I'd simply be counting down the hours!

ANOTHER MAY DAY MISADVENTURE STORY

CHAPTER ONE

At 4am on Tuesday the 27th of April, the six of us aboard the Marovonne were up and about, busying ourselves with the critical list of tasks that each of us had specifically been delegated with, by myself of course. Roger The Cabin Boy was casting off our springs and neatly packing them away, whilst Seaman Staines had taken charge of the galley and had mugs of tea and bacon sandwiches underway. I myself was down in the engine room making final checks to all systems, having already ensured that everything was ready to roll the previous afternoon anyway. We had around seven hundred gallons of diesel aboard in the two main tanks, a little under a hundred in the service tank, plus twenty-five in the gravity-fed day tank. Plus the 6.5KVA Deutz generator was also full to the brim. We had just over four hundred gallons of fresh water, along with a recently replaced pressurised water pump, and after the major repairs programme following the somewhat tricky return voyage from Lundy the previous August, during which the Marovonne had suffered several other mechanical failures, I now felt entirely confident that all systems were up and running precisely as they should be. The ship's wonderful old Gardner 8L3 engine had already been warming itself up for the last thirty minutes, and after one final tweaking down of the stern-gland grease pot, I headed back up to the wheelhouse to see how dear old Alf was coming along with his chart plotting.

After dropping Tori and Alex off at school first thing the previous morning, Nik and I had spent the rest of the day provisioning the ship in preparation for what was about to be our first serious voyage of the year, including a full inspection of all critical mechanics down in the engine room. Following the unfortunate succession of mechanical mishaps that could so easily have ended in disaster on that fateful day the previous year, but didn't, thanks mainly to the diligence of my trusted crew, I'd gone to great lengths, both time and cost-wise, to ensure that each and every repair had been taken care of to the highest possible standard immediately upon our return to our home port. I'd subsequently put the Marovonne back through her paces out and around the Holmes in the middle of the Bristol Channel on two occasions since, once in the autumn of '98, and again just six weeks prior to this particular planned expedition. She'd behaved impeccably, just as I'd expected her to, however the weather was virtually idyllic on both occasions, and despite the fact that many friends had enjoyed much fun and laughter during both brief little trips, it wasn't as if we'd actually gone very far, or come across any seriously blue waters anywhere. This next voyage would be the first to put the Marovonne seriously to the test since her partial mechanical refit during the September of the previous year.

After Nik and I had adequately restocked the ship's stores, including a *small* supply of alcohol, *'for special occasions only'*, of course, we headed off to the nearest petrol station to refill the fuel tank and the spare petrol cans for the high-speed 4-meter RIB that we carried aboard. One of my strictest rules as skipper has always been that no one aboard drinks alcohol whilst we're at sea. Laid to anchor, yes. In port, consume all you like. Out on the briny, that was simply a no-no I'm afraid! But hey, everyone that sailed with me already knew the rules, so I knew I had no need for concern. After collecting a refilled bottle of propane gas, I'd dropped Nik back to the ship, where she lay securely attached to her usual mooring directly outside the Arnolfini art gallery on Prince Street Wharf. After instructing him to secure all the fuel cans into their usual safe storage locations, then plumb in the new gas supply and secure the canister, I left him to it and set off around the corner in order to meet Helen from work. She was PA to a senior solicitor in an office block at the other end of Prince Street, and we generally both parked our cars in Jurys Hotel's multi-storey, which, conveniently, was not only halfway between Helen's work and the Marovonne, but also right next door to the Shakespeare Tavern. Helen and I dined out together later that evening. In fact, if I remember correctly, I believe I took her to the Golden Heart at Kendalshire, an excellent gastro-tavern near Winterbourne on the outskirts of Bristol. After dropping her back to her comfy little terraced house in St George afterwards, I hugged her and kissed her a fond farewell, and as she wished me *'bon voyage'* and a safe passage, I told her that I'd see her Friday lunchtime down in Padstow, and that I'd do my best to try and save her a parking space down in the car park on the harbourside. If not, then she'd have to take the park & ride from the field at the top of the hill a mile or so out of town, but I'd do my best to try and wangle something down on the harbour for her; *'So drive on down into town first babe, and we'll see how it goes from there.'* I left her to settle in, and headed back into town with the intention of getting a good night's kip before the inevitable early start the following day.

After parking the car back in the multi-storey, I stepped back aboard the Marovonne to be greeted by Alf, Rue, Alan and Kevin, all of whom had joined the ship following the completion of each of their own day's responsibilities. Kevin worked for Rolls Royce, so he'd taken a week's holiday. Alan worked for a local stationery company, and he'd done the same. Consequently the two of them needed to be back at work on Wednesday May the 5th. Alf, on the other hand, who'd spent twenty-seven years deep-sea in the merchant navy as a Chief Engineer aboard supertankers, lectured part-time in refrigeration-mechanics at Leyhill Hospital Engineering College, but he was currently still on indefinite recuperation leave following his recent hip replacement, from which, thankfully, he was recovering very nicely. As for Rue, I'm glad to say, he no longer owned that horrible, nasty Rottweiler dog of his, Rommel, which he'd thankfully given over responsibility of to his brother David, because David happened to own a farm down in Somerset. Rue lived on another old MFV in Bristol City Docks called the Accordance. The Accordance, however, was far from seaworthy, to say the very least, hence why Rue enjoyed sailing with as many other friends as often as he could. He basically dealt in dodgy old second hand cars, as well as dabbling quite a bit in computers, however, he had no need to take any time off for holidays, as he never had any firm agendas to work to anyway. Needless to say, they were all good guys, all four of them, and had all sailed with me on many previous occasions, and not just on the Marovonne either. Nik had already helped them unpack their gear, shown them to their respective sleeping quarters, having given over his own aft cabin to Alf, and they were all sat around the huge rosewood table in the Marovonne's expansive saloon chatting away over an assortment of nightcaps. I joined them briefly, just for the one single can of Old Speckled Hen that Nik handed to me with a smile on his face, and a glint in his eye that told me the cost of it had most likely come from my own pocket rather than his. A cunning little trick that I'd come to expect from him long, long ago. I then suggested that we all get our heads down as early as poss, on account of the fact that I was going to set my alarm clock for 3.15am!

So, now it was ten past four on the following Tuesday morning. Nik had heaved both of our spring warps aboard, then stepped back aboard himself and packed them neatly away in their appropriate storage lockers. Alan and Rue then released our bow and stern lines, pulled them back aboard and coiled them down neatly, one on the foredeck, one on the aft. Whilst Alf pored over my latest Reed's Nautical Almanac that was sat alongside an assortment of navigational instruments atop the huge, Perspex-covered chart table in the centre of the ship's wheelhouse, I gently wound the gear into astern and allowed our heavy fenders to lightly skim the side of the quay wall until I was able to spin the wheel hard to port, thus allowing the stern of the Marovonne to back a short way into the wide entrance to St Augustine's Reach. Having wound her back into neutral, I then spun the wheel all the way around to starboard, wound the gear-shift wheel ahead, and with the engine revs set to tick-over we glided silently down towards the Cumberland Basin at a little under three knots. Kev stepped out of the galley and carefully placed two mugs of tea and two small plates down on the side of the chart table between Alf and myself, each holding a delicious-looking bacon sandwich.

"One tea one sugar, one tea no sugar, one bacon sarnie with brown sauce, one with red," he stated proudly.

"Well done Seaman Staines," I congratulated him. "Just what the doctor ordered!"

Kevin placed the remaining plates of bacon sarnies and mugs of tea on a large serving tray, stepped down into the saloon, then disappeared out through the rear door and onto the aft deck, where the other three were all sat, sheltering from the breeze. Not that it was windy, in fact not in the slightest, but it was still dark, and still pretty chilly too. But the weather forecast was definitely good. I'd polled a Met-fax during each of the previous three days in a row, in order to monitor changes in the offshore forecast for sea area Lundy, and it looked as good as it was likely to get for that time of year. Wind south-easterly force three to four, which was a little unusual, but perfect for hugging a north-westerly-facing coastline. Visibility good, sea state slight, and the ship's barometer was steadily rising. Wind later that evening backing north-easterly force two to three; even more unusual, but in my eyes, perfect sailing conditions. Alf began writing notes in the ship's log, and I confirmed to him that we'd be taking last lock out of Bristol on the very top of the neap tide, which was at precisely 04.52hrs BST. He noted it in the log, and then began to tell me something that, not only was I already fully aware of, but also that he must've told me at least half a dozen times in the past.

"You're aware of the fact that we won't make Padstow on the one tide, aren't you Skipper?"

I ignored him completely and grabbed the VHF handset just as we approached the SS Great Britain off to port.

"Dockmaster Bristol, Dockmaster Bristol, this is Marovonne, over."

"Marovonne, Dockmaster, go ahead, over."

"Morning Bob, it's Chris. Could I request an immediate Junction Bridge swing please, followed by a Cumberland Bridge swing, then last lock out into the Avon, over."

"Morning Chris, roger that. Junction Bridge will already be swung by the time you reach it, come straight on through and hold steady in the basin, over."

"Thank you Dockmaster, Marovonne out."

"Yes Alf, I'm fully aware of that fact," I sighed. "So it means we'll have to stop off somewhere and wait on the tide before we can run up the Camel into Padstow's inner harbour, just like we *always* do!"

"Yes Chris," Alf confirmed. "It should be a reasonable trip down, especially with it being a neap tide, although it could get a little lumpy off Hartland Point, depending on when the wind backs exactly, if in fact it does at all. Can I suggest that we ... "

"Don't worry Alf, I'm not taking us anywhere near Hartland," I interrupted him mid-sentence. "We'll more than likely be closer to Lundy than Hartland. And *NO*, we're not stopping off anywhere along the way. Not Barry, not Ilfracombe, not Appledore, not Lundy, in fact, not *anywhere!* We'll take a straight run down to the mouth of the Camel, then drop our anchor either in the lee of Pentire, or the lee of Stepper Point, depending on what the wind is doing locally. We'll make that decision when we get there. Then we'll wait until two hours before high water when they'll open the inner harbour barrage gates and let us on through. So basically, that means we're in no hurry whatsoever, so I can throttle back a little, save on fuel, and we can all just enjoy the ride."

"Oh, okay then Skipper," replied Alf with a sigh, removing his glasses and plonking himself down on the pilot seat adjacent to the old long-range ship-to-shore radio set. "I guess you know exactly what you're doing these days then. Not like it was back in the old days then, when we used to sail these same waters together on dear old Bettola?"

"No Alf, it's not the same anymore. You taught me most of what I know about dead reckoning, and I shall be forever in your debt for that. But that was fifteen years ago now, times have moved on, technology's moved on, plus I've made this same passage now, down *and* back, more than a dozen times on more than half a dozen different ships. I've done it by day, by night, in good viz and in thick fog. I've done it in everything from flat calm to a north-westerly force eight, and I've done it both single handed as well as with a shipload of pissed-up idiots aboard. I've had both mechanical failures and Mayday relays to deal with all at the same time, lobster-pot lines tangled around the prop, and I'm even honest enough to admit that I've spent the odd hour now and again throwing up over the side from sea sickness. However, trust me, if there's one thing I know, it's how to get us safely down to Padstow and back."

"NIK! KEV! Make ready with the bow and stern lines please! NOW!" I hollered out of the port-side wheelhouse door, just as the Cumberland Bridge began to swing open.

"Already on it Skip," came back the calmest of replies from both the fore and aft decks.

"And what's more Alf," I continued, as I wound the gearshift into forward, "as you've probably already noticed, it makes all the difference having a young, fit crew aboard that I can completely trust, because they also already know exactly what they're doing."

As I gently manoeuvred the Marovonne into the half empty lock, and pulled her to a halt alongside the muddy quay wall port-side-to, Nik and Kev heaved both bow and stern lines ashore, and as I stepped up onto the ship's coachroof to say good morning to Bob, the Dockmaster, he looped each warp around an iron bollard and handed them back down.

"Nice early start for you this morning Chris," commented Bob politely. "Off anywhere nice today? Let me guess now, the Courageous 2 left last Saturday pound for Padstow, so I reckon you're following him on down for the old May Day Obby Ossin', that be about right d'ya reckon?"

"I reckon you'd be round about spot on there Bob, Padstow-bound indeed we are," I replied. "Plus, if I'm not mistaken, I reckon you'll have both the Roehampton and the Joseph to tend to on tomorrow's tide too. Just a guess mind you. See you in a week, or a month, or whatever, who knows? We'll just take it as it comes."

"Nice to have the opportunity! Safe passage Marovonne," came Bob's courteous reply, just as he disappeared from view, and Nik and Kev slipped the mooring lines and coiled them neatly back down again.

As the outer gates slowly swung open I wound the gearshift into forward once again, knowing full well that that's precisely where it would remain for the forthcoming sixteen hours or so, and at precisely five o'clock in the morning we ran out into a virtually static River Avon and headed on downstream towards Avonmouth. Alan was stood behind me in the Marovonne's little galley, washing up the plates and mugs and tidying up the usual mess that Kevin left behind every time he did any cooking. Rue and Nik were sat on the folding canvas chairs out on the aft deck chatting to each other, Kev was washing the foredeck down and cleaning up the port-side fenders where they'd scraped along the muddy wall in the Cumberland lock, and poor old Alf looked as if he just wanted to go back to sleep again. I decided it best to give him some kind of navigational responsibility, just to keep his spirits up. Once he'd confirmed my proposed passage plan in his own mind, then I'd pack him back off down into the saloon so that he could stretch himself out on the full-length, comfy-cushioned surround-seating.

MV MAROVONNE SETS SAIL FOR PADSTOW

CHAPTER TWO

It's exactly 163 nautical miles from Bristol to Padstow by sea. At the Marovonne's cruising speed of eight knots, I guess one might calculate that to take somewhere in the region of twenty hours. *However!* It's a strange and often extremely dangerous place is our wonderful Bristol Channel. It has the second highest tidal range in the world, peaking at just about 50ft above chart datum during an equinox spring, and it's essentially funnel-shaped. Hence why, further up river towards Gloucester, one can witness the often spectacular phenomenon known as the *Severn Bore,* a series of tidal surge waves which occur regularly during those exceptionally high bi-annual spring tides. Heading west however, out towards the Atlantic Ocean, and particularly in between the two islands of Steepholm and Flatholm, wind over a big spring tide can whip our local seas up into the most treacherous of frenzies on what initially may have appeared to be one of the most pleasant days imaginable. So basically, the tidal flow is much faster in the narrows of the Bristol Channel than it ever is in the open waters of the Atlantic Ocean, and rather than fighting that flow it's normal just to use it to one's advantage. On a particularly high spring I once measured the tidal flow between the Holmes at a little under seven knots, and as high water at Avonmouth occurs roughly an hour and a half after high water at Padstow, we comfortably made Padstow to Bristol in just under thirteen hours, taking the top of the tide out of Padstow followed by second lock into Bristol, an hour before high water, with no delays whatsoever. Sailing in the opposite direction, however, poses a problem every time, no matter what. At eight knots through the water, it simply isn't possible to reach the open entrance to Padstow Inner Harbour on the one tide, because their high water time is an hour and a half before Bristol's. So essentially, the faster you run down the Bristol Channel on an outgoing tide, the longer you'll have to wait outside Padstow until you can run up the Camel estuary, then enter the gated inner harbour at the earliest available opportunity, that being two hours before local high water. Furthermore, as the prevailing winds in this part of the world are generally south-westerlies, a strong wind over a fast outgoing spring tide is going to give you one hell of a bumpy ride, *especially* through the Holmes and off the headlands. So, a simple word of warning to those who may not know, *BEWARE THE POTENTIAL DANGERS OF THE BRISTOL CHANNEL.* Oh yeah, and the mud!

Today we were sailing in fine weather over neap tides, so I was expecting an entirely uneventful trip all the way there. I'd calculated a sailing time of around sixteen hours, arriving at the entrance to the Camel estuary at 21.00hrs. Whereupon we'd have to wait for three hours before running up the Camel and entering Padstow Inner Harbour, once they'd swung the paired barrage gates open at bang on midnight, local high water being 02.00hrs the following morning. As we ran past Avonmouth Signal Station off to starboard and headed on out into the Bristol Deep channel, I aimed the ship's compass directly towards the Clevedon North Cardinal Buoy, then asked Alf if he would kindly double check my calculations for me. He immediately obliged, and after gingerly pulling himself back to his feet, he went to work over the chart table, concentrating intensely on cross-referencing his measurements with my Breton plotter, and an old pair of brass dividers, with the relevant open page in the Reed's Almanac. Shortly before crashing directly into the tall, brightly lit, yellow and black striped Clevedon Buoy, I hung a sharp right and headed for the next waypoint on the GPS's wide-angle screen, which I'd installed just above the Kent Clear-View, right next to the fixed VHF radio. Alf confirmed that, by his calculations, given our estimated speed over ground versus the three different tidal flows that we'd encounter, as in outwards followed by inwards followed by outwards, coupled with the fact that we had a light south-easterly wind over a neap tide, with no noticeable cross-flow currents along the way, we should arrive at Newland Island just outside the entrance to the Camel estuary at; *'By my dead reckoning,'* he'd confidently calculated, *'precisely 21.00hrs BST, fifty-five minutes after low water.'*

"Well done Alf, it's good to know that your calculations fit in with both mine and the GPS's!" I said, without even the vaguest hint of sarcasm. "Once we reach the English & Welsh Grounds Racon Beacon in about ten minutes time, could you plot me a compass heading that takes us directly through the middle of the Holmes please."

Alf went straight back to work again with the chart, the plotter and the almanac. Kevin had joined Nik and Rue out on the aft deck, and Alan had come back into the wheelhouse and was standing between Alf and myself. I looked up at Al and whispered quietly;

"When we pass English & Welsh Grounds, can you take the wheel for me please mate, I need to use the head. I'll turn the nav lights off first, it'll be clear daylight by then, so when I say, bring us around to 225 degrees please, and hold us steady at that until we reach the MacKenzie Buoy in between the Holmes."

"Roger that Skipper," replied Alan obediently.

Alan had acted as helmsman for me for many an hour on the several long-haul passages we'd made together, and I trusted his judgement and accuracy implicitly. Just as I spun the wheel to port, then straightened it up again, then stood back down from the skippers seat in order to hand over control of the ship to Alan, Alf chirped up from the far side of the chart table, confirming words to the effect of; *'I believe from here to the MacKenzie marker buoy, some twenty-eight minutes ahead of us, we should steer a course of 225 degrees magnetic.'* I thanked Alf for his perfect timing and advice, switched off the nav lights, then dashed down below to relieve myself. On my return from my for'ard en-suite, I walked straight through the wheelhouse, down the steps into the saloon, then out through the back door onto the aft deck to join the others, who were sat there lazily watching the sun, as it pulled itself gradually above the horizon into a bright, blue, cloudless sky.

"Kev," I began my series of instructions with, "can you sit up in the wheelhouse with Alan and take a four-hour watch shift please. I'm gonna go do a full engine room check now, refill the day tank, etc, and then once we reach the Breaksea Light in about an hour from now, I'm gonna go get my head down for a few hours. Nik and Rue, I'd like you both to take the next four-hour shift after Al and Kev please, so can I suggest you both go get your heads down for a while too, starting from now please. And as for Alf, I'll escort him back into the saloon and prop him up against a comfy pile of cushions in the back corner of the sofa. He'll more than likely sleep for exactly the same length of time as me, knowing him as I do. So, Al and Kev can take seven 'til eleven, Nik and Rue, you can take eleven until three, and Alf can just sit out back and enjoy the ride. After which, we'll just see who's the least tired until we drop anchor at around nine o'clock this evening. Everyone okay with that? If anyone wants an alarm clock just give me a shout, although I doubt you'll need one, these things have a habit of working out quite naturally at sea."

"Once we reach the Breaksea Buoy," Kevin asked, "why don't we just run the ship on auto-pilot from there on down to Lundy Skipper?"

"Because, Mister Staines," I replied knowingly, "last time I tried that, a couple years ago when it was just me and Alf aboard, we ran through a series of unflagged lobster-pot buoys off Bull Point, and ended up getting a whole load of ropes tangled around the prop. There's no space on the back end of the shaft to install a rope cutter, so needless to say, the drag stalled the engine, and I had to call Ilfracombe lifeboat out to tow us into Appledore. We then sat down on the bottom overnight, leant up against the town quay wall, so that I could cut all the ropes away from the shaft with a hacksaw. Great fun, that was. *NOT!* So sorry guys, but no auto-pilot I'm afraid. And when I say take a watch, I mean it. *Please,* keep your eyes peeled for pot buoys, flagged or unflagged, and just avoid them like the plague."

I stepped back into the saloon then climbed down the aft stair-well and walked through into the engine room to carry out my normal regular checks. At seven knots the twenty-five gallon die-sel-fuel day tank would last for about seven hours, but I preferred to check it, along with everything else, roughly every two hours. I ran my hands along the top of all eight cylinder covers on my beautiful Gardner engine, which was purring away at just 700rpm at a mere 95 degrees Fahrenheit. *Spot on!* As indeed were the fuel filters, the oil levels, the batteries, the grease glands, the bilges, and everything else on my thorough check-list. I topped up the day tank, gravity-feeding more fuel down into it from the header tank, then climbed back up topsides. Thankfully, just for once, Roger The Cabin Boy had done precisely what I'd asked, and him and Rue had gone to get their heads down in the far for'ard bunk room. Kev was sat on the watch bunk just for'ard of the chart table, chat-ting to Al, who was steering with his knees whilst rolling a cigarette between his fingers, and clearly keeping one eye firmly fixed on the ship's compass at the same time.

"Come along then Alf," I said encouragingly, "you can leave all this chart-work stuff for the time being, Kevin and Alan are going to take the next four hour watch, and they both totally know the score, so I'm gonna go get my head down myself for a few hours, and I suggest you do similar. I've made up a bed for you on the sofa in the saloon, there's a quilt and as many cushions as you can throw a heaving line at, so just make yaself comfy and sleep for as long as you feel like it. I'll wake you if anything comes up that I might happen to need you for."

And with that, Alf stepped carefully back down into the saloon and took up his comfy little corner at the back of the long cush-ioned sofa-bench. Once I was sure he was suitably catered for, a large glass of orange squash sat next to his leather brief case on the saloon table, smack bang in the middle of his extensive scat-tered collection of packets of prescription drugs, I stepped back up into the wheelhouse, leant against the chart table and chatted to Alan, ensuring that young Kevin was also listening, which he very clearly was.

"Okay guys, we have the Breaksea Racon Buoy directly ahead of us now, can you alter course to 260 degrees please Al, and hold steady at that for the remainder of your watch. We'll be some way past Foreland Point when you swap over with Nik and Rue at 11am, pretty much bang on low water, after which I want Nik and Rue to continue keeping us steady at precisely 260 degrees, which will take us halfway between Bull Point and the Horseshoe Rocks, and on out into the open Atlantic towards Lundy Island."

Just for the record, I had all these waypoints clearly marked on the chart that was right beside them, and I made a point of showing them so that they knew exactly what I meant. As if they didn't already know! I also wrote every detail in the ship's log, along with every regular engine room check, the idiosyncrasies of which both Nik and Kevin already fully understood.

"I shall take the wheel myself at 3pm, by which time we should be able to clearly see Lundy some three to four miles ahead of us, then I shall alter course to 207 degrees, heading just north of Pentire Point towards the entrance to the Camel estuary, whilst using little Newland Island as our waypoint. So, that's the plan fellas. I'm gonna go get my head down for a bit, keep us steady at 260 degrees for the next eight hours please, *don't touch the throttle lever,* and if you don't see me before 3pm, *PLEASE,* just come get me!"

Before I retired to my cabin, I grabbed the VHF and transmitted on Channel 16;

"Swansea Coastguard, Swansea Coastguard, this is Marovonne, Marovonne, over."

"Marovonne, Swansea Coastguard, reading you loud and clear, go to Channel 67 please."

"Roger Swansea, Channel 67."

"Swansea Coastguard, this is Marovonne, do you read, over."

"Marovonne, Swansea, go ahead, over."

"Swansea, this is Marovonne, I'd like to report our passage plan for information purposes only please, over."

"Marovonne, this is Swansea, go ahead please, over."

"Swansea, this is Marovonne. We are a sixty-five-foot single engine MFV out of Bristol, currently off the Breaksea Light, destination Padstow. ETA Stepper Point 21.00 hours this evening, and we are a total of six male adults aboard, over."

"Roger Marovonne, thank you for your report and all understood. Keep a listening watch on Channel 16 please. Swansea Coastguard out."

"Will do Swansea, Marovonne out."

Whereupon, after replacing the handset, I bid Alan and Kev an uneventful watch, headed back down to my cabin and hit the sack.

PASSAGE PLAN FROM BRISTOL TO PADSTOW

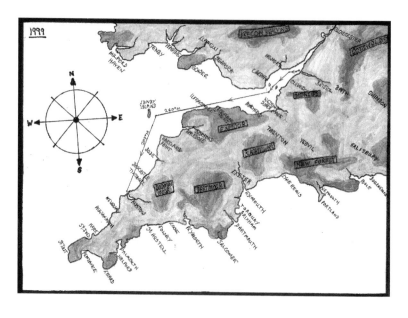

CHAPTER THREE

I'd grown used to sleeping in four hour stints whilst at sea over the years, as well as automatically recognising whether all was well or not whilst I slept. Consequently I awoke, without the need for an alarm, at precisely 11am, and headed back up to the wheelhouse just as Nik and Rue were swapping watch with Alan and Kevin.

"Nothing to report Skipper," stated Kev with a yawn. "I did a full engine room check two hours back, topped up the day tank and wrote it in the log. I also made a note as to when we passed Foreland Point, and I'm guessing we're now at low water, because what little tidal flow there was has clearly now gone slack. So now it's mine and Al's turn to catch up on last night's missed kip, Nik and Rue's watch, catch ya later folks."

Alan handed control of the wheel to Rue, then headed back into the saloon and lay down on the bench-sofa opposite the one that Alf was still asleep on. At the same time Kevin took the for'ard stairwell down to what he considered to be his own private quarters, the twin-bunked starboard-side cabin opposite mine.

"Thank you for your watch Seaman Staines," I called after him.

"Pleasure Skip," came back the simple reply.

I was about to say the same to Alan, but I'd got the distinct impression that he'd already fallen straight to sleep. Still, Nik, Rue and myself were all suitably refreshed, and after reminding them both politely to keep a careful eye out for pot buoys, whilst sticking strictly to 260 degrees for the next four hours whilst we ran past Ilfracombe and then Bull Point, I disappeared off down into the engine room for yet another full inspection. As it so happened I was pleased to report that, as expected, everything was absolutely spot on. So I climbed the stairs back up to the saloon, and then on up from the wheelhouse and outside onto the coachroof. I plonked myself down in the shelter of the ship's funnel, out of the wind but still in the beautiful, bright, warm sunshine, and in pure peace and solitude I allowed myself to become entirely mesmerised by the Marovonne's own wake through the dead-flat-calm waters, whilst I did absolutely nothing but watch the world drift by. A rare moment of uninterrupted pleasure, where I even allowed myself to believe in the misconception that I had not a single care in the entire world. I remember savouring that moment for as long as I possibly could, maybe even as long as a whole hour, right up to the point where Nik shouted up at me through the open doorway that led out onto the coachroof;

"Skipper! Alf said he's hungry! What's for lunch?"

Hey ho, little pleasures and all that...

I skipped back down into the wheelhouse and asked Nik if he'd mind cooking lunch for whoever was awake and hungry, whilst I took over his essential pot-watch and Rue stayed in control at the helm. Nik gladly agreed, mainly on the basis that he was a far better cook than myself, and I took up his position on the bench-seat in front of the chart table whilst he headed back into the galley. Some twenty minutes later Nik arrived back in the wheelhouse with a tray loaded with goodies. He'd cooked fried chicken thighs in a very light garlic-butter sauce, boiled new potatoes and peas, and carefully placed the tray down in the centre of the chart table. There was a whole pile of slices of buttered white bread, along with an assortment of condiments, and three mugs of coffee.

"Well, well, looky here," I exclaimed, "looks like our Roger The Cabin Boy has morphed into Roger the Ship's Chef all of a sudden. You might possibly have got yaself a job for life there young lad, well done."

"Alf's already got his in front of him Skip, and I reckon he's pretty happy with it too," beamed Nik.

"Well in that case," I continued, "if you guys would be so good as to continue your watch, whilst gorging yourselves on this delicious looking nosh at the same time, I do believe I shall go and join the dear old chap."

I took my plate of food, a couple of slices of bread, my coffee and cutlery, stepped back down into the saloon, slid along the long sofa-bench behind the table, and made myself comfortable right next to Alf.

"Good enough lunch for you my old matey?" I asked him with a certain degree of pride.

"Absolutely delicious sir," he replied with a mouthful of chicken. "Fair play to young Nik."

After we'd finished our excellent lunches, I stacked the dirty plates in the sink in the galley, then took Alf out onto the aft deck with me, leaving Alan still sprawled out and snoring on the smaller of the two sofa-benches. I felt that Alf could do with some fresh air, as well as the fact that he'd be missing the wonderful views if he remained inside. So I sat him down on one of the folding canvas chairs, sat myself down on the one next to him, and that's exactly where we stayed, reminiscing amicably together right up until the next scheduled change of watch. As we sailed halfway between Bull Point and the Horseshoe Rocks, then headed on out into open Atlantic waters towards Lundy, Alf mentioned that we should probably make a slight left turn and head across the outer reaches of Bideford Bay towards Hartland. Whereupon I reiterated the fact that, given the weather forecast had suggested the wind direction may potentially back from a south-easterly, which thankfully it still was, to a north-easterly, then I was determined to steer well clear of Hartland Point, knowing full well it's reputation for being one of the most treacherous headlands along the whole northern coast of the UK's south-west peninsular. Not that it was likely to be in the slightest bit treacherous on a day such as this, however, my mind was already made up, and my passage plan set accordingly. Alf simply sat back and enjoyed the soft, gentle ride, along with the gorgeous clear views of the North Devon coastline, as indeed did I. I also, however, kept a relatively frequent check on my watch, as was a constant habit of mine whenever at sea.

Just before three o'clock, Kevin stuck his head out of the back door, tapped me on the shoulder to ensure that I was still awake, which I was, and pleasantly informed me that he'd just carried out another full engine room check, topped up the day tank, and was about to write it in the log.

"Well done Mister Staines," I applauded him, "first-class seamanship. I suppose I'd best come take the wheel myself now then, and alter course for our chosen destination. By my reckoning matey, if you go take a glance directly forward through the wheelhouse windows right now, you should be able to see Rat Island, just off the south-east tip of Lundy, some three and a half miles distant. Alf, fancy grabbing yaself a hand-bearing compass, plotting our position on the chart, and letting me know whether I'm right or not?"

Alf and I wandered through to the wheelhouse, whereupon I took over control of the wheel from Rue, and thanked both him and Nik for their excellent uneventful watch. They both left us to it, retreating to the aft deck and waking Alan up for no reason whatsoever along the way. Kevin stayed with us, pointing directly ahead at the clear, huge outline of Lundy Island. At precisely 3pm Alf took compass bearings towards three static landmarks, drew them on the Perspex-covered chart with a fine-line dry-wipe marker pen, then measured the distance from where the three lines crossed to the southern tip of Lundy.

"Precisely three and a half nautical miles Skipper," he confirmed confidently. "Well done on the accuracy of your navigation my boy."

"Thank you kind sir," I replied, altering the ship's compass course to 207 degrees, "although I must admit, it does help to a certain extent when I get given the odd hint along the way from my old mate Garmin!"

We were on the top of the tide once again, not that it was much of a tide to speak of. The wind had begun to calm a little as it started backing more easterly, and with six hours remaining until our destination I expected nothing but calm seas and good visibility all the way. I settled back in the comfort of my luxurious skipper's seat whilst Alf made further notes as to the time and our precise position in the ship's log. Some thirty minutes later, after very little in the way of conversation, Kevin suddenly shrieked and pointed excitedly out of the starboard-side for'ard window. Running along-side the Marovonne, leaping gracefully over our bow wave and beyond, was a pod of maybe a dozen or more common Atlantic dolphins, clearly males *and* females, adults *and* juveniles. It was a wonderful sight to behold, and although I didn't expect them to hang around for very long, on account of them generally swimming a lot faster than the Marovonne was capable of, they actually stayed with us for a good thirty minutes or so, tracking our path in exactly the same direction we were heading. Both Kevin and Rue stood out on the foredeck taking photos with their little portable digital cameras, following which, upon zooming in on the images, it was clear that the closest of the dolphins most definitely appeared to be smiling at us. Or maybe they'd just learnt to smile for the camera, who knows?

It's a bit of a long drag from Lundy down to Padstow. Dangerous waters indeed during bad weather conditions, because, with the exception of Bude's wide sandy beaches, there's abso-lutely nothing but sheer, rocky cliffs all the way there, with not one single safe anchorage available at any point for a ship the size of the Marovonne, let alone a suitable harbour. However, not only would we be more than twelve miles offshore at one point, but instead of being rough we had exceptionally fair weather with us for a change, and a rather slight following sea, with clear blue skies overhead for the majority of the voyage. A couple of hours before reaching Pentire Point it began to turn to dusk, and whilst still sat at the wheel myself, I switched the navigation lights back on. With the exception of a few supertankers way off in the distance, and the dozen or so yachts that we'd motored past as they sailed slowly towards us out of Bideford Bay, we'd passed virtually no other ship-ping whatsoever after leaving the Holmes far behind. I called Alan up into the wheelhouse and asked him to take over at the wheel for me whilst I conducted yet another full engine room check, and topped up the day tank once again. After that I left Nik on watch, accompanying Alan at the wheel, and joined the other three guys out on the foredeck, where it was still just about light enough to see land several miles away off to our port side. Our plotted course took us just half a mile north of Rumps Point on a direct path towards Newland Island, neither of which were even remotely visible in complete darkness. Which it wasn't quite, not just yet, however Alf and I left Rue and Kev keeping watch together out on the foredeck and climbed back up into the wheelhouse. The wind had fully backed by now to a north-easterly, just as predicted, and as we were running with the outgoing tide at eight knots over ground, despite the fact that it had gone off slightly chilly, the atmosphere outside felt eerily strange, with no movement of air whatsoever, regardless of our own movement through the water. Still, despite knowing full well where I was, what I was doing, and where we were heading, I still needed to concentrate carefully on the ship's instrumentation.

At 20.30hrs the GPS told me that we were four nautical miles from Newland Island. Thirty seconds later, after making significant calculations over the chart, Alf told me that we were precisely four nautical miles from Newland Island.

"Thanks for letting me know Alf," I said calmly, pulling back ever so slightly on the throttle lever.

Both Alf, the GPS, as well as my own initiative, told me to alter course in sixteen minutes to 189 degrees magnetic, given the five degrees westerly variation from true at the time. Experience and local knowledge told me to wait until I could see the bright, white-flashing light halfway up the cliff face on Stepper Point, count to ten whilst chugging along at just four knots, then hang a sharp left, run alongside the inner faces of Pentire Point's steep cliffs, and drop anchor in their lee at the very northern end of Hayle Bay. I pulled the throttle back to just above tick-over, registering our speed over ground on the GPS at precisely four knots. I actually spotted Stepper Point Light just before I noticed the outline of Newland Island looming up through the gloom less than half a mile ahead of us. Had the wind been blowing from the south-west, I would've aimed straight for Stepper Point, and set the anchor in it's lee in the deep water area some half a mile distant from the northern reaches of the treacherous and aptly named Doom Bar. However, light and little though the breeze may have been at the time, it was still blowing, unusually, from the northeast, so I'd already made the decision to use the lee of Pentire Cliffs, and lay to anchor to the north of Hayle Bay. I counted to ten, nervously watching off to starboard as Newland Island loomed ever closer, then swung the wheel hard over to port, straightened up, and slipped silently along towards Hayle some three hundred meters out from the towering cliffs of Pentire. Nik and Kev both stood out on the foredeck together in preparation for releasing the winch-brake that held one of the Marovonne's two heavy-duty Stockless anchors. I kept a close eye on the GPS's depth reading whilst allowing us to drift a little closer to the shore, and on a neap tide that had just turned after low water some thirty minutes previous, once we reached a depth below the keel of just six meters, I brought the ship to a halt and gave one short blast on the horn. That was the specific instruction for Nik to release the anchor brake, and for Kevin to stand close by and observe. I jumped down from the wheelhouse and told Nik to pay out thirty meters of chain, allowing sufficient for the minimal neap rise that we were soon to encounter, and then clamp off the brake. Having done so easily, given that every ten meters of the ship's sixty-five meter anchor chain was colour coded, I then wound the gear astern, set the anchor, then wound it back to neutral again. Before shutting down the engine I took a full walk all the way around the ship, just to ensure that we were fully clear of any other craft laid to anchor, or indeed any other potential obstructions in our local vicinity. There were none whatsoever, so, entirely happy with our anchorage location, I shut the engine down, and asked Nik to jump down into the engine room and fire up the diesel-powered two-stroke Deutz generator. I then switched all but the masthead anchor light off, plonked myself down in one of the folding canvas chairs out on the aft deck, and cracked open a pre-prepared can of Old Speckled Hen.

MAP OF THE MID-NORTH CORNISH COAST

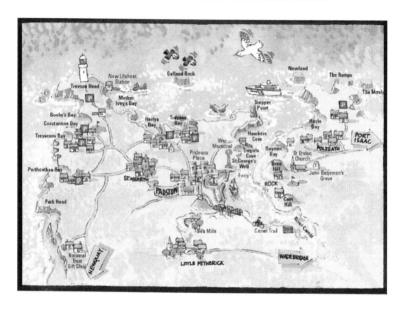

CHAPTER FOUR

"Ooh, that looks like a jolly good idea," said Alf cheerfully, "I do believe I'll join you. D'you happen to have a small lemonade by any chance?"

"Already in hand my good friend," I replied, pulling a small hold-all out from under my chair.

A few seconds after I heard the genny kick in, Nik threw the switch that activated the 240-volt exterior bulkhead lights, and the Marovonne lit up like Blackpool illuminations. Before stepping back out onto the aft deck to join the rest of us, he also switched the stereo system on, slotted in a CD, and as I began pulling cans from the little hold-all, so began the start of Pink Floyd's A Momentary Lapse Of Reason.

"Good choice young Roger," I complimented him, *"if a little cynical!"* I then passed both him and Seaman Staines each a can of the old Hen Juice.

I handed Alf a can of Sprite, already well aware of his taste in beverages, and passed cans of Thatcher's Gold across to both Al and Rue. Each of us cracked our cans open, and sat there together in silence, listening to the soft, gentle sounds of Signs Of Life coming from the inner depths of the saloon, whilst staring up into an ever darkening cloudless sky. We'd had the perfect, and probably *the* most uneventful trip down, and were now laid to anchor in a place of such beauty, solitude and tranquility, that the moment was simply worth savouring for as long as was humanly possible. Which is precisely what we did, right up until the song One Slip started playing, whereupon I jolted myself back to reality, and realised that it only took about ten minutes to empty a can of ale. Strange really, the way that a melodic swaying motion can sometimes play tricks with the mind. Hey ho.

"Okay folks," I began, after crushing my empty beer can with one hand, "we now have two and a half hours to wait here on the tide. They'll open the gates to the inner harbour at midnight, and all being well, we'll be first ones in. So, what does that mean exactly?"

"More beers Skipper!" shouted Nik and Kev in unison.

"*No!* Ya cheeky pair o' youngsters, it doesn't mean more beers at all. One each is enough for the time being I'm afraid. Consider that one a pre-docking celebration, but no more until we're safely moored alongside the inner quay wall. So, empty cans in the trash bin under the sink in the galley please, nothing goes overboard, not *ever!* Well, unless it's Nik of course! And then we need two volunteers to cook dinner. By the time we've got ourselves sorted and settled up in town, everywhere's gonna be shut. However, there's sausages in the fridge, beans in the top cupboard, and a huge bag of spuds in the cupboard next to the bin. So who's up for it then?"

"Er, I think I need to use the head quite urgently," said Nik, dashing off down below like greased lightning.

"I'm happy to cook for everyone," chirped up Alan enthusiastically. "*Especially* seeing as I somehow managed to miss lunch! How about it Rue? You peel, I'll boil and grill?"

"Sounds good to me matey," replied Rue, patting his stomach in an attempt to alleviate his hunger pangs.

"Well done guys," I commended them both, "you know where everything is. Mister Staines, could you lay up the saloon table for six in preparation for dinner please, there's a good chap. In the meantime, I shall just sit here with my dear old friend and reminisce for a little longer. Shout if you need anything."

They didn't need anything at all, not any of them. Nik helped Kevin clean all the sea salt off the outside of the windows, and wash down all the steelwork around all three sides of the wheelhouse, whilst Alan and Rue took around an hour to serve up six perfectly presented plates of bangers and mash with baked beans, along with six more mugs of coffee. And delicious it all was too, enjoyed by one and all, but especially by Alf, who hadn't really been expecting an evening meal on top of his earlier lunch. After we'd all finished I left the lads to clear up and pack everything away, and whilst Alf lay back and relaxed to the dulcet tones of Fleetwood Mac's Rumours, I wandered up onto the peaceful silence of the coachroof in order to survey the current state of our surroundings.

It was a little before eleven o'clock, and we were more or less on half tide, with the neap flowing back into the Camel at it's fastest rate for that particular night. A half moon had risen low in the cloudless sky towards Wadebridge, and in the absence of any wind in the location of our anchorage, it shone an eerie reflection off the unusually calm waters of Padstow Bay. A mile or so across the bay, as I stared inland from the stern edge of the Marovonne's roof, I could not only here the gentle lapping of waves across the leading front edge of the Doom Bar, but I could also see the irregular splashes of their little white-tops as they crested atop the dangerous lay of soft yellow sand. How many tales? How many tragedies? How many deaths over the years, along with brave and daring rescues by the local volunteer RNLI? I shuddered at the thought. I've witnessed the Doom Bar at it's angriest from the safety of the shore on more than one occasion. Thirty foot killer breaking waves created by a northerly force eight wind over an incoming spring tide. Even whilst stood safely on terra firma it scared the living pants off of me at the time! Still, I guess that's what knowledge and understanding does for you. This particular night however, whilst the wind was still blowing from the north-east at a gentle force three, the Doom Bar appeared to be relatively peaceful. Laying a way off to our stern, sparkling softly in the moonlight, it seemed somehow as if the great beast had been tamed. Still, no matter what state the tide, or indeed the weather, I knew full well she was a monster best left well alone!

I climbed the stairs back down into the wheelhouse just as a trio of small yachts sailed into Hayle Bay and dropped their anchors not far from our own location. At a rough guess I'd say they'd probably hailed from Bideford, bound for the same destination as ourselves.

'Best we get ourselves in there first then guys!' I commented positively when Nik and Kev pointed out what I'd already noticed.

"Okay folks, not long now before we weigh anchor, I'll just do one final engine room check, switch off the generator and the deck lights, top up the day tank, fire up the engine, and we'll be on our way. *Beware Padstow, here comes The 21 Gang yet again!*"

I jumped back down below and went through my extensive check list yet again, and with all being exactly as expected, I fired up my beautiful old Gardner 8L3 once more. Back topsides, sat in my comfy old skipper's chair in the wheelhouse, at precisely 23.45hrs, I switched the nav lights back on, wound the gear into forward, and brought the bow to roughly above where I'd guessed the anchor lay. One quick blast on the ship's horn was the signal for Nik to hit the retrieve switch on the side of the electric anchor windlass, and as Kev watched over the bow whilst the anchor climbed back into it's holding location, once he was happy with it's positioning he gave Nik the thumbs up, and Nik hit the switch for a second time, then re-secured the chain-lock and tightened the brake. I wound the gear into forward once again, swung the ship around until the compass read 185 degrees, and notched her up to five knots as we headed up the Camel's deep water channel, leaving the Doom Bar safely off to starboard, whilst passing the Greenaway red channel marker buoy just off our port beam. Next we passed the green Bar Buoy on our starboard side, and upon reaching the red Brea Hill Spit Buoy at 23.55hrs, I throttled our speed back to three knots, altered course to 170 degrees, reached for the VHF and flicked it round to Channel 12.

"Padstow Harbour, Padstow Harbour, this is Marovonne, Marovonne, over."

I was half expecting the reply to come back; *"Oh God, not you bloody lot again!"* Fortunately, it didn't.

"Marovonne, this is Padstow Harbour, go ahead, over."

"Padstow, Marovonne, good evening to you sir. We're a minute south of the Brea Hill heading towards Channel, can we request first entry into the inner harbour following midnight gate opening please, over."

"Roger that Marovonne. Take your time, we're not busy tonight. The gates will be fully open by a minute after the hour, come through into the inner harbour and take up a mooring position immediately alongside the right hand North Quay wall, starboard-side-to. I'll have young Steve waiting on the quayside to take your lines, torch in hand, over."

"Padstow, Marovonne, roger and understood. ETA in approximately eight minutes. For information, we have three small yachts tailing us up the Camel, most likely also inbound. Marovonne out."

Once we reached the Channel Buoy, just before *'The Pool'* at the leading front edge of the *Town Bar,* I altered course again to 203 degrees magnetic, after which it was quite difficult to follow the leading lights that led up to the entrance to the larger outer harbour, because the whole area became illuminated by the lights of the town itself. Whilst the accuracy of navigating a ship with a two meter draft through this extremely narrow channel was of critical importance, it was made all the more easy by the street lights that ran alongside the long harbour wall, and at precisely four minutes past midnight we glided silently between the walls of the outer harbour, across the short reach, and on through the open gates of the inner harbour into what, to all intents and purposes, was essentially as good as daylight. Steve, the Harbourmaster's assistant, was clearly visible as he stood at the far edge of the North Quay, waving a torch that he barely needed to use, and as I pulled the Marovonne gently to a halt right next to where he was stood, Nik and Kev simultaneously heaved our bow and stern lines ashore. Whilst Rue and Al checked that our fenders were correctly positioned, Steve ran the mooring lines through the ring bollards on the quayside and passed them back across to Nik and Kev, who secured them firmly to the ship's fore and aft cleats. I asked Kev to grab the spare shore-power cable from the store room, plug it in aboard, and run it along the quayside to the nearest Lucy box. I gave him a fifty pence piece to slot into the meter, guessing that 50p should probably last for a whole day. Steve leaned across the gap between the quay wall and the ship's coachroof and shook my hand.

"Evening Chris," he greeted me with, "welcome to Padstow for yet another May Day. Safe passage down I trust?"

"Yes thanks Steve, went like clockwork, couldn't have been better. You expecting a huge crowd again this year?"

"Yep, we sure as hell is buddy, bigger than ever I'm reckons," he replied. "Anyways-up, 'tis perty late be now mind, best I leaves ee to it, oi'l catch up with ee sometime in't mornin'. And don't thee go gettin' up to no more mischief afore the night's out mind!"

"Not a chance matey," I stated innocently. "Been a long old day, best get some beauty sleep now me thinks."

Steve wandered back off along the quayside, and I climbed the stairs back down into the wheelhouse, shut the engine down, switched off the nav lights, and now that Kev had plugged the ship in to the power supply from ashore, I switched all the interior mains lighting on. Alf was looking a little on the tired side once again, but when everyone else stepped back into the saloon, I could clearly see that they were all buzzing ever so slightly from the novelty of being back in port once again, albeit still with ever so slightly wobbly sea legs. I felt both excited and joyful, comfortable in the knowledge that I'd successfully completed yet another reasonably long passage plan. And despite the late hour, I also felt just a tad elated at being back in Padstow once again. I stood in the centre of the saloon, and with my most serious of skipper's heads on, I confidently and determinedly announced;

"OKAY FOLKS, LET THE MAY DAY MAYHEM COMMENCE!"

"Oh dear," said Alf wearily, "I think I'm gonna go get my head down."

PASSAGE PLAN FOR THE CAMEL ESTUARY

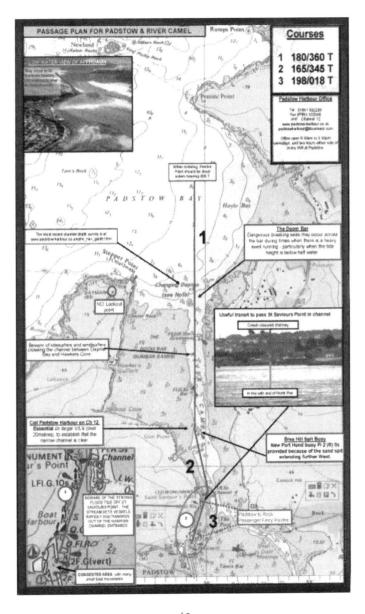

CHAPTER FIVE

Whilst Nik and Kev safely escorted Alf and his assortment of medication back down into the aft cabin, I skipped down the for'ard stairwell into my own cabin and pulled five more cans out from their secret stash at the back of my wardrobe. I handed them around, and the five of us sat happily together out on the foredeck, each swigging slowly on our chosen poisons whilst surveying our new surroundings. The Courageous 2 was moored up directly opposite us, halfway along the South Quay, a little way up from the Old Custom House Inn, the one appearing to be equally as closed up for the night as the other, with no signs of life aboard Ronnie's little ship in the slightest. Steve was stood on the quayside immediately astern of the Courageous, furiously waving his torch above his head, and once the leading yacht of the three that had entered the harbour shortly behind us finally spotted him, they all pottered line astern over towards that corner of the harbour, whereby Steve instructed them to raft up three abreast and secure their mooring lines ashore directly astern of the Courageous 2. After much noisy kerfuffle and argumentative faffing, the crew of the three little yachts finally managed to get themselves sorted out, and eventually, once Steve slumped wearily back off towards his office, they each switched their little engines and navigation lights off one by one, and peace and tranquility returned once again to the beautiful centre of Padstow. *'Enjoy it while it lasts folks,'* I mused to myself, *'this little town's gonna go full-on bat-shit crazy in a coupla days time!'* At shortly before 1am, the five of us finished our drinks, crushed the cans, deposited them in the bin in the galley, then headed off to our respective sleeping quarters. Well, all apart from Nik, that was. Nik hopped ashore, cheerfully called out *'G'nite fellas, pleasant dreams'*, and headed off into town. For the life of me I couldn't think of anywhere that might still happen to be open, but hey, good luck to him, maybe he knew better than me.

I had a bit of a lie-in the following Wednesday morning. Well deserved in my opinion, given the hectic schedule that the previous week or so had comprised of. I'd run myself ragged at work for well over a week in order to prepare for cutting myself a bit of slack for a few days, and what with having my two youngsters on my hands the weekend before sailing, then preparing the ship in readiness, and then the sailing down, all in all I'd felt just a tiny bit exhausted come the previous evening. However, a good, solid nine hours sleep soon put me back to rights again, and by 10.30am I was back up in the wheelhouse, wide awake and ready to party. Well, ready for a hearty breakfast at least.

"Morning Mister Staines," I greeted Kev with, as he leant against the chart table staring vacantly out through the front windows, "slept well I trust? Where is everyone then?"

"Ah, morning Skipper," he replied with a yawn. "Yeah, just up meself as it 'appens, but yeah, all good thanks. I think Alf'll be on his way up drektly, I heard the bath in his en-suite pumping itself out just now."

"Oh dear," I tutted, "that'll leave a nice soapy mess around the harbour then! We're not supposed to use the facilities aboard ship whilst docked in here, we don't have a holding tank. That's why I gave everyone the code to the shower block on the quay. 1 2 3 4, it's not like any of you are gonna forget it. Still, given his recent hip op, I guess it can't be easy for the poor chap, so I'm not gonna berate him over it. How about the others?"

"I've just seen Al and Rue disappear into the Quayside Café over yonder," Kev replied, pointing directly across our bow, "I was just about to go join them when you stepped up. And then there's young Nik, he's flat out on the sofa-bench back in the saloon, totally away with the fairies. No idea what time he got back in, but it weren't all that long ago by the looks."

"Okay buddy," I said, simply happy with the fact that all my crew were at least accounted for on the first morning of our visit, "you go join Al and Rue, I'll wait until Alf's ready then we'll both come and join you."

"Roger that Skip," said Kev, as he climbed the stairs and stepped out onto the coachroof.

I watched him as he hopped down from the coachroof onto the quayside. High tide would be around three o'clock in the afternoon, and the barrage gates to the inner harbour would remain open from two hours before high water until two hours after, so there's always a four-hour access window on every high tide. During neap tides, which we were currently on, the rise and subsequent fall of the water level over that period amounts to approximately one meter. During spring tides it amounts to approximately two meters. Kev's little hop from the coachroof to the quayside would prove difficult enough for Alf as things currently stood. At high water, not only would it prove impossible, but also the ship wouldn't have risen sufficiently to make the climb upwards from the main deck any easier for him either. Oddly enough, when the Marovonne was moored in Padstow on a spring tide, the coachroof was at the exact same level as the quayside whenever the barrage gates were shut, and on the top of the tide the main deck was level with the quay, thus making access on and off the ship significantly easier. And whilst it wasn't a huge step that Kev had just made, it wouldn't prove easy for poor old Alf. So best I go try find a way of dealing with it then! I climbed the stairs onto the coachroof myself and hopped down onto the quay, easily clearing the three-foot gap in between.

After using the shower block briefly myself, I took a wander around the back and across into the single lane car park that runs along that side of the harbour wall. At the far end, where it led back out onto the road, there was a chained-off area used by the harbour authority for the storage of assorted clutter. There were two builder's skips shoved up against the wall behind the chain, safely blocking in their little JCB mini-digger, and after rooting around behind the skips for a couple of minutes I found precisely what I was looking for. Two half-length scaffold planks. *Perfect!* I grabbed them up and strolled back across to the Marovonne, then laid them side by side leading comfortably from the quayside up onto the coachroof. I jumped back aboard and clambered down into the store room, just aft of the engine room, and cut ten feet of tough polyester cord from a hundred-meter roll. Just as I was about to climb the stairs back up to the saloon, Alf stepped out through the aft cabin door, and after exchanging the usual morning pleasantries, I gave him a helping hand in negotiating the stairwell himself. I then stepped back up onto the coachroof, lashed the two short scaffold planks together, then tied them down securely to a pair of scupper holes that drained the steel kick-plate which ran all the way around the roof's perimeter. I then jumped up and down in the centre of the pair of planks just to test their strength. Confident in the fact that they were in no way rotten, despite being rather old, I considered that to be '*job done*', and stepped back down into the wheelhouse. Alf was in the galley, having just switched the electric kettle on in preparation for making himself a coffee.

"Don't you go worryin' yaself about that me old mucker," I said cheerfully. "Come on, let's go catch up with the others, breakfast is on me this morning. Have you taken all your medication yet?"

"Indeed I have Chris," replied Alf with a smile. "First thing I do every morning, just as soon as I'm out of bed. However, I don't feel entirely confident about stepping ashore right now, I reckon I'm going to have a bit of trouble with that."

"No probs Alf, 'tis all sorted mate," I said with a wink. "Come along, let me show you."

I reached over and switched the kettle off, then carefully escorted Alf up the stairs and out onto the roof. He seemed pretty impressed with the set-up that I'd lashed together as a boarding platform, and didn't even need any assistance whilst casually walking ashore. Before I left the ship, I reached into a locker and isolated the gas supply, something that I'd stupidly forgotten to do the night before, despite the pair of active gas detector alarms located down in the bilges. I then skipped ashore myself, leaving every single door aboard wide open, as is generally the done thing in little old Padstow town, and Alf and I walked across the narrow shop-lined street that ran around the western perimeter of the harbour and walked into the Quayside Café. It wasn't busy, but then, certainly for the town's regular inhabitants, it was simply an ordinary Wednesday, just like any other day. During the day, everyone worked as normal. It was on a night time that the locals stayed home, busying themselves with their secret preparations for *Obby Oss Day*. So, other than early arrivals such as ourselves, the town remained relatively quiet in the days leading up to May the 1st on the forthcoming Saturday. Next Friday, however, would prove extremely manic, on account of their being literally *thousands* of early arrivals. As we entered the caff, Kev had just been served up with a full English, black pudding 'n' all, and Rue and Alan were still licking their lips after their empty plates had been cleared away. Alf and I took up seats alongside them at the same table, just as a pretty young waitress dressed in a dainty little blue and white checked frock approached us and waited patiently for our order. Apparently Kev had copied Rue and Al, so Alf ordered a child-sized equivalent of the same, and I asked for Eggs Norwegian, *'with spinach, extra smoked salmon, and don't skimp on the Hollandaise, thank you my dear! Oh yeah, I almost forgot, and two coffees, and another extra-large pot of tea please, thank you.'*

"I don't suppose anyone happens to know what Nik got up to last night then?" asked Alan inquisitively.

"Knowin' 'im like I do," answered Kev with a mouth half full of sausage and fried bread, "that's probably yet another poor young local lass 'e's gone and got up the spout."

"Nah, that'll be young Johnnie's job, that 'un will," came a voice from behind us, just as I heard the front door clatter shut. "I can tell you exactly what the pair o' them mutinous little pirates got up to last night, if you really wanna know."

"I recognise that voice," I said without turning round, just as Ronnie from the Courageous stepped over and took up the last remaining chair at our old pine table.

"Mind if I join you chaps?" he asked politely

"T'would be our pleasure my friend," I replied, reaching across and shaking his hand. "Please, sit and eat, Alf and I have only just ordered. So, what exactly d'you know that we don't then?"

"Johnnie woke me up when he came crashing back aboard at four-thirty this morning," began Ron, after ordering the same as Alf from the young waitress. "Him and Nik walked up the hill together late last night and went in to the Metropole. Apparently there was a pre-Oss local's-only disco on all night long, and 'cos our Johnnie considers himself a local wherever he goes, the doorman let 'em both in. Not that you'd ever want to argue with our Johnnie mind, he's been known to make that pretty clear from time to time, but he don't normally ever need to, he's just got the gift of the gab has that lad. Mind you, so's your Nik when it comes down to it. But Johnnie's already got a girl with a kid down here somewhere, so he kinda thinks he's got the rights to anyway. That said, he's got one in Falmouth too, and I think also maybe one in Penzance; although, to the best of my knowledge, none back home in Bristol. All he does back home is work, and drink. But when we go sailing together, which is often, he just seems to substitute working for shagging."

"Well then," I concurred, "I guess that makes him and Nik two peas in a pod, so it does. Talking of which, maybe it's time to go wake the little shit up."

"I'll do it Skip," chirped up Kev enthusiastically, "it'll give me untold pleasure! Anyway, I'm all done here, and cheers for covering everyone's bill, come on you guys, let's go drag Nik from his pit."

Rue and Alan also thanked me for paying for their breakfasts, then the three of them left, leaving Alf, Ron and myself chatting together about the voyage down. Turns out Ron and Johnnie had sailed down overnight on the previous Saturday, anchored off Stepper Point in the lee of the south-westerly, as it was then, and slotted neatly into Padstow at 10am on the Sunday morning tide. Pretty flat most of the way down apparently, apart from a bit of rock 'n' roll during wind over tide off Hartland Point. *Hmmm . . .' I thought to myself!* I asked him if he'd heard anything from the Roehampton or the Joseph yet. He said he'd spoken to

Ray, confirmed that there were very few boats arrived as yet, but Ray would definitely be leaving Bristol on today's tide anyway, stopping overnight in Penarth, then he'd be with us somewhere around tomorrow's 4pm high water. As for the Joseph, Rick wasn't entirely sure, because he hadn't been able to confirm all of his passengers as yet. He was still waiting on quite a few arrangements to be made, but all being well he hoped to arrive sometime during Friday afternoon's tide. Well, that looked like it was all pretty much set up ready to go then, so fingers crossed we'd all be having a great old Ossin' time together! We sat and chatted lazily together for a while longer, after which I paid everybody's bill, including Ronnie's, which was a bit of a struggle when he attempted to not let me. However, I justified it on the basis that I hadn't had to pay for Nik's, and so he capitulated. The three of us left the caff together, Ronnie turning right and heading back towards the Courageous, Alf and myself strolling back across the street towards the Marovonne.

Before reaching the quayside, I noticed that Nik and Kev were both up on the coachroof preparing to crane the RIB down into the water. *'Amazing how quickly that kid comes back to life sometimes!'* I thought to myself. I asked Alf if he wanted to go back aboard, but he said he'd rather spend a few hours strolling around town and looking in many of the quirky little gift shops. Alan and Rue, who were both still sat on the quayside watching what Nik and Kev were up to, said that they'd be more than happy to accompany Alf, they'd both love to wander around town themselves, and they'd take good care of him if needs be.

"Oi youngster," I shouted across to Nik, "welcome back to the land of the living, what've you got in mind with that there speedboat exactly?"

"Ah, yeah, like, hi skipper," replied Nik, with a devious tone to his voice that I instantly recognised. "Well, it's like this ya see. It's 12.30pm now, so the gate's gonna open in thirty minutes, and if something big comes in and moors alongside us, then we won't be able to get this little beauty off at all. So I thought it best we get it off now, so it's already in the water and tucked out of the way behind our stern."

"Good thinking young Roger," I commended him with, "and ...?"

"Er, yeah. So, and ... well, seeing as how I managed to miss breakfast, me and Kev thought maybe we'd go get some lunch somewhere instead."

"Oh yeah, you *and* Kev eh?" I replied sceptically. "So, where were you thinking of exactly?"

"Well," said Nik with a broad, cheeky grin, "we was thinking about the Rock Inn over in Rock. That'd be okay wouldn't it Skip?"

"Here we go then guys," I said to Al and Rue in a tone of inevitable acceptance, *"let the mayhem commence!* So, here's a thing Alf. Come three o'clock this afternoon, the ship will be one meter higher up than it is right now. Which means, of course, that this boarding platform will be much steeper. So guys, I'd very much appreciate it if you would just keep a close eye on Alf whilst he's getting on and off the ship. At 5pm this evening, when they shut the gate again, it'll be back down to where it is right now, but he still needs a hand getting down the stairs into the wheelhouse, so if it's okay with you, I'd appreciate it if you could just watch his step for him if you don't mind."

"Not at all Skipper, that's all good by us. We'll just stick more or less together now for the rest of the day," said Al, with Rue happily nodding in agreement. "Why, what are you thinking of doing?"

"Keeping a very tight rein on these pair of idiots!" I replied jovially.

With that, Kev pressed the remote control and hoisted the Avon 4-meter RIB, with it's 40hp Johnson outboard bolted to the transom, up out of it's cradle, then swung the crane's boom out over the side of the ship. Nik swung himself back down onto the main deck like the little monkey that he was, and as Kev winched the inflatable down into the water, Nik hopped aboard, secured the painter to one of the ship's starboard-side handrail stanchions, released the lifting strops and shouted up to Kev to winch the gear back up and secure the boom, which he immediately did. Some five minutes later, after Rue, Alan and Alf had all wandered off into town, the powerful hydraulic barrage gates slowly began to creak open as the water levels equalised on either side, and then forced themselves right back into their fully open position, thus doing away with the narrow footbridge that the top of the gates doubled as for pedestrian use at low tide. The opening of the inner harbour gates was followed some ten minutes later, whilst Nik, Kev and I were getting changed into more appropriate clothing, by the entry of HMS Dasher, the Royal Navy's 65ft Archer-class fast patrol boat, registered number P280, for her regular official May Day courtesy visit to the town that she had proudly *'adopted'* some years previously. Although technically based in Gosport, the Dasher was a regular visitor to both Bristol and Padstow, Bristol for it's annual Harbour Festival, and Padstow, *always,* for May Day. Well, *almost always!* But that little story can wait until another chapter. The Dasher turned immediately to port upon entry into the inner harbour, whereupon Steve was obligingly on hand to receive her heaving lines, thrown ashore by whichever training cadets aboard had been delegated to do so by the ship's *female* captain. As her fenders were dutifully lowered along her port side, with mooring warps now correctly attached, she shut down her twin Caterpillar engines just as Kevin appeared back in the wheelhouse from his for'ard cabin down below.

"Ooh, look folks, it's the Dasher," said Kev excitedly. "We know a story about her, now don't we children!"

MV MAROVONNE AND HMS DASHER MOORED IN PADSTOW

CHAPTER SIX

"Oi, dudes," shouted Nik from outside, "come on, get both your asses aboard this 'ere RIB, I'm bloody starvin' I am!"

"Will do Roger," I shouted back dutifully, and with that both Kev and I jumped down into the RIB and hopped over into the front two seats, with me behind the wheel.

I checked that Nik had correctly connected the plastic four-gallon fuel tank, and pumped the bulb to prime the carburettor, then I attached the kill-cord to it's cut-off switch, wrapped the cord around my leg and clipped it back onto itself. I then told Nik to pull the rope and fire up the manual-start outboard, and with one easy yank she started first time, just like she always did. I patted the side of her grey, starboard, inflatable tube just as Nik untied the painter, gave us a quick shove away from the hull of the Marovonne, and plonked himself firmly down in one of the two rear-facing back seats. Only then did I carefully clunk the throttle lever into forward gear, and we slowly pottered off towards the harbour entrance. As we did so, *JAWS,* one of the fast passenger trip-boats that ply the Camel estuary on a daily basis, at up to 40mph down and back again for a fiver a head, passed us on it's way in to see if anyone was waiting for a go yet. It didn't look like anyone was, the town was still eerily quiet in preparation for the forthcoming weekend.

Consequently, the other two fast trip boats, the *THUNDER* and the *SEA FURY* (they've added a forth too nowadays, the *FIREBALL*), along with the 82-foot, 200-seater *JUBILEE QUEEN* scenic tour ship, were all still laid to anchor out in The Pool, a deepish area of water just north of the Town Bar. On a low neap tide, the Town Bar becomes a small, yellow, sandy island, about a quarter of a mile square, and is perched midway between the deep-water channels of the River Camel where it splits into two, one half flowing alongside the entrance to Padstow Outer Harbour, the other flowing alongside the beach resort of Rock approximately one mile away on the other side of the estuary. The two separate flows rejoin each other close to The Pool, which remains adequately deep for anchorage of shallow-draft or flat-bottomed boats during a neap low tide. On a neap high tide, the Town Bar is submerged under approximately one meter of water. During a low spring tide the Town Bar becomes a sandy island of approximately three-quarters of a mile square, and The Pool dries out entirely, with the two flows converging considerably further north. And on a high spring, the Town Bar becomes submerged under approximately two meters of water *(Please don't quote me on the accuracy of these statistics, this is purely from memory from some twenty-odd years ago!)*

Anyway, as we were now about an hour away from a neap high, I estimated there'd be around three feet of water covering the Town Bar, and therefore probably best if we just follow the same route that the *BLACK TOR* passenger ferry takes. Although the Black Tor is a purpose-built flat-bottomed landing-craft, which plies the waters back and forth from Padstow to Rock daily from 8am until 6pm, potentially carrying up to fifty passengers per trip, she always takes the deepest channels possible, always erring on the side of caution as per her MSA rules and regulations. That said, rules and regulations were never made for pirates, however, initiative and common sense certainly were, and after leaving the walls of the outer harbour behind us, I pushed the throttle fully open, powering the little RIB immediately up on to the plane, and aimed her a little way seaward of where the Jubilee Queen was laid to anchor, drifting lazily in The Pool underneath yet another cloudless blue sky. I banked the RIB steeply and swerved it tight around the stern of the Jubilee Queen, then shot forwards on a direct heading towards Rock, making I would guess somewhere around 30mph. Less than a minute later we pulled up slowly alongside a long series of wooden pontoons that stretched out into the channel from what was clearly marked as Rock Yacht Club. The pontoons were packed, with yachts and dinghies taking up every available space, and whilst searching for a surreptitious spot that I could slot our little RIB into, all I managed to find was a large, bold sign proclaiming *"PRIVATE MOORINGS ONLY – Vessels moored here without authorisation will be impounded!"* 'Well that's bloody nice then,' I thought to myself, *'nowhere to bloody park! How very accommodating, NOT!'*

"Sod it," said Nik in a huff, "let's just go leave it on the beach outside the pub. I'm bloody starving!"

I spun the RIB around and gunned it back out into the channel away from the yacht club pontoons. A couple hundred meters downstream, shortly after we'd passed the Rock Inn, we came across a small section of yellow sandy beach that looked perfectly suitable, and I ran the RIB ashore, pulled away the kill-cord to stop the engine, and stepped out of the boat onto the soft, warm sand. Kev had already lifted and locked the outboard, even before we'd hit the beach at around ten knots, and I grabbed the long painter and tied it securely to a conveniently located channel marker, a tall iron pole that had been driven deep into the sand, and which had an inverted black triangle mounted on top of it. I wrapped the kill-cord neatly around my waist and fastened it securely in place.

"Sorted!" I said confidently, "let's go get drunk!"

"Yeah," agreed Kev immediately, "watch out Rock, *The 21 Gang's* in town again!"

"Food! I need food!" wailed Nik, heading up the beach towards the drystone wall that separated us from the narrow lane that led past the pub and on towards the yacht club.

"Beer! We need beer!" wailed Kev and myself in unison.

The Rock Inn was a great pub back in those days, for one specific reason. It had a pool table. Not one single pub in Padstow had a pool table at the time, they were all essentially about bums-on-seats for the sake of food. However, the Rock was a lot more laid back, and although it served excellent food downstairs, upstairs there was just a pool room, along with sliding glass doors that led out on to an expansive balcony with simply stunning views across the Camel estuary towards Padstow. At three o'clock Nik plonked himself down at a table by the bar and ordered gammon, egg and double chips. I ordered three beers, left one on Nik's table, and Kev and I wandered upstairs and shoved a fifty pence piece into the pool table. Twenty minutes later Nik joined us, with another round of drinks on a tray and a pocketful of fifty pence pieces. We took it in turns to play each other, not one of us any better than the other particularly, but we managed to match every single game with yet another pint. In fact, we'd actually got a pretty good rhythm going, as well as running up a pretty damned good tab at the bar. Two hours and some eight pints each later, I decided it probably best to go settle up said tab, then go check on the status of the RIB and see if it might be possible for us to get our drunken asses back across the Camel somehow. And pay I certainly did, for all of it, including Nik's dinner. *Hey ho!* We said thank you to the landlord, tripped over the threshold on the way out, picked ourselves up out of the road, and staggered back towards the little beach with our arms wrapped around each other in a vain attempt to hold each other up.

After toppling over the drystone wall and landing headlong in the one and only gorse bush growing immediately beneath it, I peered through the prickles towards the beach and immediately recognised the predicament we now found ourselves in for what it was. The tide had receded, and was still doing so at a considerable pace, and the RIB was sat high and dry on the sand some fifty feet away from the water. Even if we managed to spin it around, there was no way we'd've been able to drag it that far, *especially* in the condition we'd gotten ourselves into, it was way too heavy. Just as Kevin managed to mutter; *'Oh fuck!',* and Nik began to mumble something entirely incomprehensible, not only did I laugh, then cackle; *'Now THERE'S a surprise!',* but as I looked up, what should I see swinging her bow around the stern of the Jubilee Queen and heading over towards us, but the Black Tor.

"Looks like we might be in luck lads," I dribbled into the sand. "Gert follow I like, I's got a plan!"

We left the RIB tied to the tall iron post and stumbled off along the sand, past the Rock Inn, and up to the next beach, which I knew to be the drop-off point for the ferry. They'd even constructed a walkway across to the road for wheelchair access, and erected a huge sign saying *'STRICTLY NO MOORING'. Enough said!* The Black Tor reached the landing point way before we did, even though we only had about a hundred yards to stagger across the fine sand, but the skipper clearly noticed the three of us frantically waving our arms, and was kind enough to wait for us to stumble aboard, grab a seat each, and stare at him blankly with our *totally wasted* expressions.

"'At'll be three pounds each for you'm lads please," demanded the skipper with a snigger. "Left 'ees RIB 'igh'n' dry now 'as we? You'm's gert lucky mind, this 'ere's me last trip o' the night!"

I handed him a tenner, managed to slur the words; *'Keep the change mate',* as well as somehow giving him the clear impression that I'd be needing his services again at some point the following day. He dropped the three of us off at the Black Tor's usual low water drop-off point, which is a good mile's walk from St Saviour's Point up the hill, through the fields, and back into town. By the time the three of us had staggered that *enormous* distance, in the still-sunny spring air, and reached the harbour itself, we'd all more or less sobered up again.

"Ah, I see the three musketeers have finally returned then," said Alf sarcastically once we'd all stepped back aboard, and then, immediately upon smelling our breath, he added, "So, what's y'all done with that tidy little RIB then, ya drunken bunch o' pirates?"

"Long story buddy," I replied, "I'll tell ya later tonight. I'm gonna go get my head down for a couple hours."

"So's me 'n' Nik too," slobbered Kev.

"Not together I trust?" queried Alan with a spontaneous laugh.

Whereupon, Nik and Kevin did indeed crash out on the sofa together, with *CRASH* most definitely being the operative word, and I headed off down the for'ard stairwell to my own little cabin for a badly needed couple of hours R&R!

Having rested, sobered up, cleaned up, and dressed a little more appropriately, the six of us decided to dine out that particular evening, and we wandered across the road to the Shipwright's, then upstairs into their posh, first-class restaurant. Whilst Kev was explaining to Rue and Alan that *The 21 Gang* comprised of himself, me and Nik, simply because all three of us were born on the 21st of various different months of the year, Alf informed me that he was going to head back off home the following morning. He'd really enjoyed the trip down, and offered to thank me for it by paying for everyone's dinner that night. So I offered to let him, and cheekily ordered myself a Lobster Thermidor. Alf explained that he'd done enough May Day Ossin' over the years, he wouldn't cope too well with the crowds, and he was struggling somewhat with getting up and down the stairwell to his aft cabin onboard ship because of his hip. I fully sympathised with him, and offered to cover the cost of a cab to Bodmin Parkway the following morning so that he could get the train back to Bristol. He said that wasn't important, he'd take care of it himself, and he thanked Alan and Rue for both their help and the pleasure of their company during the course of the day. Having spent the rest of the evening gorging ourselves on rich, exotic seafoods, and drinking expensive wines as accompaniments, all apart from Nik that was, who'd made do with yet another gammon, egg and chips, accompanied this time by copious bottles of sparkling spring water, we all headed back aboard the Marovonne for a decent night's kip. By my reckoning, the three of us should be able to spin the RIB around and have it's bow back in the water by about 2.30pm the following afternoon, high tide being around 4pm, which was roughly when the Roehampton was due in. Later that evening I fell into a comfortable sleep whilst mulling those thoughts over in my mind.

The following morning all six of us had breakfast together, once again in the Quayside Café, simply because it was easy, cheap, and of a reasonable standard. Halfway through, Ron and Johnnie walked in for the very same purpose, but unfortunately they had to go sit at a separate table, as ours was full. Nik and Johnnie started ribbing each other about their shenanigans two nights previously, and both Ronnie and I had to intervene when they playfully began throwing scraps of food across the room at each other. Kevin apologised to the same young waitress on their behalf. Once breakfast was finished I asked Alf if he was all set to leave, and he said yes; other than collecting his briefcase and overnight bag from his cabin, he was packed up and ready to go. I settled up the bill, once again covering the costs of my fellow companions, and then called the one and only local cab company to come and collect Alf from the Quayside Café. The driver said he'd be around ten minutes, which allowed me the perfect amount of time to dive down into the Marovonne's aft cabin and retrieve Alf's lightweight baggage for him. I wasn't in the least bit worried about Alf taking the train home from Bodmin Parkway all on his lonesome, he'd made the journey several times before over the years, as indeed we all had. As I stepped back ashore using the makeshift gangplank, which was thankfully still holding fast, I was immediately confronted by Steve, the young Harbourmaster's scruffily-uniformed errand boy.

"Morning Skipper," he greeted me pleasantly with. "Just another day in a sunny Cornish paradise?"

"Yeah, I guess that's one way of putting it," I replied, a little wary as to why he might be asking. "Are you gonna try putting it another way by any chance?"

"Er, well, actually, yes Chris," he said, "I'm afraid I am. We're going to have to move you, and the sooner we do it the better."

"Why so?" I asked politely.

"Ronnie on the Courageous 2 tells me that you Bristol folks have got the Roehampton and the Joseph arriving shortly, and the Border Force Office in Portsmouth has just informed us that HMCC Vigilant, a 70-ton Protector Class Customs Cutter, will be mooring alongside the Dasher at 16.30hrs today, and then tomorrow all hell breaks loose, with God knows who coming from God knows where, which, if we're not *extremely* careful, is gonna cause one hell of a log-jam. And as the Vigilant's gonna be one of the first to leave on Monday morning's early tide, I need to keep her and the Dasher closest to the entrance, as well as clear of all other craft, so we need to have a bit of a shifty around before the chaos commences."

"No problem Steve," I replied willingly, "where exactly would you like us to move to?"

"So Chris, as well you know, the inner harbour is roughly hexagonal, with six specific quay walls. The Dasher is currently moored to the Outer Quay, immediately inside the barrage gates, and that's where she'll be staying. The North Quay, the one that you're currently on, is where the Jubilee Queen generally picks up from, but she'll be using the outer Ferry Slip during the course of the festivities, as will the Jaws Speedboats, or at least until everyone's settled they will. Which means we'll need to use the North Quay for the half a million Welsh yachts arriving on Friday. The Town Quay, where the pontoons are all set out, is obviously for much smaller craft, and there'll probably be another half a million of them coming in too. And the South Quay, running up to the slipway corner where the Courageous currently lies, is reserved for vessels of a similar size to the Courageous, and we've already got at least twenty of them booked in too. Now, the quay wall adjacent to the shower block building, immediately inside the entrance on the right, pointing directly towards the North Quay that runs alongside Harbour Road, we always keep that clear for late arrivals, as well as the RNLI's emergency services, should they ever be required whilst the gates are open. So, that leaves one quay wall remaining, does it not?"

"Yes Steve, indeed it does," I replied with a shudder. "So, you'd like us to run across to what I've always referred to as 'Car Park Quay' and moor up ahead of the Dasher, am I correct?"

"Indeed you are sir," Steve replied with a huge grin. "I reckon we can get at least six ships the size of yours moored to that quay, two lots of three abreast. So, if you could move across there this morning please Chris, then later today we'll moor the Roehampton alongside you when she arrives, and then we'll see what the state of play is whenever the Joseph turns up. All okay with you?"

"Yes Steve, all understood," I replied in a dull, sullen voice. "So, just to be clear, you want me to go tie the Marovonne up right next to where they're currently setting up that god-awful, brash, noisy amusement park, with it's antiquated funfair rides that we all threw up on as a kid, am I right?"

"Yes sirree Mister Chris," replied Steve, still wearing the same old grin, "you'm be spot on there my luvver, way t' go."

"Humph . . . " I grunted, and walked back across the road with Alf's bags.

Alf was already sat in the front seat of the cab, the driver facing in the right direction with the engine running, and becoming just a mite impatient. I opened the back door and placed Alf's small hold-all and his briefcase on the back seat, shut the door, and warmly shook hands with him through the open front window. I thanked him for the unnecessary aid that he'd given me with his navigational skills on the way down, then waved him goodbye as the taxi pulled away from the kerb. Kevin, Nik, Rue and Alan remained stood on the narrow pavement, each having already wished him a safe journey home, and I looked across at them and announced in a very matter of fact tone;

"Come along fellas, we gotta go move the ship."

With my trusty crew knowing precisely what they were doing with the Marovonne's mooring lines, the process was simple, and made even simpler by the fact that there were very few other vessels moored within the inner harbour as yet. Some thirty minutes later I shut the engine back down, after adjusting our fenders somewhat and mooring port-side-to against Car Park Quay about a ship's length ahead of the Dasher. That would leave plenty of space for both the Roehampton alongside ourselves, as well as the Vigilant alongside the Dasher, despite the fact that she was twenty feet longer than the Dasher. Still, I was well aware of the fact that the Harbour Commissionaires were highly experienced at cramming a massive armada of ships into a very small space for this exception-ally special occasion. Whilst the barrage gates were still shut, I sent Kev across their little footbridge to retrieve our shore-power cable, told him to use some of his winnings from yesterday's pool tourna-ment, and plug it in to a meter in the nearest Lucy box to our new location. He carried out this simple operation with all the efficiency of an unemployable electrician, and eventually slotted just the one single fifty pence piece into the empty coin meter. Hey ho, it would suffice for the time being. I checked my watch, it was a little before noon. We'd have a real struggle if we attempted to drag the RIB down to the water anytime before half past two, sober or otherwise, but I couldn't see any reason why we shouldn't catch the ferry across to Rock in readiness for doing it anyway, so I checked with Rue and Al that they were quite happy for the three of us to shoot off together, which they were. After grabbing the kill-cord from the chart table, Nik, Kev and myself took a stroll together. We crossed the bridge over the harbour gates and walked along to Harbour Road, then turned right and strolled up past the cottages towards the fields. The little lane ended at a five-bar gate with a kissing gate next to it, and we carried on through, then up over the long grassy hill, which had a dozen memorial bench-seats located every fifty meters or so, each one having the most glorious views across the Camel to the lush green hills the other side of the estuary, just beyond the long, wide expanse of golden-yellow sand known as Daymer Bay. I don't think I'll ever stop thinking what a perfect retirement location Padstow would make *(if it wasn't so Goddam expensive nowadays, thanks mainly to Mister Padstein himself!)*

The little footpath forked off to the right and took us down the other side of the hill, then along a carefully carved pathway across the rocks at St Saviour's Point, where the Black Tor Ferry was already sat waiting for passengers at the little landing stage with her engine running. The three of us walked aboard using the ferry's lowered forward ramp, to be greeted, *thankfully,* by a different skipper than the one in charge the evening before. However, I still managed to blag the crossing for free, on account of the fact that this was our return trip, and as the cost was supposed to be £3 per *return,* then I'd already paid for this one the previous day. Whilst crossing the Camel I explained to the skipper exactly what had happened, and after letting it sink in, he not only agreed to let us off paying, but also muttered words to the effect of; *'Hmmm, happens all the bloody time round 'ere!'* I don't suppose we helped his cause too much with the fact that we were the only three passengers that he ran across with, but hey, with huge grins we each extended him our most sincere gratitude, stepped back ashore at the landing stage on Rock beachfront, then ambled across to the road that leads towards the Rock Inn. I strolled up to the bar, and offered apologies to the landlord for our previous afternoon's behaviour, should he deem them necessary. He said he didn't, in fact, not in the slightest, as it would appear he'd made a pretty decent profit out of the three of us. Not that I remembered a huge amount about it. *'Well on that note sir, could I just order three half-pints of bitter shandy today please',* I asked politely. We didn't bother going upstairs, we just sat at a table in the corner by the front window that looked out onto the little lane, and the landlord brought our drinks over on a tray.

"Right guys," I said with all good intentions, "let's try going steady today eh? Try and make these last until we set off to float the RIB, then we'll catch up a bit more later on tonight."

"Hey Skip," piped up Kev suddenly, "why don't you remind me and Nik of that story about the Dasher? Always makes me giggle that one does."

"Okay then lads," I happily agreed, "well it goes like this ya see..."

BLACK TOR FERRY ROUTES FROM PADSTOW TO ROCK

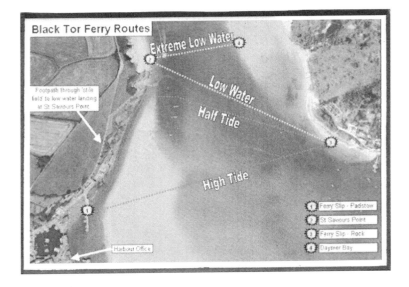

CHAPTER SEVEN

HMS Dasher, a 65ft P2000 Archer-class fast patrol boat, registered number P280, is exactly the same length as the Marovonne, although considerably lighter and an awful lot faster, with a top speed of around twenty-two knots. She's generally based in Gosport on the south coast, but as a training vessel she's affiliated to Bristol University, and her adopted town, or *twin* town you might say, is Padstow. As such, she's always attended Bristol Harbour Festival during the summer, as well as visiting Padstow every year for May Day. Well, *almost* every year that is. I was there in '97, and I remember her visiting that year. And the three of us were all there for May Day '98, but for some reason or other the Dasher wasn't, she didn't show up. Anyway, shortly after that I took a few mates away on a fishing trip to Guernsey. We'd caught the Condor Fast-Cat from Weymouth and stayed in a hotel on the harbourside. Anyway, I was sat in the hotel lounge one morning reading a previous month's local magazine, and somewhere inside I came across this article headlined;

'WOMAN CAPTAIN CRASHES WARSHIP!'

"Well, that sure grabbed my attention lads, I can tell ya! So I read on."

'One of the first women to act as a captain in the Royal Navy has crashed her ship. Lieutenant Sue Moore's vessel HMS Dasher hit her sister ship HMS Puncher just 10 days after she took control. The 29-year-old had ended centuries of male domination in the Navy as one of the first two Wrens to command a warship. She beat male *colleagues competing against her for the prestige post, and was thrilled to strike a blow for female equality. However, her 65ft-long fast patrol boat collided with Puncher as she was attempting to berth it in Guernsey. Following the collision in St Peter Port in the Channel Islands, the captains of both vessels filed reports, but their superiors decided to take no further action. At the time of her appointment to the 43-ton ship, Lt Moore said; "I was in direct competition with a lot of other people, and by dint of my work, I have been selected. I don't see any problems with the post, as for the last six years I have been commanding other sailors, most of them men. I am still ambitious to go further, perhaps to a frigate or even a destroyer. But for the moment HMS Dasher is absolutely perfect for me, especially now I have found where reverse gear is!" Yesterday a Royal Navy spokesman was keen to play down the crash. He said; "Because we're in a dynamic environment, minor bounces like this are not unusual." The Royal Navy said that Lt Moore would not be commenting on the incident, however she's clearly in good company. Prince Andrew was in command of HMS Cottesmore in 1995 when it hit a riverbank in Lincolnshire.'*

"So there ya have it lads, straight from the horse's mouth, *'one of the UK's first-ever lady skipper's of a Royal Navy warship managed to crash it after just ten days at sea.'* And that, my boys, I'm pretty sure, is the reason why the Dasher failed to make it round to Padstow last year. One of the local Guernsey fisherman told me at the time that she'd had to stop over briefly for some *'minor repairs!'* However, to the very best of my knowledge, Captain Moore is still in command of the Dasher, and consequently she'll be aboard, and around, all weekend. Hmmm ... what could possibly go wrong eh? *I wonder now!"*

I took a quick peek at my watch. It was two o'clock, and all three of our glasses had been empty for more than just a short while. I suggested maybe we should go get our butts back over the other side of that drystone wall, hopefully a little more comfortably this time, and check out how the tide's coming along. Nik and Kev were both in agreement, so I placed the empty glasses back on the bar, thanked the landlord, and we stepped back out through the front door, once again into gorgeous sunshine. We strolled along the lane, and then, unsurprisingly, found hopping over the wall to be considerably easier than I'd remembered it from the previous evening. The RIB was still sat in more or less the same position on the soft yellow sand, having been floated back and forth ever so slightly by the high neap tide at three-thirty in the early hours of that morning. Thankfully I'd taken that into account when I'd picked on that particular safe little beach that we'd left it stranded on. I untied the painter that was still securely fastened to the tall iron post in the centre of the beach, and with a grunt here and a heave-ho there, the three of us managed to spin the bow around 180 degrees so that it was pointing towards the water. Actually, it was better than that, the front of the hull was now in the water itself, but we still had to wait a further twenty minutes for the tide to rise sufficiently for us to drag the boat in so that it was fully afloat. It's quite surprising just how heavy those old 4-stroke 40hp Johnson outboards are, added to the significant weight of the boat itself. Still, now that she was fully afloat, the three of us jumped in, and I sat behind the wheel, attached the kill-cord and clipped it around my leg again. Nik lowered the outboard into nearly three feet of water, yanked on the starter cord and fired her up. Once I was sure that both Nik and Kev were sat comfortably in their respective bucket-seats, I clunked the throttle lever into forward gear, and we pottered off down the Camel against the steadily incoming tide.

It was exactly 2.30pm, the sun was shining, it was warm and dry, we had a little bit of time to kill, and lot of fuel to burn. I felt a bit of a spin coming on. Padstow's harbour gates had opened thirty minutes previously, and the Jaws speedboat was just making it's way out into the river, having picked up half a dozen thrill-seeking passengers. I already knew the RIB couldn't keep up with any of the fleet of Jaws boats, I'd tried racing them on several previous occasions, even with just myself aboard, but I also knew that if we got a head start on them we could have a bit of fun jumping their wake further down the Camel.

"Okay fellas," I said wickedly, "hang on to yer hats, let's go play!"

"Er, we're not wearing hats Skip," said Kev innocently.

"Grab-handles buddy," I said, pointing them out, "grab-handles."

Nik already knew. He'd done this on his own on more than one occasion, although I considered him to be significantly more reckless than myself. Still, I immediately slammed the throttle fully forward, and the RIB leapt straight up onto the plane as I pointed us towards the stern of the Jubilee Queen, which was still lying at anchor in The Pool. We shot past the Channel marker buoy at our top speed of a little under thirty knots, and just before we reached the Brea Hill marker buoy the Jaws speedboat, with just half her maximum capacity of twelve passengers aboard, shot past us at her top speed of a little under forty knots. Not bad going for an old heavily-moulded boat with a noisy old Ford Sabre inboard engine. The best thing about being so heavy though was of course the wake that she left behind her. As soon as the excited passengers stopped waving at us once they'd gone past, I spun the wheel hard to port, and we flew off the top of the first three-foot-high wave and landed smoothly in the trough of the second. Our engine screamed as the prop left the water, then quietened as it dug back in, and then screamed once again as we flew off the top of the Jaws' other wake, before landing gently again, this time on their opposite side. Their passengers all turned around and stared at us in amazement as we repeated the exercise once more, this time over even larger waves that were spread farther apart. With Nik and Kev gripping the grab-handles for dear life, and me clinging tightly to the wheel, I spun the RIB back into the calming wake of the Jaws boat and continued to follow her as she powered on ahead of us, past the Greenaway, past the gently breaking waves that were about to cover what little remained visible of the Doom Bar, and on towards Polzeath Beach at the southern end of Hayle Bay. Exhilarating though that was, unfortunately there was no way that I could keep up with these powerful trip boats.

"She'll turn around and head back home once she nears Polzeath," I shouted at Nik and Kev, "we'll get her again on the way back. You'll have to hang on even tighter next time mind, we'll be crossing her wake from the opposite direction. I'll try for another two jumps again, but we'll just have to see how it pans out."

As we passed the Greenaway Buoy ourselves, I watched as the Jaws boat made a series of fast spins and turns just south of Polzeath Beach, and then began heading directly back towards us. Neither of us slowed, however I took great care to ensure that the skipper of the Jaws was well aware of my intention to pass port-side to port-side, as dictated by International Maritime Law, regardless of our combined closing speed, which I estimated to be about seventy-five miles per hour! The beautifully flared bow of the Jaws steadily grew increasingly larger in my field of vision through the RIB's little Perspex windscreen, and as I shouted at Nik and Kev once again to hang on tight, I kept my head down and gritted my teeth. Other than the disturbance in the water left behind by the Jaws previous pass, the sea state was virtually flat-calm, however, as the Jaws sped ever closer, so the size of the wave that trailed across in front of us in it's wake appeared to grow ever higher, and I knew that I'd have to catch it just right in order to give us the perfect landing. Closer . . . closer . . . easy does it . . . We were about to pass each other with nothing but a boat's length in between us, although the skipper of the Jaws was very clearly aware of what my intentions were. In fact he'd even witnessed me executing it perfectly on several occasions over previous years, so we kind of had a mutual respect for one another. Closer . . . closer . . . now don't get this wrong Chris . . . you've got to catch that big old wake just right! Closer . . . closer . . . the two boats shot past each other in less than the blink of an eye, immediately after which I spun the wheel hard over to port and held my breath as we flew off the top of the wave and headed skywards. *Shit!* I hadn't hit it right! I should at least still be able to see land, *not the bloody sky!* Any second now we'll land flat on our hull and continue spinning around to port in the centre of the Jaws' wake. Won't we? *Wishful thinking I'm afraid!* Seconds later the engine stopped screaming as the prop dug deep back into the water. And then the engine dug deep into the water. And then the transom, followed immediately afterwards by Nik, round about up to his waist, along with the bases of the two rear seats.

"Er, sorry guys," I muttered from behind the wheel, as I brought the throttle lever back into neutral, "looks a bit to me like we didn't hit that one quite right. *Oops!*"

We'd flown off the top of the right wave in the right direction, but it's a very fine line between going up and over, or just going straight on up. Ask any football striker who's taking a free kick just outside the eighteen yard box! Anyway, instead of landing as intended, it would appear that we'd managed to land *arse-first!* Up forwards, down backwards, and now there was half a ton of water sloshing around in the bottom of the boat. Hey ho, *thank God for the safety of inflatables!* Not that I would have attempted such a leap in anything other than, nevertheless I was happy enough simply to have been saved by the very nature of our air-filled Hypalon sponsons. Not only that, but after it's brief but complete dunking, our little Johnson outboard was still quietly purring away on tick-over. Just as well really I suppose, as I watched the skipper of the Jaws check his rearview mirror, cheerfully wave one hand high in the air, and charge on past the Greenaway without a single thought of altering course or speed. Nik stood up in the back of the boat in an attempt to drain some of the water from his trouser pockets, and then Kevin stood up in the front and cracked up laughing, after which, I immediately did the same, I simply couldn't help myself.

"Mister Staines," I said, trying my best to keep a straight face, "if you lift your seat cushion sir, underneath it I do believe you'll find a life jacket. And underneath the life jacket I do believe you'll find a battery drill. Would you be so kind as to drill a couple of decent-sized holes straight through the bottom of the hull please, so as to let some of this damned water back out, there's a good chap."

"Right on it Captain Pugwash," replied Kev obediently. "By the way Skip, why have all these life jackets got RyanAir printed on the back of them?"

"Er, I think you'd best be asking young Nik that question buddy, not me." I replied, clunking the gear back into forwards after they'd both sat back down again.

"So, there'll be no fast planing on the way back to Padstow then," Nik moaned jokingly, "just a slow old chug and a whole lot of sloshing about. Never mind, *worse things happen at sea!*"

Not five minutes later, before we'd even reached the Greenaway, I heard a long single blast on a loud ship's horn, and I spun my head around just in time to see the white bows of the Roehampton settle into the calmness of the middle of Padstow Bay as she prepared to traverse the partially-filled Camel. It was 3.45pm, so she'd be entering the inner harbour at high water, precisely four o'clock, exactly as expected. The three of us were all extremely pleased to see her, and despite our additional load that we now carried aboard, I knew we'd easily be able to run alongside her as she negotiated her way into port. I slowed the RIB a little, and the Roehampton caught up with us just before the Brea Hill. Allowing her to hog the centre of the deepwater channel, we stood twenty feet off her port side, and we looked up at Jamer, who'd just stepped out of the wheelhouse, with huge grins on our faces.

"What's 'appened to you daft old buggers then?" Jamer called across from the Roehampton's handrails. "'As it bin chuckin' it down with rain down 'ere or summut? Why's thee boat 'alf full up wi' watter then?"

"Hey there buddy, great to see you," I called back. "No, the weather's been absolutely gorgeous so far, couldn't be better. We've just been out doing a bit of wave-hopping with one of the Jaws boats. Kinda caught one ever so slightly wrong, that's all. D'ya have a good trip across from Penarth?"

"Flat as a witch's tit," replied Jamer, using a good old-fasioned nautical expression.

"Glad to hear it matey," I called back. "So, the Harbourmaster wants you moored alongside the Marovonne, *s'il vous plaît*. When you run in through the gates and look across to your left, you'll see us tied up just ahead of HMS Dasher. Once you're round the corner I'll run on ahead of you and make sure someone's out on deck to take your mooring lines, most likely Alan and Rue I expect."

Ray suddenly stepped out onto the ship's walkway too, greeted us with a cheerful; *'Ahoy there me old shipmateys'*, and then asked a particularly relevant question;

"Is the Marovonne pointing inwards or outwards Chris?"

"She's pointing inwards Ray," I said.

"Okay, well I'm gonna spin the Roehampton around so she's pointing back out before I moor her alongside you," he said positively, "otherwise it's gonna be a total ball-ache if we decide we wanna leave early. So, is there plenty of room inside for me to make that manoeuvre safely mate?"

"No problem at all buddy, there's not many boats in yet, there's plenty of space at the mo," I confidently confirmed back to him. "Not only that, but what with you having twin engines, and us being alongside to give you a gentle nudge, should it prove necessary, 't'will be a piece of piss buddy, let's do it."

Ray stepped back up to the wheel, and expertly guided the Roehampton past St Saviour's Point, up through the deepwater channel, and in through the wide opening to the outer harbour. I then ran ahead of him in the RIB, entered the inner harbour, and stood by whilst the Roehampton slowly made her way in. Steve was standing on the quayside in between the Dasher and the Marovonne pointing to where he wanted the Roehampton located, and I gave him the thumbs up to let him know that we already knew what we were doing. Fortunately there was very little breeze at the time, and Ray brought his ship to a dead halt parallel with the Marovonne some fifty feet distant. In one simple manoeuvre he then put his port engine into forward gear, his starboard engine into reverse, and by feathering each of the throttles in turn he spun her around a full 180 degrees, as if balancing on a sixpence, so that she was pointing directly back the way she came. *Oh the joys of having two engines!* Had there been significant windage within the harbour this manoeuvre would have proved extremely difficult, however, as the only wind at the time appeared to be coming out of Nik, Ray made it look like child's play. Now to get him alongside the Marovonne.

I'd already shouted out to Rue and Al, but they'd not appeared out on deck, so I guessed they must've gone ashore somewhere. I quickly ran the RIB alongside the Marovonne and told Nik and Kev to jump back aboard and give a hand. I then ran the RIB, still half full of seawater, around to the port side of the Roehampton's midships, then gently pushed it's soft rubber bow up against her white-painted mahogany hull. Jamer and Arthur were now stood out on her aft deck, with Dave on the foredeck, each holding coiled mooring lines in preparation for throwing, but the distance between the two ships was a little too far for that just yet. I clunked the RIB into gear and increased the revs a little, and very slowly the Roehampton approached the Marovonne, side-on, just perfectly. When they were close enough, Jamer and Dave heaved the lines across, Nik and Kev took a single turn of each around the Marovonne's starboard-side fore and aft cleats then heaved them back across, and after Arthur had carefully positioned the Roehampton's fenders, Jamer and Dave pulled her in tight alongside the Marovonne then made the mooring lines fast and secure. Ray shut the engines down and stepped out onto the deck to say; *'thanks for the shove mate',* but I'd already disappeared back out of the inner harbour again with the RIB, leaving Nik and Kev aboard ship so they could change back into dry clothes.

I ran the RIB up into the far top corner of the northern side of the outer harbour, just past the old wooden grid-iron that was very rarely used, tied the painter to a chain-ring attached to the harbour wall, removed the kill-cord, raised the engine, and left it quietly drifting amongst a couple of other old wooden dinghies that were both tied to the same steel ring. As I climbed the rusty old iron ladder that was bolted into the solid stone wall, I was comfortable in the knowledge that the RIB would dry out at low tide on the one and only small patch of firm yellow sand, the entire remainder of the outer harbour consisting solely of dark grey, deep, oily mud at low tide. Shortly before pub closing time later that evening, or in other words, at precisely low tide, 10.15pm, providing I remembered of course, I'd climb back down, remove the bung from the base of the transom, and let the water drain out of the RIB. I pulled myself up off the top of ladder back onto the harbour wall, then jogged all the way around the inner harbour itself and stepped back aboard the Marovonne. Ray was down in the Roehampton's engine room faffing around with his *perfectly-paired* Gardner engines, as he so often did, but Jean and Sheila had both climbed up from the galley down below and stepped out onto the aft deck, and along with Jamer, Arthur, Dave and Nik, they all appeared to be having a good old laugh together. Kev had neatly laid the Roehampton's shore-lead across the Marovonne's bow, and was plugging it into an electricity supply right next to ours, and when Dave said that Ray wouldn't be long, I told him in no uncertain terms that he'd be allowed to take no longer than it took me to get changed, after which it was beer o'clock!

Christopher John Reason

TS ROEHAMPTON ENTERING THE CAMEL ESTUARY

CHAPTER EIGHT

Fortunately Ray *had* got the message, and as all eight of us stepped ashore together, myself now wearing a clean pair of white shorts and a bright yellow, very loud Mambo shirt, he put his arm around my shoulders and quietly confided in me that him, Dave and Jamer were absolutely gagging for a beer. None of them drank a single drop at sea, the same rules as applied on my own ship. Jean wasn't overly keen on too much alcohol anyway, and Arthur and Sheila were both tee-total, basically because he often had really bad attacks of gout, and she didn't want to encourage him into bringing it on. However, for the majority of us, once ashore; '*Come on guys, let's go for it*', was generally the order of the day. The nine of us marched enthusiastically into town together, heading purposefully for the London Inn, a small backstreet pub that was most definitely a favourite amongst the locals. Strangely enough there'd been no signs whatsoever of Ron and Johnnie anywhere. They clearly weren't aboard the Courageous as we all wandered past. However, deep down I had a vague idea that we might stumble across them at some point fairly soon. Padstow wasn't exactly big enough to get lost in! That point, as it happened to turn out, was a lot sooner than I expected. As we all stepped in through the narrow front entrance to the London Inn, who should we happen to see all sat at the bar together, but Ron, Johnnie, Alan and Rue. They were in the middle of a four-man game of spoof, with coins all over the bar and empty pint glasses littered all around them, the four of them not so much drunk as just extremely merry. Upon spotting Raymondo and the crew of the Roehampton they immediately scrapped their game, pocketed their coins, and everyone began hugging each other with warm and genuinely affectionate greetings. I stepped straight up to the bar and ordered three pints of Tribute, then Ronnie ordered seven more, plus a gin and tonic for Jean, a large orange juice and lemonade for Arthur and a small one of the same for Sheila. It was five o'clock. I had to be somewhere at ten o'clock. I sincerely hoped that I'd remember. I set an alarm on my phone. I sincerely hoped that I'd hear it when it went off!

And fortunately for me, yet again, I did hear it. In fact, we'd vacated the London Inn in favour of the safety of a much needed measure of fresh air and sobriety, along with the peace and quiet of the still, cool, night air outside the Padstow Fish & Chip Café, where all twelve of us had been sat for the last hour, right on the harbourside. This had simply amplified my alarm, and it made everyone jump when it went off, including myself. We'd been eating some of the best-ever freshly caught battered cod and chips available anywhere in the UK, in my own humble opinion that is, and we'd all been sat there completely transfixed. Firstly, by how much the harbour had started to fill up with more and more vessels whilst we'd been in the pub, buying Jamer's drinks for him all evening because he'd won virtually every single game of spoof. And secondly, by just how busy the local Town Council had been over the last couple of days decorating the entire town with mile upon mile of colourful bunting. The HMCC Vigilant had docked shortly after the Roehampton, mooring herself alongside HMS Dasher, which now appeared diminutive by comparison, and at 85ft in length, the Vigilant's bow was very nearly touching the stern of the Marovonne. Immediately forward of the Marovonne lay a rather beautiful 60ft twin-masted ketch, and a multitude of other slightly smaller yachts and motor cruisers now surrounded the Courageous 2. She was moored directly in front of where we were all sat, just beyond the inner slipway, which had been cordoned off for health and safety reasons, and almost every vessel in the harbour had also hoisted a colourful array of flags and bunting to the top of their masts. Several vessels were flying the Scull & Crossbones, however, the Marovonne's was by far the largest. I finished my final mouthful of delicious battered cod, left the annoying hoard of *bastard* seagulls to squabble over the remainder of my chips, excused myself from my exceptionally pleasant and cheerful group of companions, and jogged around the quayside towards the outer harbour wall. I climbed the ladder back down to the tiny little beach, removed the bung from the back end of the RIB, and stood there for a good fifteen minutes whilst all the water gradually drained out. I then replaced the bung, climbed back up the ladder, and walked across the barrage gates footbridge back towards the Marovonne.

Alan and Rue were back aboard, sat out on the foredeck with a selection of tinnies that they'd bought from the little Spar store just around the corner from the fish & chip shop, and marvelling at how the little town was suddenly coming alive with people, despite the relatively late hour.

"Emmets!" I declared bluntly, following their gaze. "Looks like lots of folk have taken the day off tomorrow to make an extra-long weekend of it. I'm guessing most of them will be staying in local hotels and B&B's, although looking at the weather forecast it's clearly gonna turn out to be a good weekend for camping too. Not long arrived by the looks of it, most of 'em, they're still just wandering. Talking of which, any idea which way Nik and Kev went?"

"Take a guess!" replied Al with a lighthearted degree of sarcasm.

"Hmm, let me think now. Which pub's most likely to be having a lock-in tonight I wonder?"

"I'll give you a fairly hefty clue," said Rue with a grin. *"The London!"*

"Cheers buddy," I thanked him, "best I get my ass back over there before they lock me out."

"Permission to come aboard Skipper?" I heard Jean call down from the quayside.

"No permission required my lovely," I called back up. "Please, feel free to come and go as you please, any number of you, any time, night or day. This is party season now."

With that, Jean, Arthur and Sheila walked across the makeshift gangplank onto the Marovonne's coachroof, which I'd conveniently swapped over from starboard to port, then climbed the stairs down into the wheelhouse and out onto the deck. It was then a simple step-over from the Marovonne onto the Roehampton, as their bulwarks were virtually level with ours, with just one row of slim fenders in between, and Arthur went first in order to assist the ladies with their easy little climb. Fortunately they were both wearing trousers and not skirts!

"No sign of Raymondo and the rest of the crew yet then Jean?" I asked innocently.

"Not a bloody hope," she replied, laughing, "not as long as there's a local pub still open!"

"Wouldn't be the London by any chance would it?" I queried knowingly.

"Apparently they're staying open 'til twelve tonight," Jean replied. "Special dispensation by all accounts. Anyway, Ray, Jamer, Nik, Kevin and John, they all headed straight back to the pub as soon as they'd finished their chips. Ron and Dave said they might catch up with them a bit later, but they were going to take a wander up through the town together first to check out the decorations. I must admit, they do look rather stunning, especially all the beautiful flowers in everybody's window boxes all over town, but it really is getting rather busy out there, and it's been a very long day for us *'ever-so-slightly-older-folks'*, if you know what I mean, so we're just going to go put our feet up and relax for a bit with a nice cup of tea."

Jean and Shiela had a good old giggle to themselves as Arthur helped them in turn across the gap between the two ships, after which they bid the three of us pleasant goodnights and disappeared back into their well-appointed saloon. *'Hmm, midnight eh?'* I thought to myself. *'Time for another couple of ales at least, but maybe a quick wander up into Broad Street Square first, just to see how the Maypole's coming along.'* I wished Rue and Al a pleasant evening, climbed back ashore, and headed along the quayside back towards town. Just past the Custom House Inn, one of my favourites it has to be said, I took a left at the corner and walked up through the narrow cobbled streets, up to where they opened out into a small cobbled square, fronted on all four sides by pretty little gift shops, and with two more narrow streets running off at different angles from both top corners. In the centre of the square was a tall, white-painted Maypole, the top of which was adorned with a huge array of brightly coloured flowers, and from which ran a long row of colourful bunting to the top end of every little wooden flagpole that was fixed to the wall above each of the ornate shopfronts. Each shop flew the colours of their choice from their own flagpoles, however, there was a very special difference between anyone flying blue colours, or wearing blue clothing, or sticking blue posters up in their windows, compared to those who either flew or wore the opposing colours of red. The Maypole itself was wrapped with a hundred long silk ribbons in alternate colours of blue and red, each attached to a traditional steel ring at the top of the pole, and neatly tied in a bow near the bottom with a bright yellow ribbon. That bow was not to be undone, and the Maypole not to be used for dancing around, until later in the evening on Saturday the 1st of May, and the reason for the blue and red colours will all become clear in due course. In the meantime I continued on up through the square, walked underneath the fabulous array of colourful flowers, ribbons, flags and bunting, took the right hand lane at the top, and dropped back down through yet another narrow cobbled street which brought me out not fifty yards from the London Inn. Thirty seconds later I found myself fighting my way across the rugged flagstone floor towards the bar, and shouting above the din at Johnnie, the first of our crowd that I could actually see, to get me in a pint of Walter Hicks ale, *por favor señor*. The place was heaving! Mainly, I must admit, with local fisherman, as opposed to the recently arrived hoard of emmets that were still just wandering the streets, but I was grateful to Johnnie for shouting me in a beer because it was clearly going to take me some considerable effort to get to the bar to order it myself. *And it was still only Thursday!*

"Hey, Chrissy-boy," shouted Raymondo from over in one of the far corner window recesses, "over here buddy, we've saved you a stool."

"What kind of stool?" I asked, staring directly at Johnnie as he threw me a look of disgust.

"Quit with the wise cracks and come take these glasses off of me please," he replied in anticipation.

"Anyone else fancy another drink whilst I'm *almost* at the bar?" I called across. "If I can actually get to the bar that is!"

"Tribute for me and Kev please," shouted Nik from somewhere totally unseen.

"No thanks matey," chirped up Jamer from a stool beside Ray's, " I think we'll make these our last thanks."

"No worries guys," I shouted back.

Johnnie passed me over my pint of Hicks, spilling not just a small amount in the process, and I asked him to grab two more Tributes, get one for himself, and handed him a tenner. He passed me his own pint, which had already been poured for him, and I fought my way through the crowd towards the little stool that Ray had saved for me, where the four of them were crowded around the one tiny little round table. To be fair, there weren't exactly hundreds of people in the London Inn come midnight, it was just the fact that you couldn't move because the pub is so small and narrow. Anyway, Johnnie managed to barge his way through the throng with two pints of Tribute, handed them across to Nik and Kev, and took the last remaining stool. The six of us sat together at the tiny little table next to the window that looked out onto the still bustling street outside and drank a toast together;

"To May Day Mayhem. All for one, and one for all. Arrrrrr!"

"Walter Hicks 5% HSD Draught Ale eh?" I commented quietly to Ray as we raised our glasses. "I've got a feeling that this one's gonna slide down nice 'n' easy!"

And it did too. And so did the next one! However, although I had no idea as to roughly what time Helen was likely to be arriving, as indeed neither did she just yet, I did know that she'd be driving down to meet us in town at some point during the following day. Plus I'd promised to try and blag her a space in the car park not too far from the ship, so probably best I don't go getting myself too spannered before she arrives. Ray and Jamer had already left a little after midnight, the crowd at the bar had thinned out a little, and Johnnie and Kevin had stepped up to order yet another round.

As they returned to the table and clumsily plonked the four pints of ale down in the centre, spilling a significant amount of them in the process, I made a point of saying that I was definitely going to make mine the last of the night.

"Hey Skip," Kev slurred at me after taking a long swig of his Tribute, "I's got a gert plan fer t'morra! Why's don't us take the RIB out an' go catch a loada fish, an' then go cook 'em back up on da beach? Nik's a dab 'and at lightin' fires, so us an' the girlies can 'ave oursell's a gert beach-barbie. Wot's say boss?"

"Well what d'ya know Seaman Staines," I slurred back at him, "so you've persuaded Sarah to come on down after all eh? Well done sir! And I tell 'e what, that ain't half a bad ideal neever, innit! What's reckon Mister Cabin Boy? Y'up for it 'er no?"

"Defo Skip," replied Nik, looking a tad like he might be about to fall asleep in his beer at any moment. "Yep, that gets my vote any day, defo, defo, defo, let's do it."

"Right then boys," I concluded, "well we's got us a '*grey tide eel*' then, dunnit!. Kev, first thing in't mornin', you go grab three rods and a box of assorted tackle from the ship's store room, carry 'em down onto the RIB, then bring the RIB round to one of them floating pontoons just outside the harbour entrance. Otherwise, come 11am, it'll be sat firm down on the sand yet again. The kill-cord's sat on the chart table as per usual. Nik, drag yaself outta ya pit, take a wander down the fish market t'other end o' the car park and blag a handful of unwanted stale mackerels, then go give Kev a hand. Make sure the fuel tank's at least half full, and if it ain't, top it up from one of the spare cans that's stored inside the spare dinghy up on the coachroof. As for me, I gotta take a walk into town and make a quick visit to Halfords."

"What you gotta get from 'alfords?" asked Kev after downing the remains of his last pint.

"Never you mind matey," I replied secretively. "Let's just day I feel a cunning little *Chrissy-plan* coming on! Right then lads, back aboard now I s'pose, specially if we're gonna be up and about by 10am in the mornin'."

"Er, well, me 'n' Johnnie thought maybe we'd stop for just one more," retorted Nik, much to John's surprise.

"Okay buddy, no worries," I said calmly. "Mister Staines, do me the honours please. Kick his butt outta the sack by nine-thirty tomorrow morning please, there's a good lad."

"Aye aye Skipper," slurred Kevin drunkenly.

Kev and I got to our feet and stepped back out into the street, leaving the pair of them to get even more drunk than they already were. I wasn't particularly bothered, I already knew that much worse was inevitably still to come. On the way back to the ship, I hit upon another cunning little plan. It was almost 1am in the morning, the streets had quietened significantly, and the long-stay section of the south-side car park, which ran all the way along the harbour wall right down to the fish market at the far end, was now mostly devoid of vehicles. The short-stay on the opposite northern side of the harbour, along with the streets around the harbour itself, had all been fully cordoned off for the health and safety's sake of the tens of thousands of visitors that would undoubtedly be attending the weekend's traditional festivities. In addition to this, the area of the quay that the larger private ships, such as our own, along with the quay that the Naval vessels were berthed against, which would ordinarily also have been used for car parking purposes, was now taken up by an extensive assortment of *not-quite-yet-ready* bright, noisy, adrenaline-pumping fairground rides. This meant that, as per usual, the remaining quayside areas that were used on a daily basis for long- and short-term pay & display parking, whilst they were still considerably extensive, would become fully jam-packed right up to the hilt from first thing the following morning until at least late Monday night, or possibly even early Tuesday morning.

"Do me a favour please Kev," I asked, as we staggered back along the quayside together, "pop down into the Marovonne's stores and grab me a large, black, permanent marker pen out of the top compartment of my small, blue toolbox, and bring it back over to me, along with a Stanley knife and some string. Fishin' line or simlar will suffice, cheers mate."

Kevin obligingly wandered across the quay and stepped carefully aboard ship. In the meantime, I'd spotted something out of the corner of my eye that I'd figured I could make very good use of. Virtually the whole of the harbour had been cordoned off with tall, heavy duty, red and white plastic traffic cones, with red and white striped plastic tape tied around the top of each one which linked them all together. However, the job hadn't been fully completed, and the unused traffic bollards, along with several rolls of tape, had been stacked up around the back of the Tourist Information Centre. The first three long-term car parking spaces alongside the harbour wall opposite had been taken up by the huge generators that powered the fairground rides, so I picked on the three parking spaces next to them, and with the use of six strategically placed traffic cones and about seventy feet of the stripy tape, I cordoned them off in precisely the same way that most of the town had already been done. I then rummaged through another skip which I found wedged up a side alley, halfway between the Custom House Inn and Rick Stein's Fish Restaurant, until I found exactly what I was looking for; a large, strong, empty, white cardboard box, most likely packed earlier that day with a food delivery for the pub. Kev returned at precisely that moment, handed me the Stanley knife, and I very carefully cut a perfect two-foot by one-foot rectangle out of one side of the box, then tossed the remainder back in the skip. Sat on the pavement, keeping a keen eye out for the possibility of any passing officialdom, of which there was clearly none around at that time in the morning, I took the black marker pen, and in my tidiest semi-drunken handwriting possible, I wrote the neatest words I could manage across the front of the plain white cardboard. I then punched a small hole in each of the top two corners, and using two cut lengths of string from the ball that Kev handed me, I hung the sign from the middle of the tape that cordoned off the centre of the three parking spaces. Kev kept hold of the ball of string whilst I pocketed the tools, then we both stood back a good few paces and delivered our professional opinion as to how acceptable the set-up looked, and whether we thought I might get away with taping the area off in exactly the same way as the rest of the harbour, then clearly labelling it as follows;

NO UNAUTHORISED PARKING – STRICTLY FOR THE USE OF FAIRGROUND VEHICLES ONLY – By Official Order Of The Commissionaire's Office.

"That should do the trick then," sniggered Kev, as he stifled yet another yawn.

"We'll see," I replied, not entirely convinced, "but if it works it'll save her having to drive back up to the top of the hill again, and then wait half an hour for the park & ride bus back into town. Come on buddy, let's go hit the sack, we've got another long, fun-filled day to look forward to tomorrow."

"Oh God," said Kev morbidly, "what could possibly go wrong?"

THE LONDON INN, PADSTOW

CHAPTER NINE

I awoke early the following morning, if indeed you can call 9.15am early! I had to shout loudly through Kevin's solid rosewood cabin door to wake him, and subsequently Kev had to physically drag Nik from his bed, which he'd reclaimed in the aft cabin immediately after Alf's departure, by one of his still-fully-dressed legs. I even heard the soft thud from the aft deck above as Nik's sleeping fully-clothed body landed on the carpeted timber-planked cabin floor, followed by Kev's deep voice hollering just the one word; *'MACKEREL!'* Well remembered Mister Staines! Rue was also sat out on the aft deck, a half-eaten plate of bacon, eggs, beans and toast sat squarely in his lap, and as I'd passed the galley on my way to the saloon in search of my trainers, Alan called out from beside the gas cooker asking if we'd like him to plate up three more breakfasts.

"Very kind of you to offer Al," I replied pleasantly, "but the three of us have a pretty busy schedule booked for today. Helen and Sarah are coming down by car sometime later, and I've kind of, well, *hopefully* kind of, saved them a space in the car park, over by the fairground generators. No idea yet as to what time they're likely to arrive, but in the meantime we're off out on a little fishing jaunt, see if we can't rustle up something half-decent for lunch. Three coffees in about half an hour would be bloody marvellous though mate, cheers."

I'd absolutely no idea how the heck Nik always managed to do it, but he wandered up into the wheelhouse, out onto the coach-roof, walked across the twin planks onto the quayside, and headed off through the car park towards the fish market with his eyes still fully closed. Or at least, so it had appeared. Plus, as Kev and I jointly acknowledged, undoubtedly without a single penny in his pocket either. Meanwhile, Kev grabbed the kill-cord off the chart table and headed across the footbridge towards the far north end of the outer harbour, and after finally retrieving my trainers from the ridiculous place that I'd thrown them the night before, I grabbed my wallet from my bedside table and headed off into town. We each had our own separate agendas, and I was praying that all three of us managed successfully to achieve them. As I wandered around the quay, I opened the steel door to the Lucy box and checked the electricity coin meter, knowing that we'd only slotted the one 50p into it so far. Oddly enough, it still registered 50p on the dial, power consumed to date; nil. *'Hmmm, how very odd,'* I thought to myself, but then, who the hell was I to argue with a potential fault in my favour. I wandered through the still-sleepy little town until I reached the small Halfords store, tiny by comparison to the norm, albeit one of the largest shops in Padstow at the time. They had precisely what I wanted, and I paid just £2.99 for a pack of two at the counter, pocketed the receipt and stepped back through the door. Immediately opposite Halfords I noticed a small Supasnaps photographic franchise, and another wicked thought immediately sprang to mind. I stuck my head through the door and asked one simple poignant question, then, happy with the answer, I left the store and headed back towards the harbour.

As I stepped back aboard the Marovonne, Kev handed me a coffee, whilst Nik, eyes now wide open and wearing a huge grin, opened a cheap, white carrier bag and proudly showed me the four half-pound mackerel that he'd managed to blag from the market. I didn't bother questioning him about it; I knew better not to!

"The RIB's now moored to the outer rising pontoon Skipper," Kevin confirmed, "with the three rods and reels aboard, a small box of assorted tackle, plus it's all fully refuelled and ready to go."

"Good job Mister Staines, well done," I commended him. "As for Roger The Cabin Boy here, well, what can I say? Looks like you've scored yaself a half-decent bag o' bait there young laddie. I've no idea how you constantly manage to keep up this crazy pace of yours mind, you're nothing but a true enigma young lad, but again, well done, well done indeed. Now, if you'll excuse me lads, I have a little *Chrissy-mission* to take care of before we set off in search of some exceptionally fresh lunch."

I downed the remainder of my coffee, left the mug on the side, then hopped down into my cabin and changed into a pair of swimming trunks. Next I grabbed a roll of black gaffer tape from the aft storeroom and tore strips of it to the required lengths up on the chart table in the wheelhouse. Whilst Nik and Kev stood watching, looking moderately perplexed, I tore open the polythene wrapper that I'd bought in Halfords, pulled out one of the red and white plastic L-Plates, and carefully stuck four strips of black tape around it's square perimeter. I grabbed my little waterproof camera, strapped it tightly around my wrist, then keeping a tight hold of the L-Plate I strolled purposefully back out onto to the aft deck. I was pretty sure that Nik and Kev had guessed what I was up to by then, but as for Rue and Alan, who were just chilling out in the sunshine sat right next to me, I seem to recall them both being somewhat gobsmacked when I boldly shouted;

"Hooray, hooray, the first of May. Outdoor swimming begins today!"

I then stepped up onto the ship's stern gunwhale and made a perfect swallow dive into the deep, chilly waters of the inner harbour. *'Brrrrrrrrrrrr' would've been a bit of an understatement at that point!* On top of that, needless to say, it wasn't a perfect swallow dive in the slightest, it was simply a clumsy back-flip that looked as if it had gone horribly wrong! But no matter, it had the desired effect. So I began swimming. Whether I was swimming with the stealth of a Navy Seal, or more likely that of an Atlantic Seal who's pregnancy term was way overdue, I really had no idea, however I managed to glide effortlessly around the stern of HMCC Vigilant without a single member of her crew noticing me, and as silently as I could manage I approached the wide stern transom of HMS Dasher. I then carefully stuck the L-Plate in what I considered to be the perfect location, smoothed the tape down with my hand so that it couldn't possible come unstuck, then swam back a few meters towards the harbour's tightly-closed barrage gates. I lifted up my camera and quickly shot off half a dozen photos, surprisingly to the sound of cheers and laughter coming from the increasingly busy hoards of emmets that had by now begun crossing the barrage gates' footbridge. Once again I swam silently and stealthily back to the stern of the Marovonne, keeping myself well away from the broad starboard hull of the Vigilant, then climbed the ship's permanently-trailing emergency ladder back up onto the aft deck.

"Successful mission Skip?" Kevin asked, as I brusquely rubbed myself down with a towel.

"Successful first half buddy," I replied with a wicked grin, "we'll see how the rest of it pans out later on this evening."

I pulled on a pair of shorts, tee shirt and trainers, grabbed my camera, then jogged back through town and walked into Supasnaps. I scanned the half dozen pictures that I'd taken, selected which one I thought was the best, and after handing the camera over to the young girl behind the counter, I asked her if she'd kindly print off a full-colour A4-sized copy for me, and I'd be back sometime before five o'clock to collect it. I then jogged back to the ship, and calmly informed Nik and Kev that we'd best bloody well catch something out there, on account of the fact that the three of us had eaten absolutely zilch so far that morning, and I'd just worked up a bit of an appetite..

"You just leave that to me Skip," said Kev confidently, "I've never not caught nuffin' yet!"

"Confession time!" Nik said cheekily. "Me and Kev just had a bacon sarnie each whilst you was off in town."

"Ah, so it's just me then," I sighed. "Hey ho, you'd best be right about your fishing then Mister Staines. Come on, let's get going, we've got a lot to get through today."

I fetched my grab-bag from my cabin, which contained standard emergency kit such as a portable VHF radio, a flare pack, first aid kit, torch, knife, whistle, etc, etc. Kev grabbed the killcord, along with a hold-all that he'd carefully packed earlier, at my request, and the three of us bid Rue and Alan a pleasant day, stepped ashore, then climbed the ladder down onto the pontoon.

It wasn't too far off midday, shortly after low water, and the atmosphere was already quite clearly buzzing in town. Not that there was any sign of either of the Oss teams as yet, although they wouldn't be commencing their street-dance routines until the following day anyway, so it was mostly still just emmets wandering around the harbour, trying desperately to shut their whinging youngsters up with ice creams, whilst fending off the dive-bombing seagulls as they tried to steal them in the process. As the three of us stepped aboard the RIB I looked forward to the tranquility of the ocean once again. Kevin took the wheel, connected and attached the kill-cord, and as Nik started the engine and then took his seat, I patted Kev on the shoulder and said; *'Run us out to Newland Island please Mister Staines, there's a good chap.'* I then took my phone out of my trouser pocket and dialled Helen's mobile number. She answered it immediately, and quite clearly, by the sound of it, on hands-free, which I was pleased to note meant that she was already on her way.

"Hi honey, how's ya gettin' along?" I began.

"Just passed Exeter Services on the M5," she replied. "Traffic's been quite heavy most of the way so far, but it seems to be easing up a little now. Hopefully it'll thin out even more when we hit the A30. I couldn't persuade Michelle to come down with me I'm afraid, she just said that something was bound to go horribly wrong at some point over the weekend, especially with *The 21 Gang* being out of town together, and she seriously needed to be in work for 9am Tuesday morning. Anyway, Sarah's with me, so all's good, and she's just said she's beginning to feel a little peckish, so we'd both like to know if you've got anything particular planned for lunch?"

"I do indeed babe, but I can't tell you what it is I'm afraid, it's a surprise. Anyway, it'll more than likely be a late lunch/early tea by the time you're with us. Not that I want it to be overly late, we're expecting Rick and his crew on the Joseph to arrive somewhere around high water, which is just after five o'clock, so it'd be nice to go grab a coupla pints of ale with that good old bunch of pirates once they're all moored up and sorted out, maybe around six-ish. Anyway, in the meantime babe, just listen up for a mo please. When you get here, drive in through the bottom entrance to the car park, then follow it all the way around to the Tourist Information Centre. Look across to the harbour wall on your right, and next to the fairground generators you'll see three taped-off spaces with a sign saying *'reserved for fairground vehicles'*. Get Sarah to lift up the red and white striped tape for you, then park in any one of those three spaces, and I'll sort the payment side of things out later. Then you've both got to take a bit of a stroll. It's not too far, and I know you've done it before, plus the weather's gorgeous down here today, so I'm sure you'll both enjoy it. Walk across the barrage gates bridge, then take the lane off to the right that leads up into the fields, towards where the low tide ferry pick-up point is. You with me so far hun?"

"So far I am, yes. I'm just hoping you're not going to lead us both off on some long-winded wild goose chase out into the middle of nowhere!" Helen tutted, knowing me as well as she did.

"I wouldn't dream of it sweetie," I replied innocently, "there's no feathers involved in this little plan whatsoever. Anyway, don't fork off to the right to where the ferry takes you across to Rock, just keep on going straight. Walk on past St Saviour's Point, and about a quarter of a mile after that you'll come to a sharp hairpin bend in the footpath. Halfway round that bend there's a stile on your right. Climb over the stile, then walk down the narrow little path through the trees that leads you down to St George's Cove, and we'll meet you down there on the beach. All good?"

"Hmmm," replied Helen sceptically, "we'll see!"

"Great! It's a date then!" I answered her back enthusiastically. "Picnic on the beach, St George's Cove, three o'clock. See you there girls." And with that I hung up.

No sooner had I hung up than Kevin slammed the throttle wide open, and we shot off down the narrow deep water channel, in between the half a square mile of golden-yellow sands that constituted the Doom Bar off to our left, and the lush green hills surrounding the village of Trebetherick away to our right. Not long after that, as the incoming tidal stream very gradually began to increase, Kev pulled the RIB into the eastern lee of Newland Island, and as we appeared to be holding our position within the eddy created by the island, he cut the engine and allowed us to just drift. And if it were ever possible to say that the instantaneous silence was almost deafening, then that's how I'd've described it. Serenity at it's very best!

"Okay guys," I said, as Nik pulled the first of the mackerel out of the bag, "rule number one! *Fishing hooks, rubber boat!* The two simply don't mix I'm afraid. Same applies to knives. So, if you're swinging something in or out over the side, *PLEASE,* be careful. And when you're slicing up the bait, use the solid fibreglass floor please, and *NOT* the tubes or the seats."

"Aye aye Skipper," they both acknowledged together.

"By the way Skip," Nik said, as he began carving strips of blue and silver striped flesh from the flanks of the first mackerel, "I've not had the chance to say 'til now, but when I walked back past the parking spaces that you'd taped off earlier, there was a scruffy old Ford Transit van already parked in one of 'em. Just thought I'd mention it."

I simply shrugged, as Kev baited his first hook, and carefully swung his weighted line out over the side of the boat. Nik had cut several strips of bait, and was preparing his own rod for casting, whereas I was simply sat there relaxing, loving the situation we'd now found ourselves in.

"There's a shallow water sandbank that surrounds this island, and we're hovering right above the centre of it at the mo. What I suggest you do Kev is let your bait all the way down to the bottom, and then very gradually..."

That was it, I didn't get any further than that before Kev's line was suddenly yanked tight, and he shouted excitedly; *'I'm in!'* From the fight it was putting up, it clearly wasn't just another small mackerel, however, before he'd had the chance to reel it in and retrieve it, Nik also shouted; *'I'm in too!'* Okay, let's take a look and see what we're all gonna have for tea then! Kev was still playing his fish, as he had a much lighter tackle set-up than Nik, and having already decided to leave my own rod untouched, I leaned over the side of the boat to see if I could help Nik with bringing his fish aboard. Moments later it broke the surface, thrashing around like a good'un, and I reached down, hooked my fingers under it's gills, and lifted it up over the side. A beautiful 2lb sea bass, *well caught young Roger!* Kev's was next, once he'd finished playing around with it. Same principle, different side of the boat. As Kev's fish thrashed around on the surface under the strain of the line, I hooked my fingers under it's gills once again, grabbed a tight hold and raised it aloft. A two-and-a-half pound sea bass this time, and a gorgeous looking fish it was too.

"At this rate we're gonna be early for our own party lads," I stated in disbelief. "Still, keep it up, there'll be five of us for tea altogether, so three more o' them would be bang on the nail."

The initial excitement of hooking straight into a decent shoal of sea bass didn't last for very long though, as we appeared to have scared them off, but trotting our lines very slowly all the way around the island appeared to generate the required results, and within the hour Kev had another two, and Nik had managed to land a 3lb pollack. The incoming tide would be flowing at it's fastest rate at around 2pm, three hours before high water, shortly before which it would easily be possible to run the RIB up onto the sand just off St George's Cove, so with our picnic basket now adequately full we packed the rods away and pottered sedately back inland. Ten minutes later, as Nik tilted the outboard and Kev pulled the cord to cut the revs, I stepped out of the front of the boat onto pristine, golden-yellow sand, grabbed the hold-all full of goodies that Kev had bought from the Spar store earlier, whilst I'd been off in town on my secretive mission, and strolled purposefully up towards the high water mark. I was intent on searching for driftwood, however, it wasn't as if I had to search very far, it was littered all around the top of the cove in abundance. Clean, attractive, arguably decorative, but most importantly bone-dry. Kevin and I managed to collect up a pretty decent-sized bundle and set it down in the centre of the beach just below the next incoming tide's high water mark, and within fifteen minutes Nik had a good old-fashioned roaring camp fire on the go. I placed half a dozen slightly larger dry logs over the top of it, then suggested we let it burn down to just embers whilst we gut and prepare the fish.

"Good plan Captain," said Nik enthusiastically. "In fact, I'll tell ya what, I'll do the gutting, Kev can do the wrapping, you can do the pouring."

"What a damned civilised idea young Roger," I agreed, unzipping the top of the hold-all.

BEACH BARBECUE AT ST GEORGE'S COVE

CHAPTER TEN

The first thing I pulled out of the bag was a large, black bin liner, which I handed across to Nik so that he could account for every single scrap of our rubbish, and ensure that absolutely nothing whatsoever got left behind on the pristine beach, other than the dying embers of the fire, which would be entirely consumed and returned to nature by the next high tide. As Nik gutted each of the fish in turn, using the super-sharp filleting knife from the tackle box, he placed all of their heads and innards carefully into the black bag. The last thing we wanted was to compete with the local chip shop over another annoying hoard of seagulls. I then passed Kev a cheap roll of Bacofoil, and he carefully washed, cleaned, and then wrapped each of the fish, and having cut and trimmed a few thin green branches from a nearby lime tree, he speared each of the foil-wrapped fish from end to end, then laid them side by side on the sand, waiting for the fire to die down a little more. In the meantime I pulled a pack of white disposable plastic cups out of the hold-all, along with a half-gallon plastic flagon. After wedging three of the cups firmly into the sand, I carefully filled each of them to the brim with Cripple Cock scrumpy cider.

"Five sticks ain't gonna be enough Kev," said Nik with a grin, as he slit open one of the three remaining mackerel that we hadn't needed to use for bait, "and to be honest mate, I ain't all that keen on pollack anyway, so I'll just get stuck in to this little lot instead. Go cut three more buddy."

"Good job Helen likes pollack then," I said cheerfully. "So, Mister Staines, if you could manage to eat two of the sea bass my good lad, then that'll mean nothing will get wasted. Happy days!"

"I can't see that being a problem Skip," announced Kev enthusiastically, his multi-tool knife blade poised aloft in readiness, "I'm bloody starving already. Wish these fire embers would die down a little quicker."

Ten minutes later Nik was carefully positioning all eight foil-wrapped fish into the red hot embers of the log fire, Kev was dragging the RIB a little further up the beach so that it didn't drift off with the incoming tide, and I was in the process of pouring three more small plastic cupfuls of Cripple Cock. It was just after two-thirty, and I hoped that Helen and Sarah had already crossed the barrage gates' footbridge, because the gates themselves would be opening very shortly after three o'clock. I knew that initially we'd begin to see some of the smaller boats begin to sail up the Camel from where we were sat, and as the water gradually deepened, so both the size and the quantity of boats would steadily increase. Next, as it became ever-closer to high water, at precisely 17.06hrs BST, so the onslaught of the Welsh armada would dramatically dominate the skyline. All being well we'd be comfortably ensconced in one of the town's waterfront taverns with Rick, Kim and Lloyd, and whoever else they'd managed to persuade to sail down with them aboard the Joseph, long before the screaming and shouting and jostling for mooring positions drowned out all other sounds around the centre of town. My guesstimates were generally pretty accurate time-wise though, and at ten to three, whilst Nik was in the process of lifting each of the fish out of the dying embers of the fire in order of size, having placed the pollack in first with the intention of taking it out last, both Helen and Sarah skipped out from under the trees and down onto the sand, their handbags swinging wildly around their shoulders as they threw their arms into the air with screams of joy and delight at finding us precisely where I'd said we'd be. Kev and I immediately got to our feet, threw our arms around each of our respective girlies, and welcomed them to our little picnic with what appeared to be the most immaculate timing. Nik had pulled five large white paper plates out of the hold-all, and was in the process of laying the baking-hot foiled fish down on them one at a time to cool. I set another pair of plastic cups firmly down in the sand, pulled a screw-top bottle of Sauvignon Blanc out of the bag, removed the lid, and poured the girls a cup each.

"Sorry it's not chilled babe," I said, passing a cup to Helen, "it's the best I could manage under the circumstances, we've been ever so slightly busy so far today."

"It's absolutely perfect my darling," she replied, smiling broadly whilst kissing me at the same time. "*Everything's* absolutely perfect! I can't believe you've got all this done, and ready, and, and, and just sat here waiting for us, with such perfect timing. In such a perfect location. With such perfect weather. It's just, it's just, well, *unbelievable!*"

"Listen sweetie," I said calmingly, "I know you've had a long stressful drive, but all I've done is exactly what I said I was gonna do. Now take ya shoes and bags off, plonk yaselves down on the sand, and chillax. This is Padstow, not Peckham!"

Once Kevin had finally put Sarah down, I gave her a big welcoming hug too, and she sat herself down next to Helen. We kept ourselves well away from the smouldering fire, because although I was now very much in the mood for telling campfire stories, we were sat under a bright-blue cloudless sky in warm sunshine, surrounded by trees and rocky outcrops that sheltered us entirely from what very little wind there was, and perfectly comfortable wearing just shorts and tee shirts. So there was no need whatsoever to head back into town afterwards stinking of wood smoke to top it off. I asked Helen about the final leg of their journey, and whether she'd managed to park the car successfully.

"There was a queue of traffic from the Metropole all the way down to the car park," Helen began, "but other than that, and the M5 of course, the roads were surprisingly clear most of the rest of the way, even around the lanes, as well as through Wadebridge. Took quite a while to get into the car park though."

"But you did manage to park where I said okay though, didn't you?" I asked nervously.

"Yeah, we found it straight away, no problem," she replied. "Sarah lifted the tape up and I drove right up close to the harbour wall, right in front of the little sign that says *Strictly No Parking*. I do hope that'll be okay though, there were two scruffy old Ford Transit vans parked in the other two spaces, one either side of us, so we just parked in between them."

"Perfect!" I beamed back at her. "Absolutely perfect! I'll sort that little lot out later this evening. So, who does, who doesn't, and who would like to know what the Padstow May Day Obby Oss festival is all about then?"

"Me please," said Sarah excitedly, sticking her hand up in the air. "I'd never heard of it before until Kev mentioned it a couple of weeks ago, it sounds totally mystical and intriguing, I'd *love* to know what it's all about, and where it originates from."

"Nik...?" I began, nodding towards the fish.

Nik set the five paper plates down in a rough circle on the dry sand, and expertly burnt every single one of his fingers whilst he peeled the blackened foil away from around each of the perfectly baked fish, discarding the foil, along with a significant amount of scaly skin that came away with it, into the bin bag. I noticed that the RIB was gradually drifting along the beach from left to right with the current, so I sent Kev off to retrieve it and drag it a little further up the beach again, whilst I pulled a large clear plastic dish of potato salad, a packet of six cheap plastic sporks, and a large pack of white serviettes out of the hold-all, set them down in the centre of the circle, after which i poured more drinks out for everyone. Once Nik and Kev were both sat back down, noticing that the girls were still eagerly waiting to find out exactly what it was we'd caught for them, I handed the plates around to each in turn.

"Okay folks," I began, "so, we've got one sea bass for Sarah, one pollack for Helen, two sea bass for Kevin, one sea bass for me, and Nik gets to eat the three remaining mackerel that we didn't use for bait. Help yaselves to potato salad, get stuck in and enjoy."

"I'd like to propose a simple toast," said Kev, picking up his refilled cup of cider. *"To the Osses of Padstow."*

"To the Osses of Padstow!" we all shouted out simultaneously, raising our cups and downing a good old slurp.

"So, what are these Osses all about then exactly?" Sarah asked, whilst easily pulling the top layer of beautifully cooked white meat away from the bones of her delicious sea bass.

"Okay children, are we all sitting comfortably?" I asked rhetorically. "Then I'll begin. No one really knows the true origins of the Obby Oss May Day festival, although it's believed to stem from ancient pagan fertility rites. Some say it's related to the Gaelic festival of Beltane, others proclaim it to be solely Padstonian, but either way it's certainly by far the oldest annual ritual of it's kind throughout the whole of England. So anyway, they have this Obby Oss, which is essentially just ancient Cornish lingo for Hobby Horse, and it's basically comprised of one of the young, single, local lads, who hides himself underneath a heavy black costume and spins around whilst leaping up and down, provoking thoughts and images of a young rampant stallion leaping wild and free. Then, at certain times throughout the day, prompted and led by the *Teaser,* he dances and prances and galavants all around town in search of a fair maiden to both capture, woo, and I guess to ultimately marry and procreate with. Fortunately, from my own observations, most fair maidens find themselves lucky enough to escape, hence why the whole ritual tends to last from dawn 'til dusk. You'd be very fortunate if you found yourself close up to the actual Oss himself mind you, as he's always surrounded and followed by a whole host of *Mayers,* or townsfolk, but you'd stand no chance of getting chosen as a fair maiden anyway, they only pick on their own down here I'm afraid. Still, you'll certainly hear the whole crowd approaching along any given street by the noisy playing of accordions and banging of drums, and the loud, joyful chanting and singing of the *Morning Song.* You'll be singin' it non-stop yaself come Sunday, I guarantee it! Anyway, if the opportunity arises, don't go getting' yaself too close to one of them there Osses, they behave a bit like *Whirling Dervishes,* and their black capes are made out of literally half a hundredweight of three-quarter-inch plywood. Accidental injuries *have* been known to occur, although they're extremely rare, but take heed, and if you happen to come across one of the processions, just stand back and marvel, then let them pass on their way, don't try to join in. After all, it's *their* day, not *ours!*"

"You said there were Osses," said Sarah, her eyes glued to me with keen interest, whilst clearly loving her sea bass, "does that mean there's more than one Oss then?"

"Before the First World War there was only one Oss, the *Old Oss,* also now referred to as the *Red Oss,* but in 1919 the *Blue Ribbon Oss,* occasionally known as the *Temperance Oss,* was introduced, and ever since then there has always essentially been the Old Red Oss, with it's local team of loyal supporters, and the Blue Ribbon Oss, again with it's own dedicated group of followers. So there's just the two Osses, a Red Oss and a Blue Oss, and during the hours of daylight, in the *Merry Morning of May,* as the repetitive words constantly, joyfully, and often addictively ring out, custom dictates that '*never the twain shall meet!*' The two parades are led separately around the town by their respective *MC's,* with their top hats and decorative sticks, followed by their bands of musicians, and then their Oss, spinning like a lunatic to the encouragement of his Teaser, and closely guarded by his loyal crowd of Mayers. They'll all be repetitively singing the Morning Song whilst looking for young fair maidens, who are then invited to dance briefly in front of the Oss before quickly making their escape, with each of the maidens wearing beautiful, highly decorated costumes sporting the colours of their own favourite Oss team, and dancing joyfully as if they had not a care in the world. And all of this takes place regularly throughout the day, through the tiny narrow streets of pretty little Padstow, without either Oss team meeting, bumping into or coming across the other at any point during the proceedings. It really is very, very clever, beautiful to watch, and exceptionally well put together, even if it does appear to most outsiders to be entirely random."

"Is it just entirely random then, or is there some kind of fixed programme that they work to?" asked Sarah, still fixated by my words whilst pouring both her and Helen another cupful of Sauvignon.

"More Cripple Cock Skip?" asked Kev, with immaculate timing as ever.

"Fill me up Mister Staines," I replied greedily.

"Mister Staines?" Sarah queried, looking to Helen for an answer with a puzzled expression on her face.

"Never mind hun," Helen answered her with a smile, "I'll tell you about it later."

I was downing large mouthfuls of fish and potato salad in between each sentence, washing it all down with cider, and loving every single bit of it. To say nothing about being the centre of attention, as well as just the five of us having the whole beach to ourselves too. Oh well, just another day in paradise I guess! On with the story then, but not before asking Kev to drag the RIB a little further up the beach yet again.

"Okay, so if you're still around in town at midnight tonight, you may well here a whole bunch of locals, many of them dressed in costume, singing the *Night Song* outside the front door of the Golden Lion Inn. Just ignore them, they're basically just begging for ale. They'll get it though, with smiles and thanks from the landlord and landlady, and then they'll move on to the next pub. Could be the London, could be the Shipwrights, could be the Harbour, could be the Custom House, who knows, but wherever they stop they'll be welcomed with free glasses of ale. By the early hours they'll all be drunk and asleep, however, come 8am, when all the children come out to play, the whole town will somehow have magically been decorated with tree branches tied here, there and everywhere; to lamp posts, drainpipes and street signs, and many of them ornately draped with colourful flowers. The children dance and play in the streets, often accompanied by the musicians, and sometimes singing their own made up versions of the Morning Song. Then, at 10am, the Blue Ribbon Oss leaves the Padstow Institute to begin it's tour of the town. The Old Oss makes it's appearance next, outside the Golden Lion at 11am. The two Oss teams dance merrily around the town together, equally without fear of crossing one another's paths, until 12 noon, when the Old Oss happens across Prideaux Place, and is Teased into performing a particularly long and energetic dance in front of the gathered and waiting crowd. I should add at this point that there is never just the one single person that performs either of these ritual Oss dances, as that would certainly prove to be *more than* exhausting. I would estimate thirty minutes to be the most that any young fit lad could manage at any one go, so consequently a variety of volunteers tend to take it in turns, returning to the responsibility now and again once suitably refreshed."

"Talking of suitably refreshed young Roger," I said, holding my empty cup out towards Nik, who dutifully topped it up with cider right away. They didn't appear to hold very much, those little plastic cups. Hey ho!

"Roger? WTF?" queried Sarah yet again, although this time both Helen and Kevin simply laughed.

"Anyway, once the Old Oss has exhausted itself to the satisfaction of the gathered crowd, having still failed to capture a suitable maiden, it then heads on back to the Golden Lion. At some other point during the day the Blue Ribbon Oss will also perform the very same ritual, this time to the raucous applause of a completely different crowd surrounding the centre of Prideaux Place. Similar exhaustive parades will be carried out by both Oss teams at various different locations throughout the town, not normally announced in advance, but generally at around 2pm, then randomly during the course of the afternoon, and then a little later at 6pm. Finally, shortly before dusk, neither the Blue nor the Red Oss having successfully managed to capture a single fair maiden, the two Osses are allowed to cross each other's paths, and they meet up, along with their respective Teasers, Mayers, musicians, supporters and hangers-on, at the Maypole in Broad Street. Briefly the two Osses try to outdo each other with all the rapidly whirling and spinning energy that they have remaining in their bodies, whilst both teams of Mayers dance merrily together around the Maypole. On the odd occasion the two Osses even manage to clash, whereupon they are both very quickly brought back under control by their MC's, and just before dark, each are returned peacefully and without protest to their appropriate stables; the Old Red Oss to the Golden Lion Inn and the Blue Ribbon Oss to the Padstow Institute. At precisely midnight, all the supporters gather together once again around the Maypole in the centre of Broad Street and have themselves a jolly good old drunken sing-song together, mainly relating to the sudden recent deaths of each of their own beloved Oss's, and looking forward with great fervour to it's passionate resurrection on the following *Eve of May*. So, in a nutshell folks, there ya have it. Twenty four hours that act as a celebration of the coming of summer, explained in brief summary from start to finish."

"Wow, what an awesome ancient ritual we're about to witness then," said Sarah excitedly.

"Hooray, hooray, the first of May, outdoor sex begins today!" I said, acknowledging reality. "Anyway, Padstow's a cold, lonely, isolated place during the depths of winter, and hardly surprising, what with the inability to successfully harvest the local seas due to the regular ferocity of the Atlantic storms that constantly batter the whole of the northern Cornish coastline, so they have every good reason to celebrate the coming of summer, along with the onset of harvest time, and the arrival with monotonous regularity of their massive trade in tourism. Personally I'm of the opinion that it's all just one big excuse to get pissed-up and go shag in the fields. Come on, let's get this stuff packed away and get gone from here, the tide will be upon us before we know it. Nik, are you done with all them mackerel yet?"

"Picked 'em right down to the bones Skip," replied Nik, bin bag in hand. "All three of 'em!"

"Good lad, good lad," I said. "Everyone else happy with their afternoon tea then?"

The answers that came back were entirely unanimous. My picnic plan had clearly worked out well, Nik's cooking had definitely put a big smile on everyone's faces, and I do believe the Cripple Cock cider had added an extra dimension to the smile on mine. Time to get going then. The fire had all but burnt itself out, but it wouldn't be long before it was entirely consumed by the incoming tide anyway. Nik made a point of collecting every single scrap of rubbish and placing it in the bag, including all the fish bones, as well as both the empty wine bottle and cider flagon. Satisfied that not one single scrap of evidence remained, he knotted the bag and placed it carefully in the back of the RIB. As the five of us stood, at a little after four o'clock in the afternoon, we could clearly see the flotillas of increasingly-larger yachts and motorboats heading up the Camel towards Padstow, however, as yet, there had been no sign of the Joseph.

"Okay guys, looks like we gotta go mingle with the Welsh for a bit," I said in a mock Welsh accent to no one in particular, "those legs of yours gonna cope okay with a bit more walking then girls?"

"It's okay Skip, I'll take a walk back with them," Kevin gladly volunteered. "You and Nik go ahead with the RIB whilst me, Sarah and Helen take a nice steady stroll back through the fields. I'm sure a peaceful sunny walk in this warm light breeze will do the three of us the world of good, and help to digest all that delicious fish too. Plus it's only less than half an hour, so you two go ahead, we'll meet you back aboard the Marovonne."

"Okay, will do Mister Staines," I agreed, "enjoy the walk, you enjoy the walk too girls, and take ya time, there's no hurry, nothing to rush back for, we're all on holiday remember."

As Kev set off up the little path through the woods with both girls in tow, I grabbed up the now almost empty hold-all, shoved the RIB back out into deeper water, and said to Nik with an air of urgency;

"Come on Roger, get that engine fired up quickly please, I need to get myself back into town before the shops shut!"

Christopher John Reason

KEVIN AND SARAH STROLLING BACK INTO TOWN

CHAPTER ELEVEN

As we reached deeper water, Nik lowered the outboard and pulled the start cord, then I span the RIB around and headed out into the melee of inbound vessels. Half an hour to go before high water, and they were coming in thick and fast now. I was pleased to see that both the Jubillee Queen and all three of the Jaws Speedboats were laid to anchor in The Pool, but I still didn't fancy being in Steve's shoes at that particular moment in time. On our way back towards the entrance to the harbour we happened across another couple of friends who'd sailed down from Bristol via somewhere or another, namely Tom and Catriona aboard their 30ft motor cruiser, the Kathleen B. I briefly pulled alongside them and said; *'Hi guys, a warm welcome to sunny Padstow, and good luck with the parking!',* to which, after getting over their initial shock at seeing us suddenly appear out of nowhere, Tom replied with a huge, confident smile that Ronnie had promised to try and save them a space alongside the Courageous 2. *'Hmmm . . . '* I thought to myself, as we waved them a cheerful *'TTFN'* and headed in through the wide open space between the outer harbour walls. Once inside the outer harbour it immediately became apparent that all vessels were being requested to hold back before entering the port itself, presumably in order that Steve could direct them individually to specific locations, and consequently they were rafted up in rows of ten abreast all alongside both of the outer rising pontoons. I swapped seats with Nik and gave him control of the wheel.

"Drop me right up in the top north corner by the old iron ladder please buddy," I asked him calmly, "then as soon as you get the chance, run the boat inside the harbour and shove it somewhere in between the Roehampton's bow and the Marovonne's stern, *right underneath the Vigilant's fo'c'sle!* Then you've gotta get rid of that bagful of rubbish asap, otherwise it's gonna reek like a good'un come nightfall. Shove it in one of the Harbour Authority's wheelie skips down by the end of the fairground, right by the barrage gates. And if you wouldn't mind just sticking my grab-bag back down in my cabin, that'd be marvellous too matey, cheers."

"Will do Skipper, leave all that to me," Nik replied, just as I stepped off the side of the RIB and began to climb the rusty old ladder.

I jogged into town, stepping constantly from side to side to avoid the myriad of people, pets and pushchairs, and made it through the front door to Supasnaps at just ten minutes before closing time. The young girl behind the counter handed me back my little camera, then pulled an A4 high-gloss photograph out of it's large white envelope to show me. *'AWESOME!'* I declared, not expecting quite such a spectacular result, and wondering just how much trouble it was going to get me into exactly. I thanked the young girl for her first-class service, then she took £9.99 off my credit card and slid the photo neatly back into it's sleeve. I jogged steadily back towards town, once again making every effort to avoid bumping into the marauding hoards of emmets. With the barrage gates still firmly open, the latest arrivals pouring in like bees to the honeypot, I had to circle the entire harbour to get back to the Marovonne. No mean feat given the density of the crowds, *and it wasn't even May Day yet!* As I reached the Padstow Fish & Chip Café at the harbour's south-west corner, I noticed Ronnie stood out on Courageous's foredeck, gesticulating wildly at Tom and Catriona, who were poised motionless together in the centre of the harbour stood aboard the Kathleen B. Steve was clearly directing them in one direction, whereas Ronnie was pointing exactly towards where he'd left just enough room between the Courageous and the end of the slipway for the Kathleen B to slot into. I strolled back towards Steve and sidled up next to him.

"Hey Steve," I began calmly and politely, even though I could tell that he was all in a flap over everything, "Tom on the Kathleen B is best mates with Ron on the Courageous, and the Kathleen B will be staying on for a few days after the festival, which is why Ronnie's saved him a neat little space right under his bow, tight up against the wall. Once he's slotted in there you can raft as many more 30ft yachts up alongside him as you consider safe, and then the fifty-footers can sit alongside in front of them. Good plan buddy?"

I actually had no idea when Tom and Catriona were intending on leaving, but Steve appeared to be grateful to me for pointing out a small space that he'd clearly not noticed, and directed the Kathleen B over in front of the Courageous. I shouted across to Ronnie; *All sorted mate'*, and he gave me the thumbs-up. Johnnie, on the other hand, was clearly nowhere to be seen. *Surprise surprise!* I stopped off at the Spar store and bought another half-gallon of Cripple Cock, as I'd rather enjoyed that last one just a little more than I'd expected, and two more bottles of Sauvignon Blanc to boot. I also asked for ten one-pound coins by way of change, then headed on over to the car park. Thankfully there was no parking ticket on the front of Helen's car, so I walked across to the long-term pay & display machine, slotted in eight of the pound coins, took the little printed ticket and walked back to the car. Helen had left the key where she always did when we were out and about together, Blu-Tacked to the underside of the front number-plate holder. I placed the ticket on the dash, locked the door and replaced the key, then carefully undid the two lengths of knotted string and removed the fake sign from the taped-in compound. I left the tape and bollards in situ however; *nothing to do with me your honour, honest!* I then walked back along the quayside, back past the noisy, brightly-lit fairground rides that were all now in full swing, screaming away with deafening music and crowds of shrieking kids and adults alike, along with increasingly longer queues of emmets also awaiting their turn. I hated to think how raucous that was likely to become shortly before midnight, at just thirty feet away from the water's edge and the gangplank that led up onto the Marovonne's coachroof.

I stepped aboard and hopped down into the saloon, where the noise became significantly quieter as it radiated outwards over the top of the ship's roof. Nik had safely secured the RIB well out of sight, removed all the fishing tackle and stashed it back down below in the stores, and was in the process of getting changed into something a little tidier. I dumped the drinks on the side in the galley, took a quick strip-wash down in my cabin, then changed into some tidier togs myself too. I stepped back up into the wheelhouse at around five-thirty. Still no sign of Kev and the girlies, still no sign of Rue and Alan, and still no sign of the Joseph. Oh well, at least there's the sign of a pub! From where I was standing there was anyway, directly ahead of me! Through the ever growing collection of tall, swaying masts, I could still very clearly read the bold golden letters that proudly marked the location of one of my favourite local haunts, THE OLD CUSTOM HOUSE. Time to put phase two of my naughty little *Chrissy-plan* into action. I knocked on the side of the Roehampton, climbed aboard, and stuck my head through the aft saloon door. Everyone was sat around the comfortable array of sofas watching the TV, with the exception of Ray, who was stood behind his well-appointed home-built bar pouring several pints of draft Bass off the barrel.

"So, young lad," beamed Jamer immediately upon seeing me, "come to bring us all some nice, fresh sea fish then 'ave ee?"

"Er, no, like, sorry buddy," I replied awkwardly, "we caught plenty, but I'm afraid we cooked 'em all up, then ate 'em ourselves down on the beach. Bloody gorgeous mind! Sea bass mostly. No, I've stopped off to ask if any of you fancied coming over the Old Custom House for a beer with me and Nik, but by the looks of it you'll be savin' ya pennies by stayin"ere."

"Indeed we will young Christoff me lad," said Raymond, raising a half-filled pint glass towards me. "Thanks for the offer though me babber, maybe we'll pop over and join you a little later on this evening, we'll see 'ow we goes."

"Okay guys," I replied cheerfully, "well that's just so long as I'm still allowed in of course, otherwise it'll have to be some other place, but we'll see how we get along for starters."

"What's mean, *not allowed in?*" asked Jean inquisitively. "What you been and got up to now then?"

I pulled the large photo out of the envelope and showed it around to everyone.

"Oh my bloody giddy aunt!" exclaimed Ray as soon as he saw it. "You can't go round doing shit like that my son, you'll more 'n likely get yaself arrested for that. You know you ain't allowed to go within shootin' distance of one of Her Majesty's warships without an invite, let alone take the piss to that extent. Jesus Mary Mother of God, whatever next?"

"Well," I began confidently, "firstly, 'tis done, and by the looks of it, as I stand 'ere now, 't'aint gonna get undone! Secondly, she shouldn't have bloody crashed it in the first place. Thirdly, this *IS* an official regatta, so as far as I'm concerned, providing no one gets crushed or mashed, anything goes. And lastly, whilst all their top brass, *including* Lieutenant Moore, are all uniformed right up to the nines and hobnobbing it together over in the Custom House Inn, I feel it only fair and proper that I go stick this here little picture up on the wall for all to see. My bad, but perfectly planned, and hopefully now about to become perfectly executed too."

"Well you go bloody careful over there now sonny Jim," said Dave with a scowl, "'cos if you ain't, that's perzactly what you'm might become yerself; *executed!*"

"Not only that," warned Arthur seriously, "but I happened to notice earlier, the three most senior Border Force officers that are currently escorting young Ms Moore are both wearing holstered sidearms."

"Haha," I guffawed jokingly, "bring it on! What's a coupla pop-guns up to our massive barrage of *Super-Nerf Ultra-Dynamic Multi-Soaker Water-Pistols* anyway? Huh? They might win the scrap outside, but they'll never win the final battle!"

I stepped back aboard the Marovonne, sniggering quietly to myself, grabbed a pack of Blu-Tack from a cupboard in the saloon, stuck a lump in each corner of the photo, then slid it back into it's protective sleeve.

"Come along Mister Cabin Boy," I said to Nik cheerfully, "your turn to buy the beers buddy."

"Er, actually Skip," Nik stammered quietly, "I'm totally skint if the truth be known."

"Well now, there's a fuckin' surprise!" I said, ever so slightly annoyed. "Hey ho, situation normal I suppose. Come on, let's go anyway, we've got things to do, and more importantly, ale to drink. Follow me Roger."

As soon as we stepped ashore, I wandered casually along to the end of the quay, pretending that I was just watching the steady flow of yachts and motor cruisers entering the inner harbour one by one. Still no sign of the Joseph, even though it was now pushing six o'clock, however I did have the perfect vantage point from which to wave down to two more dear friends who'd just sailed in from Bristol, namely Rob and Little Kim aboard the Clair de Lune. I called down that we'd catch up with them for a beer in one of the pubs around town fairly soon, then turned and walked back past the Dasher, acknowledging the young uniformed cadet who stood guard aboard with his *unloaded* rifle. I knew that cadets were never allowed anywhere near real ammunition whilst aboard ship, however, far more importantly, I was extremely pleased to note that the Dasher was still proudly displaying her little stern L-Plate, which, as yet, had gone entirely unnoticed by all but countless members of the public. *Best foot forward it is then!*

"Here ya go young Nikolas, here's a tenner laddie," I said sarcastically, "now get yer ass up to the bar in the Custom House and order me a pint of Hicks, and get yaself whatever you fancy too. And if you get the opportunity, try and make sure no one in a uniform catches sight of what I'm about to get up to."

"Cheers Skip, I'll do my best," answered Nik meekly.

On the way to the pub we bumped into Kev, Sarah and Helen walking purposefully towards us, carrying several bags of shopping. I asked them if they fancied joining us, and they all said yes, but not until after they'd put the shopping away, had themselves a quick wash, and changed into something a little more suitable. I said; *'Okay, cool, we'll meet you all over in the Custom House shortly, but best make it pretty soon, Nik's only got a tenner on him!'* Kev almost laughed the socks off that he wasn't wearing, and Sarah turned around and innocently blurted out; *'Oh don't you worry about that Chris, I've brought plenty of money along with me!'* Now there's an interesting thought, I thought. We left the three of them to it and walked in through the front doors of the Custom House. It was busy, very busy indeed, with probably at least a third of the customers sporting full dress uniform, but it wasn't what you'd call *packed*, not like it got in the London, because it's a very large and spacious pub, is the Custom House, with plenty of room inside for folks to spread out. Nik approached the bar and ordered two pints of Hicks, whilst I subtly blended into the background with the envelope carefully hidden behind my back. I eyeballed the surrounding area, and immediately spotted the perfect location for my cunning little prank. The high ceilings were originally beamed, but some years ago the beams had been neatly boxed in and squared off with plasterboard, then tastefully decorated. They ran from left to right across the ceiling as you walked through the main door, and the front face of the one that was nearest to me was proudly displaying a collection of assorted naval memorabilia, interspersed with framed signed photographs of the various different naval vessels that had visited the town over the years. Taking pride of place right in the centre of the beam was a wonderful picture of HMS Dasher, with her crew of cadets all stood to attention, lined up along the quayside, and saluting. The photo was clearly some years old, as the ship's captain, who was stood dead-centre of the saluting contingent and flanked on either side by chief petty officers, was sporting a grey beard to be proud of, and clearly therefore not female. However, as I sneakily looked around, there was certainly more than one fully uniformed female officer stood close to the bar at the time, laughing, joking, and generally socialising with their superiors.

Fortunately there was a good space in between the picture of the Dasher and the Commander's white and gold combination cap that hung next to it, and after carefully ensuring that no one was looking over in my direction, I pulled a chair across to the centre of the room, stepped up onto it, then quickly and efficiently stuck the A4 portrait-style photo firmly and squarely onto the cream-painted plasterwork right between the two. I quickly stepped back down, replaced the chair, folded the envelope and shoved it in my back pocket, then reached out and took the pint of Hicks from Nik that he was holding out for me. I took a large gulp, then stepped back a few paces to admire my handiwork. *Stunning! Well impressed! How much shit was that going to get me into exactly?* Shortly after that, Kevin walked in with the girls, and the five of us approached the nearest side of the three-sided bar together. None of them had noticed the picture, and to be honest, I didn't think anyone would unless it was deliberately pointed out to them. *'Now there's a thought!'* I thought.

"Look at all them suits Skip," said Nik flippantly, "them's all drinkin' half pints of shandy. Bloody bunch o' lightweights!"

"They're all on duty mate," I replied. "They're not really supposed to be drinking at all whilst on duty, but then they are on a courtesy visit to their adopted home town for the sake of a festival, so on certain occasions such as this, just as Britannia once ruled the waves, I guess they're now allowed to waive the rules."

Lieutenant Moore and her equally-ranked female colleague were still hobnobbing it around the other end of the bar with their Commander in Chief and countless other top brass, most of whom had clearly arrived by road as opposed to by sea. It wasn't the Captain of the Vigilant, but his superior officer and his two Border Force sidekicks that all wore holstered sidearms, albeit they may well have been simply a part of their dress uniforms, and therefore purely for show. *Who knew?* So, do I tell them? Do I point out my little prank purely for the sake of a few laughs? Or do I let it ride? Leave the photo there for as long as possible until someone actually notices? More than anything I wanted to see the look on there faces when they discovered it, but dare I actually point it out to them myself? *What to do? What to do? What to do?* The five of us stood at the bar together, discussing the matter between ourselves, eyeballing the enemy whilst weighing up the odds.

"Them's the Navy," observed Kevin astutely, "we's pirates! *What could possibly go wrong?*"

HMS DASHER COMPLETE WITH L-PLATE

CHAPTER TWELVE

"WHAT'S THE MEANING OF THIS DAMNED BLOODY INSOLENCE EXACTLY?" bellowed a deep gruff voice from somewhere not far behind me all of a sudden.

For a brief second my blood ran cold, and I quickly span around to see, firstly, where the angry voice was coming from, and secondly, who it might potentially have been aimed at, whilst spilling a small drop of my pint down Helen's top in the process. It was clearly one of the most senior commanding officers, a three-gold-striped top brass military chap, who'd obviously just returned from the gent's toilets, which were situated just inside the main entrance away to the right. He was stood in the middle of the floor, staring up at the photo, and fuming significantly. Several other officers rushed across to find out what he was staring at, including one of the female lieutenants, although at the time I didn't know which one was which. As half a dozen senior naval officers dropped their jaws in stunned silence, the five of us steadily began to snigger uncontrollably.

"WHO, PRECISELY, IS RESPONSIBLE FOR THIS OUTRAGEOUS PRANK? I WANT TO KNOW, AND I WANT TO KNOW RIGHT NOW!"

He appeared to be addressing his own group of subordinates gathered around the bar, more so than any of the civilian fraternity gathered within, who probably outnumbered the officialdom somewhere in the region of three to one anyway. The remainder of the uniformed personnel hesitantly stepped forward in groups of twos and threes to take a peek at what the Commander was still staring wide-eyed at, and then disappeared back towards the bar, one or two of them clearly making an effort to stifle a fit of the giggles.

"WELL?" he continued angrily, *"I'M STILL WAITING, AND I'M NOT GOING TO WAIT ALL BLOODY DAY! SOMEONE WILL BE HELD RESPONSIBLE FOR THIS, PUT ON A CHARGE, AND GIVEN A MINIMUM OF DOUBLE-DUTIES FOR A WHOLE WEEK! SO WHO WAS IT?"*

His underlings all began fidgeting nervously amongst themselves, whilst the two female Lieutenants appeared to have snuck off around the corner to chat quietly amongst themselves. Suddenly Nik gave me a sharp dig in the ribs, forcing me to spill yet more of my pint, so I took several large swigs then placed the glass firmly down on the bar. Maybe it was me, maybe it was just coincidence, but the background music appeared to have stopped all of a sudden, and the pub had momentarily become deathly silent. Whilst once again forcing myself to choke back the laughter, I stepped forward and raised my hand.

"It was me sir," I said calmly, "I'm the person responsible, both for the photo *and* for sticking the L-Plate on the back of the Dasher in the first place. No one else is to blame sir, solely myself."

"YOU? WHO THE BLOODY HELL ARE YOU SONNY?" he hollered at me.

"Name's Chris Reason sir," I replied as calm as you like, "and I'm sure we'd all appreciate it if you kept your voice down a little, there are families with children in here trying to eat their dinner in peace."

"WHAT THE HELL? DO YOU HAVE ANY IDEA WHO YOU'RE TALKING TO?" he continued.

"Who I'm listening to more like!" I retorted quietly. "Yes sir, indeed I do, now *please* sir, lower your voice a little."

"Are you not aware of the fact that it's strictly against the law to lay a single finger on one of Her Majesty's warships without prior invitation?" he asked me, lowering his voice considerably whilst giving me a cold, piercing, icy stare, *"let alone stick Goddam stickers on one!"*

"Aye sir, that I am sir," I replied confidently.

"Are you not aware, sonny Jim, that it's an arrestable offence to do so?" he questioned me, with not a single blink coming from those intense, piercing blue eyes of his.

"Indeed I am sir," I answered, allowing him to continue the charade with his brief moment of presumed power.

"And do you not care one single hoot about this fact?" he asked, now clearly becoming a little stupefied over my perfectly straightforward series of answers.

"No sir, I don't," I replied flatly.

"WHAT THE BLOODY HELL D'YOU MEAN, YOU DON'T CARE? YOU'LL PAY HEAVILY FOR SUCH INSOLENCE YOUNG MAN! WHAT IF THAT HAD BEEN A BLOODY LIMPET MINE OR SOMETHING?" he yelled, raising his voice considerably once again.

"Well it wasn't, was it!" I replied calmly. "And I'm sorry, but we don't do *'What ifs'* where I come from. Either it was, or it wasn't, and you, along with everyone else present, can quite clearly see that it wasn't. So, end of!"

The remainder of his group of senior officers and subordinates, whilst still all crowded around the far end of the bar together, were noticeably beginning to cringe, and my guess was that they'd already begun to see the joke in the correct humorous context in which it was originally intended. And although Helen and Sarah were both beginning to look just a mite worried, Nik and Kev had been forced to turn their faces away for fear of cracking up laughing. Unfortunately for the commanding officer, however, he then made one sudden fatal error. He placed his right hand on top of his service revolver.

"I must insist that you remove your hand from your weapon immediately sir," I demanded firmly.

"Under who's authority?" he queried. "And more to the point, to what end exactly?"

"To what end? What on earth are you suggesting, *sir?* Purely for the purpose of keeping the peace and not allowing this situation to escalate any further," I stated forcefully, and then added with a distinct air of pride; "I have to warn you sir, I have a 3rd Dan black belt in Origami, and if you don't remove your hand from your weapon immediately I shall be forced to tear several pages from the bar snacks menu and fashion them however I deem most appropriate to diffuse this situation."

There was a sudden explosion of laughter immediately behind me, and Nik fell to his knees, clutching desperately at Kev's trousers for fear of rolling around in fits. Kev was absolutely no help whatsoever, he was in tears himself, and even some of the other uniformed guys were openly cackling by now.

"WHO THE BLOODY HELL ARE YOU SUNSHINE? I WANT YOUR NAME AND ADDRESS RIGHT NOW!" the Commander shouted at me, thankfully removing his hand from his pistol.

"I already told you my name sir, it's Chris Reason," I answered him as calmly as a judge, "and that's Reason as in reason, if you get either mine or it's meaning. Anyway, if you'll just step outside with me for one brief moment, I'll gladly show you precisely where I live."

I stepped past him, lightly brushing his shoulder as I did so, pushed through the door and held it open for him. Tentatively at first, he turned and took a couple of steps towards the door, and then, regaining his authoritative pose once again, he pushed past me and stood bolt upright in the centre of the pavement. I let the door close on itself, reached over his shoulder, and pointed directly towards the Marovonne.

"That, sir, is *my* ship! She's called the Marovonne, and I live aboard, *permanently!* She's British registered, and the flag that we fly whilst at sea is the Red Ensign. The flag that we fly whilst attending an official harbour regatta, as I'm sure you can clearly see for yourself, is the Scull & Crossbones, therefore rendering myself and my crew official pirates of the party. And this, whether you've yet recognised it as such or not, is quite clearly *not* an official Naval exercise, but purely an ordinary civilian party. Furthermore sir, as you also may or may not have noticed, we're currently your next door neighbour, and it's always been my humble opinion that next door neighbours should make every effort to get along with one another.

Now sir, correct me if I'm wrong please, but is this an official open-to-all-comers harbour regatta, or is it not?"

The Commander simply grunted, without actually acknowledging me.

"And is it, or is it not, customary for lighthearted practical jokes to be played on one another during the course of an official harbour regatta? In precisely the same way that it's not only permitted, but *encouraged* even, to fly flags of an incorrect nautical nature. *Etcetera, etcetera, ad nauseam!* Am I correct?"

Another grunt.

"Now then sir, whilst I have the utmost respect for the Navy, for HM Customs, for both the Dasher and the Vigilant, for all of your officers and crew and the admirable and outstanding work that they carry out on behalf of our Queen and country, and also, I must add, for Lieutenant Sue Moore herself, regardless of our entertaining little prank at her expense, *but you sir,* I'm legally obliged to inform you, have no jurisdiction here whatsoever. You're clearly outnumbered here by your average gathering of common or garden civilians such as ourselves, so the best thing I can suggest you do right now, *sir,* is to rejoin your band of loyal, merry men, and ladies, *pipe the fuck down, and LIGHTEN UP!*"

I was about to add further threats relating to the enormous complexities of folding paper into incredibly complex shapes when the Commander simply spun on his heels, stuck his nose in the air, and stomped back off inside to rejoin his fellow officers. Feeling rather proud of myself as to how I'd handled a potentially worrying situation, I strolled back inside, snatched up my pint off the bar, downed the remainder of it in one go, then told Nik and Kev in no uncertain terms to pull themselves together. Helen and Sarah had ceased with their worried expressions, and even as I hastily ordered another round of drinks for the five of us, the congregation of uniforms on the other side of the bar at least appeared to have resumed relatively normal levels of conversation. All, apparently, bar one junior officer, whom I presumed had been instructed to get on the phone immediately, which was clearly what he was now urgently doing, having stepped just a few paces away from his compatriots.

Anyway, *'enough of this frivolity'* I thought to myself, my little prank had succeeded as well as I could have hoped for, it was time to move on.

No sooner had I started on my second pint, one that I was determined to savour this time, than Rob and Little Kim walked in through the front door. As soon as Kim saw Helen and myself she ran straight up to us, threw her arms around the pair of us together, and gave as a *'raht big northern-style hoog!'*

"Awww, it's sooooooo loovly ta see the pair o' ya's," she exclaimed excitedly.

After Rob had shaken my hand and given Helen a customary kiss on both cheeks, I introduced both him and Little Kim to Kevin and Sarah, who all exchanged greetings together. After which both Rob and Kim looked Nik up and down, and with cheeky grins they both sarcastically acknowledged that; *'We already know this naughty young rascal from somewhere, now don't we!'* I wondered for a second what history lay behind that, but quickly let it drop. Instead I simply asked them if they'd had a pleasant voyage down, to which they replied that they'd anchored in Landing Bay off the southern tip of Lundy Island along the way, and fed themselves on freshly-caught mackerel. *'Hmmm,'* I thought to myself, *'now that one rings a few bells!'* I asked Rob how easily he'd managed to find a mooring slot out in the harbour, and whether he'd had any contact with the Joseph on the way down.

"Mooring the Clair de Lune was beginning to look a little tricky as soon as we sailed in," Rob replied honestly, whilst Kim stepped up to the bar on tiptoe to order their drinks, "but then Malcolm, the Harbourmaster, who'd clearly left the comfort of his office to give Steve a hand, because Steve was gradually beginning to panic, he immediately directed us alongside another 30ft motor cruiser, similar to ours, three boats astern of the Courageous. So now we're right in the centre of the South Quay, three boats out from the wall. Bit of climbing around to get ashore, but it'll do fine. Safe passage yourself Chris?"

"Yes mate, no problems whatsoever. Straight here, then laid to anchor just this side of Pentire whilst waiting on the tide.

Other than local boats there were no other vessels in here when we arrived. We even beat the Dasher in for a change. Talking of which, come take a quick look at this picture I stuck up on the wall earlier."

I pointed the photo out to Rob, who stood staring at it for some considerable moments looking somewhat flabbergasted.

"You never bloody did Chris, did you?" he asked incredulously.

"Too bloody right I did," I replied proudly, "although the chances are there's probably some young uniformed cadet stood aboard as we speak, reaching precariously over her stern transom with a long sharp stick trying to scrape it back off."

"Hahaha," chuckled Rob, "one up for the lads. Bloody women drivers!"

Kim went to hand him his pint, then accidentally on purpose spilt a whole load of it down his clean white trousers whilst looking at Helen and myself with a broad grin, and winking at each of us in turn. I laughed aloud at Rob's expense, because I felt it was the polite thing to do in front of a dear friend, who was also a highly competent sailor in her own right, but at the same time I gave Rob a gentle nudge in the ribs, just to let him know that my feelings were ultimately on his side really. I asked Rob again whether he'd heard anything from Rick on the Joseph, noting that the time was getting on towards seven o'clock, very shortly after which the barrage gates would be locking everyone in until two hours before the next high tide, which was just before twenty past five the following morning.

"The last I heard from Rick," replied Rob, peering out through the window just to check that the Joseph wasn't squeezing through the gates at the very last minute, which clearly she wasn't, "he said they were going to stop off in Ilfracombe on the way down for a spot of grub. Mind you, he did give me the impression that he had one hell of a party joining him aboard, including a certain very well known Irish musician 'n' all. So who knows, maybe they're all still *'rockin' the boat'* somewhere well out to sea, so to speak. 'Tis virtually perfect conditions out there for an offshore *Céilidh*, what more can I say?"

"Nah, I can't see Rick doing that in the dark somehow," I said, disagreeing with Rob's thoughts. "If that noisy young Irish rapscallion has kicked off one of his impromptu but unstoppable Céilidhs yet again, it'll at least be within the safety of Ilfracombe harbour. Maybe the party got a little out of hand and they missed the tide or something, stuff like that happens along the way sometimes, especially in a harbour that dries out at low tide. But I know Rick well, certainly well enough to know that he'll be here at some point. If Rick says he's going to do something, he does it, no question about it, it's as simple as that. In fact, there's a group of four of us altogether that have always had that very same mindset when it comes to passage planning, and come this time tomorrow night I guarantee you that all four will be somewhere hereabouts, having a pint or three together, and drinking a toast to the Merry Morning of May. Those four being, very specifically, me, Ronnie, Rick and Raymondo. Oh look, *talk of the bloody devil!*"

No sooner had I mentioned his name, than guess who should walk through the door, but none other than Raymondo himself. Accompanied, of course, by his own loyal band of merry men, and ladies, who all approached us at the bar, welcomed Rob and Kim to the party, and began ordering their drinks. Jean appeared somewhat exuberant, and began chatting excitedly to Helen, so I made a point of surreptitiously earwigging their conversation. It seemed they'd all set their hearts on having one of *Granny's Pasties* for tea, and I couldn't agree more as to what a perfect choice of meal they'd all made. So much so in fact that I asked if they'd mind if we joined them, and when they all agreed that they'd be delighted, I shoved two long tables together over by the window, then walked back up to the bar just to check with the staff that they had more than enough pasties to feed all thirteen of us.

"Oi'l jus' pop out back an' check for ee," said the polite young waitress, "but if us a'mt, us c'n always pop down't road an' grab a few more for ee frum arr Granny, nowt stress there folks."

Granny's Pasties were the *best*, and I mean the *BEST!* They were made locally in a tiny little shop just around the corner from the London Inn, and according to Granny herself, no matter whether the shop was open or shut, she *'never ran out!'* They weren't all necessarily to everyone's taste, because they made every flavour of pastie imaginable, including peanut-butter and apricot jam ones! Flavoured ones aside however, their bog-standard traditional Cornish pastie, I can honestly say, hand on heart, was by far the best I'd ever had throughout the whole of my worldly travels, and a whole hearty meal one of those big boys made too. I congratulated Jean on her first-class choice of evening meal, and once everyone had been served with their drinks, and we'd all ordered a total of thirteen servings of piping-hot pasties, because we'd all agreed unanimously that Jean's was a cracking idea, we headed across to the table that I'd sneakily placed a small plastic *RESERVED* sign in the centre of. Before taking our seats, I pointed out my photograph stuck ceremoniously up on the ceiling bulkhead to Ray and his crew.

"So how did you manage to wriggle out of the handcuffs then, you wicked young scallywag?" Ray asked me jokingly.

"Gift of the gab buddy," I simply replied, "gift of the gab. Anyway, *my pirate flag's bigger than theirs, so there, nah nah nah nah nah!*"

We took our seats, and everyone immediately began chatting incessantly. Ray was chatting to Rob about compass bearings and waypoints, Shiela was chatting to Sarah about which different pasty fillings were acceptable and which weren't, and Jean was chatting to Little Kim about the pros and cons of cooking mackerel aboard ship on a Primus stove in the dark. Dave and Kevin were well off on one about getting the ferry across to Rock and trashing each other at pool, whereas Nik, Arthur and myself had begun a deep and meaningful conversation about the origins of the two Osses, and the likely chances of meeting one or the other the following day. As for Helen and Jamer, it was hard to make out whether they were scheming together, or just lightheartedly squabbling. However, it wasn't long before our pasties all arrived, carried out from the kitchen by the chef and three waitresses in convoy, and it wasn't very long after that either, whilst all thirteen of us silently chomped away on absolutely delicious mouthfuls of true Cornish meat and potato pie, that one of the waitresses subtly pulled a chair across to the centre of the room. When she thought I wasn't watching, which in actual fact I was, she stepped up onto the chair, pulled the photograph down off the bulkhead, stepped back down, walked across behind the bar, and handed it in plain sight to the Commanding Naval Officer, who by now was drinking strong black coffee. I was so wrapped up in both my meal and my conversation that I pretended not to notice, however the Commander was clearly waiting to catch my attention before ceremoniously tearing the photo into two pieces. And then four, and then eight, and then evidently struggling to manage sixteen, and eventually he threw all eight pieces angrily down onto the bar, whilst I made a clear point of staring intently at him as he did so. I chuckled to myself, whilst at the same time decidedly allowing him to have what he genuinely believed to be the last laugh. Even though I think most of us had clocked his inability to tear eight sheets of photographic paper into sixteen all in one go. I felt like walking over and offering him a volume of the Yellow Pages, but the joke was over, there was little point in prolonging it, let alone antagonising him still further, so I merely resumed my interest in what remained of my delicious pasty, and added just a tiny drop more Daddies brown sauce to the side of my plate.

By nine o'clock we'd all finished our delicious meals, and with another round of drinks newly delivered to our table, we renewed our noisy conversation, this time much of it aimed at the expense of the Naval and Customs officers who had all long since retired to their respective quarters. It wouldn't have surprised me in the slightest had their Commander in Chief taken a chauffeur-driven limousine to an awaiting helicopter somewhere on the outskirts of town. I doubted that our paths would ever cross again, although I suspected that mine and Lt Sue Moore's quite possibly might. Whilst halfway through our current round of drinks, everyone still deep in conversation, the debate that had being going on between Helen and Jamer appeared to be becoming increasingly more animated, even though they were both clearly laughing and joking about whatever it was they were discussing. All of a sudden, with a big grin across his face, Jamer slammed his almost empty glass down on the table, and in a deep, loud and mock-grumpy voice, he hollered;

"Listen now Helen me dear, you ain't never gonna get me up on one o' them bloody machines, not now, not never, and not for love nor money. Good grief girl, I'm damned nearly eighty bloody years old, what's the matter with ee? Think o' me 'eart, for pity's sake. Them machines is fer kids ya knows, not fer the likes of old'uns like ey. Do us a favour moi babber, leave it out now, innit."

"Come on Jamer, there's nowt wrong with ya heart!" enthused Helen encouragingly, "and you ain't nearly eighty neither, you're only seventy-six. So get with the programme buddy and come on up on the old *Wipe Out* with me. Come on me old mucker, just the one go, and I promise I'll hold ya hand for the whole ride."

The rest of us had cottoned on to where Helen was coming from by now, and as we finished our drinks one by one, we all joined in with the encouragement. Not only that, but we grew steadily louder, and by the time we'd all settled up the bar tab and removed ourselves noisily from the pub, the chanting of almost a dozen voices began resounding around the harbour, even above the noise of the fairground;

"JAMER, JAMER, JAMER," we all cheered in unison, as we gradually ambled along the quayside towards the Marovonne.

Which, *coincidentally*, just happened to be moored right opposite the Wipe Out ride. Plus, *coincidentally*, as we slowly approached the Wipe Out, it had stopped once again at the very bottom of it's high-speed revolution so as to allow one set of riders off, and a new set, who'd clearly been queuing patiently whilst awaiting their turn, to climb on and strap themselves in. Nearly a couple dozen new riders climbed on, leaving just half a dozen remaining in the queue, the safety harnesses came down and clamped them all firmly into position, and to the screaming tunes of the old pop hit *Wipe Out* by The Surfaris, off it went again, around and around and around. And off we all went again too;

"JAMER, JAMER, JAMER, JAMER, JAMER, JAMER!"

"Oh bollocks!" said poor old Jamer. "Looks like I ain't gonna get away with this one then, doesn't it girls!"

"Don't you worry Jamer," said Sarah sympathetically, "I'll come on it with you too. Helen and I can sit one of us either side of you, that way you'll have *nothing whatsoever* to worry about. Anyway, I love these rides to pieces, and I've been on this particular one loads of times. Trust me, it's child's play."

"Well, young ladies, it looks very much to me like I have no choice, doesn't it," Jamer sulked, although still with a huge grin across his face. "Come along then, let's go get in the queue."

Helen, Jamer and Sarah went and joined the back of the queue, whilst I stepped up to the kiosk, purchased three tickets, then handed them one each. Moments later the ride stopped, the harnesses automatically raised, the previous riders exited via the raised checkerplate walkway, and the next group of riders, including Helen, Jamer and Sarah, all climbed aboard and braced themselves for their brief, cheap, fairground thrill ride. The other ten of us stood back a little on the quayside, ready to cheer them on and shout encouragement every time they came around. Their harnesses lowered, and then suddenly they were off, slowly at first, but then gradually faster and faster. And the faster the Wipe Out span, the louder everyone's screams became. I couldn't hear Jamer, but I could *definitely* hear Helen's and Sarah's screams, especially each time the long row of seats reached their highest point of travel, and even above the countless decibels of 1960's pop music too. Then, all of a sudden, halfway through the ride, it began to rain. Not drops of water, but showers of coins. Little coins; pennies, two's, five's, twenty-pences, they were raining down all around us, clattering across the checkerplate and rolling out onto the quayside. And it didn't take too long for everyone to spot precisely where this huge shower of coins was emanating from either. Yep, you've guessed it folks; *Jamer's pockets! 'Oh well, not a lot to be done about that then',* I thought to myself, as half a dozen youngsters began running around, collecting them all up, and shoving them deep into their own pockets. Moments later the ride began to slow, then after one more revolution it stopped at the bottom, the safety harnesses raised themselves, and everyone stood up to begin exiting. Everyone bar Jamer that was, who, despite the broad grin still spread across his face, was clearly quite incapable of standing. Sarah was the first of the three to exit, following which she immediately dived around the back of the machine and vomited violently all down the face of the harbour wall. Ray then stepped onto the machine, and between him and Helen they carefully helped Jamer to his feet, and then slowly and steadily back along the walkway and down onto the quayside. I managed to find him an old plastic chair with a backrest, and sat him down well away from the crowds that were queuing for the next ride, in order that he could relax and get his breath back.

"Love it, love it, love it," was about all poor old Jamer could manage to come out with. *"Legs not working, love it, love it, legs won't work, love it, wanna go again!"*

"Er, I think maybe that ought to wait at least until tomorrow," said Ray and I, more or less in unison.

Meanwhile, Kevin was comforting Sarah, whilst escorting her own somewhat wobbly legs back aboard ship, whereas Helen, Ray and I were doing our best to look after Jamer in the hope that we could get his legs working once again in the very near future. Arthur had already retired back aboard the Roehampton, not in the slightest bit interested in any of our childish frivolity, and Jean, Shiela and Little Kim were stood a short distance away from us, waiting at a stall for their candy flosses to be spun for them. Dave, Nik and Rob, after cracking up laughing at the absurdity of the bigger part of our day, had set off back into town together in search of more alcoholic beverages. After resting for about five minutes Jamer was successfully able to walk again, albeit on exceptionally wobbly old pins, but with a considerable amount of help from Ray and myself we managed to get him safely back aboard the Roehampton. Helen went over and ordered herself a candy floss too, then escorted the other three ladies back aboard the Marovonne, and I simply did what I invariably tend to do on such occasions, I headed back into town in search of more alcoholic beverages too! When I returned some hours later, if I wasn't very much mistaken, the girls had gotten through at least two bottles of Mateus Rosé between the four of them, *despite* Shiela professing on numerous occasions to being teetotal. In the meantime, however, I set my sights on trying to locate Dave, Nik and Rob.

WIPE OUT AT THE FAIRGROUND

CHAPTER THIRTEEN

'Twas now the very Eve of May, with still just a couple of hours to go until midnight. I stuck my head through the front door of the Custom House, and although it was exceptionally busy, with a modicum of neck straining I managed to notice no one whatsoever that I recognised. There was little point in trying the Golden Lion, as being the home of the Old Red Oss that would've essentially been tantamount to a far left extremist walking into a Conservative Club. No, my next most logical step, before trying the Shipwright's, would be the London Inn once again. I trotted up through Broad Street, past the highly decorated Maypole, then back down through the narrow little streets until I reached the London. It was a real tight squeeze simply trying to open the front door, but once inside there was no mistaking the tall lanky silhouette of Long Tom stood over against the far wall, just to one side of the bar. I pushed my way through the crowd and eventually stumbled across one and all, hogging the whole of one of the alcoves, with insufficient chairs around the large rectangular table for everyone to be seated. Catriona was sitting though, with Long Tom, her ever-smiling boyfriend, leant against the wall immediately behind her. They were always exceptionally friendly, were Tom and Catriona, and very much loved by everyone around Bristol's historic harbour, particularly all the members of Bristol Cruising Club, especially as Tom regularly played in a local jazz band most Sunday evenings aboard Sabrina, the club's licensed static Dutch barge. I couldn't see him playing anywhere locally that particular weekend though, the traditional music of May Day was strictly for Padstonians only; evolved for, performed by, and danced to mainly by locals only, and most definitely not to be out-performed or ridden shotgun over by outsiders. *That, my friends, would be pure sacrilege!* I ordered a pint of Tribute from the bar and joined in with the general conversation. Johnnie was bragging about how many girls he had in however many ports he'd sailed into, along with *potentially* how many children may have been conceived by them entirely down to his very best efforts. Rue was desperately trying to offload some tatty old faded red Porsche 924 that he'd managed to acquire from God only knows where, to anyone who might be vaguely interested, for next to nothing, which, in reality, was exactly what it was worth. Alan was trying to join in the conversation too, but was struggling somewhat with the words that simply seemed to be dribbling down the front of his shirt. Ronnie was trying his best to keep order, whilst counting up a rather large stack of coins that he'd clearly won off everyone whilst playing *Shoot,* and failing miserably every time he got halfway through the stack. Rob and Dave were busily downing their pints in a desperate attempt to equalise their alcohol consumption with the others, and Nik was trying his damnedest to get them all to continue with their game of Shoot. *I wondered why!* Having said that, I'm actually quite a dab hand at Shoot myself too, so why not? *Let's see if we can't grab some of that little stack of loot back from greedy old Ronnie then!*

"Your deal then Ron," I shouted above the din, watching Nik's eyes pop wide open in anticipation.

And he did too. He shoved a large handful of coins into the centre of the table and dealt two cards to all but Catriona, who'd already decided that the whole idea behind the game was nothing but reckless irresponsibility, and rightly so too I might add. Johnnie immediately shot and lost, doubling the pot. Rue waged a pound and won. Alan folded, although realistically that may simply have been because he couldn't focus clearly enough on either of the two cards he held in his hand. I waged a pound and won. Nik went two pounds, and also won, and Tom shouted in a whole fifty pence, which he lost. *Second deal Ronnie!* John was a little more careful this time, he bet two pounds and won. Rue waged a pound once again, but this time he lost. Alan shouted fifty pence, just for the hell of it, but almost inevitably he lost too. I had a rubbish hand, a three and a five, so I stacked. Nik was feeling exceptionally brave, and bet three quid, but lost, and Tom managed to win back his fifty pence that he'd lost during the first round. *Third and final deal Ronnie-boy!* John stacked, slamming his rubbish pair of cards down on the table in anger. Rue tried his luck at two quid and won. Alan called a pound, and to everyone's surprise, *including his own,* he won. I ummed and ahhed for a few seconds over the two cards I'd been dealt, then called a brave three quid on them, which fortunately I won, leaving, at a very rough guess, some twenty-odd quid remaining in the pot. Nik looked at his cards once, then twice, then a third time, and then, somehow inevitably, or so it seemed to me, he called *Shoot!* Ronnie turned over the king of clubs, and everyone sucked in a long, deep breath. Nik hesitated, looked up with a glum expression on his face, which very, very slowly morphed into a wide smile, and he threw the ace of clubs down on top of the king. Leaving poor old Tom without a go, which was quite sad for him, because he happened to be holding a pair of queens. Hey ho, *the next round's on Nik then!* Nik stepped up to the bar with his hands overloaded with shrapnel, scattered it across the bar, and politely asked the young barman if he would kindly pour another drink for everyone present. *'Oh, and best get poor old dejected-looking Ronnie over there a double please!'* The shrapnel that Nik scattered across the bar more than covered the round of drinks, and he threw the remainder into the centre of the table, declaring firmly that it was now his turn to act as banker. And so the evening went on, until we were all unceremoniously requested to vacate the premises at precisely eleven thirty. Not just our crowd, but everyone. The *Eve* was upon us, the merriment wasn't far from commencing, and all pub landlords in the heart of the town were required to prepare themselves for that dreaded potential bang on the bolted and shuttered front door, starting at midnight and continuing well beyond. Whereupon, the singing outside of the infamous *May Night Song* by the locals in costume would signal the demand for half a pint of free ale each, which would willingly be given up by the landlord and landlady, with their blessings and gratitude for the final arrival of yet another summer.

"No Nik, we can't join in with the begging ritual," I reprimanded him sternly, "this is very much a locals-only tradition, and not for emmets or outsiders such as ourselves to get involved in. Stand back, watch and marvel by all means, but you're not staying up all night long, banging on closed pub doors, begging for half pints of ale. Leave that little ritual to the traditionalists all dressed up in their appropriate costumes please."

"I'm quite happy to run back to the ship and put a dress on," volunteered Dave enthusiastically.

"NO DAVE!" shouted Chris angrily!

Kicking out time had happened awfully suddenly, and as we ambled through the narrow windy streets together it was surprising how remarkably busy it had become all of a sudden. The streets were packed with both locals and tourists alike, many of the locals now wearing fancy costumes, and heading towards what appeared to be the general direction of the Golden Lion. Whether it was because we weren't in any particular hurry, or because we'd all decided just to be nosey, or because one or two of our group couldn't even walk in a straight line anyway, I wasn't entirely sure, but either way we decided to take the long route home, which just so happened to take us past the Golden Lion Inn, and eventually brought us back out by the Custom House. At precisely midnight, a large gathering of costumed locals, unaccompanied by musicians of any kind, began singing the infamous *Padstow May Night Song* in the street right outside the firmly shut front door of the Golden Lion Inn.

Unite and unite and let us all unite,
For summer is a-come unto day,
And whither we are going we will all unite,
In the merry morning of May.

I warn you young men everyone,
For summer is a-come unto day,

To go to the green-wood and fetch your May home,
In the merry morning of May.

Arise up Mr Hide and joy you betide,
For summer is a-come unto day,
And bright is your bride that lies by your side,
In the merry morning of May.

Arise up Mrs Bling and gold be your ring,
For summer is a-come unto day,
And give to us a cup of ale the merrier we shall sing,
In the merry morning of May.

Arise up Miss Lean all in your gown of green,
For summer is a-come unto day,
You are as fine a lady as wait upon the Queen,
In the merry morning of May.

Now fare you well, and we bid you all good cheer,
For summer is a-come unto day,
We call once more unto your house before another year,
In the merry morning of May.

Halfway through the song the front door was ceremoniously unbolted, and the landlord and landlady stepped outside with a tray each full of half pints of ale. Once they'd handed them all out to the locals mid-tune they then joined in with singing the remainder of the song themselves too. Once the song was sung, the ales drunk and the glasses returned to the trays, the landlord and landlady then bid the crowd a Merry Eve of May, returned back inside, and ceremoniously rebolted the door. The gathered crowd then debated noisily amongst themselves before moving on to their next pub of choice.

"Right then lads," I said, putting my best foot forward, whilst at the same time attempting to stop Alan from falling flat on his face, "this malarkey's gonna go on all bloody night long, or at least until they drop to their knees, which looks precisely what a couple of us may well be doing before too long if we ain't careful. So, seeing as this is *their* night, and not *ours,* once again, can I suggest we all just get our asses back aboard ship and grab some well-earned kip. *PLEASE!*"

"You go on ahead Chris," said Ron gracefully. "Leave Johnnie to me mate, Tom'll give us a hand getting him back aboard, no worries."

I said thank you to Ronnie, bid Tom and Catriona a pleasant night's sleep too, then told them all that we'd be seeing them again bright and early in the Merry Morning of May. I wasn't entirely convinced that many of us were going to be up particularly bright and early, *especially* Alan, but I said it anyway, just by way of wishing them goodnight. Fortunately for us the fairground had shut down by the time we made it back to the Marovonne, making it somewhat easier to help Alan across the gangplank without the fear of some kind of serious catastrophe occurring. Nik and Rue helped him down into his for'ard bunk room, although whether they'd managed that without waking Kevin and Sarah up I've no idea. Shortly after that Nik said goodnight himself and disappeared off down into his aft cabin, leaving me to clear away the empty bottles of Mateus and dirty wine glasses that the girls had left lying around on the saloon table, before heading off down to my own cabin and climbing into bed with my dearly beloved. I drifted gradually into a pleasant, relaxed sleep that night, and dreamt peacefully of fair young maidens escaping the clutches of angry red and blue stallions by rushing into the safety of my own waiting arms. *Chance would be a fine thing!*

Christopher John Reason

AN AERIAL VIEW OF PADSTOW HARBOUR

CHAPTER FOURTEEN

I awoke bright and breezy on the Merry Morning of May, which is far more than I can say for the remaining crew aboard the Marovonne. Quietly leaving Helen fast asleep, and the rest of them snoring so loudly, to the point where I swear the entire ship's hull was sending ripples out across the otherwise tranquil surface of the harbour, I pulled on shorts and a tee shirt, and shortly before 9am I stepped lazily out onto the aft deck.

"Oss! Oss! Wee Oss! I called loudly across the water, as if by way of a general early morning wake up call to all and sundry around the harbour. Not that all and sundry were by any means visible anymore, as I was surrounded on all three sides by the countless hulls and masts of ships that were, for the most part, somewhat larger than mine. And nothing but the solid granite blocks of the harbour wall up against my port side, causing a slight echo to my noisy words in the stillness of the early morn.

"Morning Chris," came the soft, calm, gentle words of a female voice from somewhere I couldn't immediately make out directly ahead of me. And then, moments later, I clocked her. A smartly-uniformed young senior officer stood at ease out on the front deck of the Dasher, inspecting and noting the entire surrounds of the ship that she herself commanded.

"Ah, top o' the mornin' to ya Sue," I replied pleasantly, in my very best Bristolian pirate accent, "I trust ee managed ee's self a good night's kip amongst all these 'ere noisy goin's on okay?"

"Indeed I did Chris, thank you," she replied, again surprisingly pleasantly. "I will add though," she continued, with a clearly lighthearted attitude that was easily noticeable by her friendly smile, "that I have now officially passed my parking test, and therefore have no further requirement for L-Plates."

"Ah, congratulations me dear," I replied with the tiniest bit of friendly sarcasm, "you'm wuz noticeably conspicuous by yer absence down 'ere last year ya knows. Anyways-up, please excuse me little bit 'o skylarkin' around, t'was only done in the best spirit o' the 'arbour festival, innit. No offence meant moi luvver."

"None taken Chris," she replied, smiling sweetly. "Just make sure it never happens again please."

"Yes ma'am," I replied obediently, "I wouldn't dare ma'am. Once wuz fer fun. Twice just ain't funny 't'all. No worries there Sue me dear."

"Thank you," she acknowledged, threw me a friendly wave, then turned and strolled back along her ship's starboard-side walkway towards the aft deck.

'Phew!' I immediately thought to myself, *'looks like I managed to get away with that one then!'*

I grabbed my wash-bag and headed on over to the shower block, and just as I stepped up onto the footbridge across the firmly-shut harbour entrance gates, I looked diagonally across to my left, and *'quelle surprise'*, the Joseph was in! *'Well, well, they must've made it in on the 05.24hrs early morning top of the tide then, or an hour or two either side of it maybe,'* I immediately thought to myself; *'Thank goodness for that!'* There were no signs of life aboard as yet, although that was clearly understandable, so I headed on into the shower block and spent the next twenty minutes luxuriously soaking under steaming hot high-pressure water, amongst other things. After towelling off and dressing again, I stepped out onto the quayside, only to notice Rick out on deck, sorting out various clutter and generally tidying up the free ends of the Joseph's mooring warps. She'd docked starboard-side-to against the North Quay, the area that Malcolm and Steve deliberately kept strictly clear for late arrivals and emergency vessels, and her bow was right up in the top corner, facing directly onto the roadside, with the Quayside Café directly opposite, more or less in exactly the same place that I'd moored the

Marovonne when we'd first arrived. I wandered over to the Joseph, exchanged polite *'good mornings'* with Rick, and asked him why the delay.

"What kept ya buddy?" I began, the relief at seeing him quite clear in my expression. "We were expecting you in on yesterday evening's tide, along with the rest of the crazy mad rush. Problems along the way or anything?"

"Nothing we couldn't handle matey," replied Rick confidently. "Had a bit of a minor delay in Ilfracombe, ended up missing a tide and 'avin' a bit of a crew change. We set off from Bristol with this mad Irish bloke aboard, you know, the one that keeps on taking his acoustic guitar out on deck and encouraging everyone else aboard to sing along with him, which, for the most part, they did, which was actually quite good fun. However, he jumped ship later that evening, said he was gonna head back to Bristol, pick up the other two members of his band, load all his amplifiers 'n' stuff in the back of his van and meet us back down in Padstow. He mumbled something to the effect of; *'If 'e was gonna do it, then 'e was gonna do it good 'n' proper like!'* So Will the Blacksmith, along with Little Dave the Shipwright and his lovely young wife Jo, they all got a bit of a late start leavin' town, so they drove on down to Ilfracombe to meet up with us. Davey then drove Will's van back to Bristol for him, which seemed like a good ideal at the time, but I reckon's we'd best keep a right proper eye on the bloke by the time 'e gets back down 'ere mind, 'e's a bit of a lad is that there Black Jack Davey!"

"Oh my God," I exclaimed, "not Black Jack Davey? Not Wylde Green themselves? *Please, no?*"

"I'm afraid so," replied Rick with a grin. "Davey, the vocalist, guitarist and comedian, Paul the piper *and* Kate the fiddle player, the entire Wylde Green outfit, amplifiers 'n' all. They're on their way down here right now, as Poseidon's my witness, and they'll be playing a coupla well know Irish folk songs aboard the Joseph a bit later on. Just for a short while. *Or at least, that's what he promised!"*

Oh great!" I said, matching Rick's grin with an even bigger one. *"What could possibly go wrong?"*

"Anyways-up, mustn't hang around 'ere chattin' for too long matey," Rick stated with an air of urgency, "we's got a right busy schedule ahead of us today. Lloyd and Cathy's gettin' married in an hours time, and I'm actin' Master o' Ceremonies, so I've got a whole programme of events to sort out, and not a whole lotta time to sort 'em out in."

"What d'ya mean, Lloyd and Cath are getting married?" I asked incredulously. *"When the hell did that all start? That's certainly the first I've heard anything about it!"*

"Well," said Rick hesitantly, "it all kinda started back in Ilfracombe, whilst we was waitin' on the tide. I just happened to mention that, being the captain of this ship as I am, I'm legally allowed to marry anyone who should choose to do so whilst sailing aboard my ship with me. So, Cath and the Master Mariner, being the fun-loving impetuous fools that they both are, they cooked up this plan together to hold an official full-scale wedding ceremony out on the foredeck first thing this morning. They're actually getting ready as we speak, best bib 'n' tuckers, flowers 'n' all. We even managed to put a printed programme together for 'em, so it all comes down to me to read them their marital rites, etcetera, etcetera."

"Ah, so it's not actually happening for real then?" I queried, breathing a sigh of relief.

"Well, no, not *really* for real," Rick replied laughing. "Firstly we'd 'ave to be twelve miles offshore for it to become properly official. And secondly, it wouldn't actually count for nuffin' as soon as they stepped back ashore anyway. And lastly, can you honestly see young Cathy and Lloyd, the old Master Mariner, actually *wanting* to get married for real Chris?"

"Er, well, no, not really mate," I answered knowingly, "although it sounds like a damned good harbour regatta jovial jest to me, so bring it on. I've played the odd regatta trick meself so far too, much to one person's disgust, but what the hell, t'was all done in the best *possible* taste, or at least I thought so!"

"Well we've even rehearsed this one on the way down already," said Rick enthusiastically, "speeches 'n' all. So even though it ain't *really* for real, we're all gonna make a damned good show of convincing both the locals *and* the emmets that it actually is."

"Hmmm ... " I enquired warily, "who's *'all'* exactly?"

"Well," began Rick, counting on his fingers, "there's me and Kim, and then there's the Master Mariner and his bride-to-be, that makes four. And then there's Shabby and Mel, and Little Dave and Jo, and Little Karen and Nikki, so that's ten. Olive-Ben & Karen are down below somewhere, although I've no idea whether they're gonna wake up in time for the wedding ceremony though, and I guess the same applies to Will, Giles and Derek; none of them have managed to get a whole lot of sleep in the last couple of days. *Or nights!* So anyway, that makes fifteen of us aboard in total, and now we're here we're gonna make a damned good job of enjoying ourselves!"

"Bloody good on ya matey," I said encouragingly, "let's hope we all get to spend a few days *'avin the craic!* Best I go wake up me own crew then, get 'em all back up 'n' lively once again. Catch up with ya very shortly Skipper."

"Will do Chris," Rick replied, coiling another length of rope around his arm, "go steady buddy."

I gave Rick the code to the shower block then wandered back across the little footbridge. Before stepping back aboard ship I checked the electricity coin-meter once again. *'Strange,'* I thought, *'still full up on just the one fifty pence piece. Hey ho!'* Rue stepped ashore, just as I was about to step aboard myself, and I greeted him with a simple; *'Morning! Happy May Day buddy,'* before he headed off, rather urgently it seemed to me, towards the shower block. *'Oh well, I'm sure he'll spot the Joseph easily enough for himself!'* I hopped back down into the Marovonne's wheelhouse, then jumped up and down noisily on the solid wooden-planked floor, whilst shouting down the for'ard stairwell; *"UNITE AND UNITE AND LET US ALL UNITE!"* Nik immediately appeared from somewhere back in the saloon and asked me what was up.

"Happy May Day youngster," I replied cheerfully, reaching across the chart table for my Oakleys. "Come on, get ya shit together, we've got some serious Ossin' to do today. Afore that mind, the Joseph sailed in during the night, Rick plus a crew of fourteen no less, so in a little under an hour from now we have a wedding to attend."

"Wedding?" queried Nik, looking puzzled. "What bloody wedding?"

"Lloyd and Cathy are getting married, out on the deck of the Joseph, in public," I enthused, "and Rick's playing the part of the *Celebrant*. They've got a programme and flowers and everything, and Mel and Jo are gonna be the official witnesses. Come on, we've gotta go watch it mate, it'll be fun."

"Yeah, I'm sure," said Nik, just as Helen appeared at the top of the stairwell, wash-bag in hand. "What d'you mean by *'playing the part of'* exactly? Surely they ain't gettin' married for real? *Please* tell me that ain't 'app'ning Skip? I always kinda fancied marryin' Cath meself if the truth be known."

"FOOL!" I smirked at him, just as Helen asked me what was going on.

I put my arm around her shoulders, kissed her softly on the cheek, and said; *"Happy May Day Princess!"* I then told her that the Joseph had arrived safely at some point during the night, and all about Rick and Lloyd's cunning little plan for Lloyd and Cathy to get *unofficially* married aboard, whilst making it appear to be genuine in front of the onlooking passers-by. Of which, by this time, there were already a great many.

"So guys," I continued, "go use the showers, and someone'll have tea and toast waiting for you as soon as you get back. Don't be too long mind, the wedding ceremony starts in less than an hour."

As Nik and Helen headed off towards the shower block, accompanied by Jean, Shiela and Arthur from the Roehampton, Kevin and Alan both stepped up into the wheelhouse simultaneously.

"Ah, just the lads I've been waiting for," I greeted them with, "and a top of the Merry Mornin' of May to ya's both. And a busy old day it looks like being too. The Joseph's in, and the ball's beginning to roll. Any chance you could have tea and toast ready for Helen and Nik when they get back from the shower block please? And Rue. And Sarah, if she should happen to wake up. I wanna go let Ron and Tom and Rob know exactly what's going on. Plus, there's a queue for the showers at the mo, so you'll all have to eat first and wash after, if that's okay with you?"

"Sure thing Skip," replied Kev, "but what exactly is going on this early in the morning? I mean apart from the young kids that I can hear running around outside, singing mostly the wrong words to the May Day Song?"

I told Al and Kev all about the wedding ceremony, and also not to bother with tea or toast for myself, I'd grab something from the caff after the marriage vows had been officially witnessed. I'd known Lloyd and Cath for a long time, I wanted to witness this fake little wedding for myself too. I wanted to be a part of their crazy little scheme. So I left Al and Kev to it, stepped ashore, and wandered around the quayside towards the Courageous. Kevin was right, it sure as hell was getting busier. And noisier. And yes, the highly excited youngsters dancing around the harbour side of town did indeed seem to be getting many of the words to the May Day Song muddled up, but it really didn't matter, it was simply a joy to hear. As the Courageous was moored adjacent to the quayside I reached across and banged on the wheelhouse. I then did exactly the same on the Kathleen B. Ronnie appeared out on deck, we exchanged May Day greetings, and I pointed across the harbour towards the Joseph. Ron immediately told me that he knew they were here, as not only had he tracked their incoming passage on his VHF, he'd even helped them secure their mooring lines ashore at quarter to five in the bloody morning! *'Such is the life of the sailor,'* we cynically acknowledged between us. *'Because as well we all know, time and tide awaits for no man!'* Anyway, I asked him if he'd been made aware of the imminently pending nuptials, to which he clearly hadn't, and he agreed that it ought to be a show worthy of a decent-sized audience. On that basis therefore, he'd have a damned good go at shaking Johnnie from his pit, although realistically he didn't hold out a whole lot of hope of that happening, at least not until somewhere towards lunchtime at least. As for Tom, he was already up and out a little earlier apparently. Ron had helped him and Catriona scramble ashore almost an hour previously and head off towards the Quayside Café. He told me to go on ahead, and he'd catch up with me as soon as poss, hopefully before the wedding began. I told him he'd got just five minutes or so before kickoff, and began walking along the harbourside towards the North Quay.

By the time I'd walked all the way around to the Joseph the wedding ceremony was in full swing. Rick was wearing his best bib and tucker, basically meaning that he'd put a button-up shirt and a clean pair of jeans on, and was reading the Words of Welcome to everyone present. Those people being specifically; Lloyd, who'd managed to pull on the least ripped pair of jeans and shirt that he could get his hands on, and Cathy of course, who was all dressed up in flowing white bin liners and adorned with pretty flowers; Jo and Mel, both dressed smartly as acting official witnesses; Will, who'd managed to locate and play some vaguely wedding-style music, inclusive of background church bells, on an old portable cassette player; Nikki and Little Karen, who were both drinking coffees for breakfast that I could've sworn we're laced with something a little stronger; Little Dave, who was sat with his back towards everyone looking as if he desperately needed to go back to sleep; Shabby, who was sat next to him looking very much the same way; and Long Tom and Catriona, who'd clearly just eaten their fill in the Quayside Caff and wandered aboard themselves. I joined them all out on the deck of the Joseph just as Rick began the Exchange of Vows between the pair of them, halfway through which we were also joined aboard by Helen and Nik, whilst Ronnie, Rue, Kevin, Jamer, Dave, Arthur and Shiela all looked on from the quayside. Will turned the music up just a little louder halfway through the proceedings, and by the time Rick had reached the end of the Exchange of Vows between Lloyd and Cath there was quite a considerable gathering of onlookers who'd stopped to watch along the quay. Finally, when Rick looked down at Lloyd and Cath and boldly announced; *'I now pronounce you man and wife',* then specifically addressed Lloyd by saying; *'You may now kiss the bride!',* not only did everyone aboard send up a great cheer, but the rather large crowd that had gathered on the quayside around the Joseph all began to whoop and cheer too. Several gents actually reached across the gap between the ship and the quay to shake hands with Lloyd, each one of which he gracefully accepted like the gentleman that he genuinely was, and some of the ladies even stepped away from their child-bearing pushchairs to blow Cathy a kiss, and to wish the both of them all the very best for a prosperous and fruitful future together. Several of the locals even commented on how very special it must feel to be sailing into Padstow specifically to get married during their very own traditional Merry Morning of May. *If only they knew!* Rick quietly read out the final blessing as the music gradually began to fade, and the applause from the quayside slowly died down, and as the congregation of tourists all began wandering off in their own individual directions, I was pretty dammed sure that not one single one of them had even remotely noticed the fact that, not only had Lloyd and Cathy not actually fancied kissing each other, but also that Cathy's wedding ring had somehow magically become completely invisible! *Hey ho, marriage null and void, better luck next time guys!* For what it was worth, I shook Lloyd's hand myself, gave Cathy a quick peck on the cheek, and said a very warm, heartfelt, and effectively meaningless *congratulations* to the both of them. Then, with a happy cheer of *'Unite and unite and let us all unite!'* I loudly announced to one and all that, on account of it actually now finally and officially being May Day; *'The pubs are open all day long folks!'* I was fairly sure that everyone present probably knew that already!

Christopher John Reason

LLOYD & CATHY'S MARITIME WEDDING CEREMONY

CHAPTER FIFTEEN

Things went quiet for a while aboard the Joseph as the participants of the wedding ceremony began to tidy the decks and clear things away, and the onlookers began to drift away towards their various assorted destinations. I believe one of those assorted destinations, at least certainly for Nik and Rue, would have been the Shipwright's Arms, however, as a general rule, I personally preferred not to start drinking at such a ridiculously early hour of the day; and as Sarah had shown her pale and sallow face shortly after the end of the marital proceedings, Helen and I, along with Kevin and Sarah, decided to head on over to the Quayside Café to order some bacon sandwiches. To the best of my knowledge Jean and Shiela were cooking a late breakfast aboard the Roehampton for Raymondo and his contingent, Ron had returned to the Courageous to have another attempt at waking Johnnie from his comatose slumber, Tom and Catriona had wandered off into town in search of some serious Ossin', and as yet there was no sign whatsoever of poor old Alan. Neither, indeed, had Rob and Little Kim put in an appearance as yet, although I felt sure we'd catch up with all of them at some point during the day. It proved impossible to find an unoccupied table in the caff, the place was full to overflowing, so after a considerably lengthy wait we were finally served with four takeaway bacon sandwiches, along with two teas and two coffees, and at somewhere around eleven-thirty the four of us sat down next to each other on the solid granite quayside wall, in the warm spring sunshine, with our legs dangling over the edge towards the water, and simply relaxed whilst enjoying our modest little breakkies together. Or at least we did our level best to relax, given that the town was becoming gradually busier and busier by the minute, as indeed was the resident flock of greedy seagulls. The harbourside car park had been closed off, on account of there not being a single vacant space available anywhere within it, so my best guess was that the majority of emmets continuing to steadily arrive were doing so via the park & ride double-decker bus that regularly ran down the hill from the large field at the top, about a mile outside of town. Needless to say there were now pushchairs and buggies bumping into each other left, right and centre, so after finishing our rather delicious sarnies we picked ourselves up off the ground, deposited our rubbish in a nearby bin, then began to push our way through the crowds as we slowly started heading into town in search of some localised traditional ritualistic merriment. In other words; *'Where's that damned Oss?'*

"Unite and unite and let us all unite . . . " The loud banging of drums and chanting of the May Day Song, accompanied by countless melodic concertinas and drums and shouting and cheering, appeared to be coming from all around us as we wandered up through Broad Street, past the Maypole, and around the little cobbled backstreets. The music appeared to be emanating from every which way we looked, other than whichever direction we decided to walk in. It was somewhat eerie in a mildly exciting kind of way, and as the sounds of the May Day Song echoed off the solid stone walls of the tall, tightly-packed buildings within the narrow little streets, with no sign whatsoever of either Oss team, it felt to me on more than one occasion that we were simply chasing shadows. Mind you, if we were, then there were certainly a whole lot of other people seemingly chasing the very same shadows. We rounded the corner walking towards the London Inn, expecting to see the Red Oss team dancing merrily down the street towards us, having just departed the Golden Lion. The music and laughter appeared to be getting louder by the minute, but no sooner had we set foot into Lanadwell Street, and stared towards the Golden Lion down at the very far end, other than the throngs of visitors there was absolutely

nothing else there, and the noisy celebration seemed to magically fade once again into the background.

"I reckon 'tis the Red Oss up ahead of us," said Kev excitedly, "and I reckon they's headed off down Middle Street, that'll be why we'm casn't hear 'em no more. What says we doubles back through Market Place and then hangs a left into Duke Street? Oi'l bet ee a pound to an Oss's tail that we catches 'em somewhere round by the old *Prawn On The Lawn,* 'alfway down Duke Street."

"Good thinking Mister Staines," I replied positively, "I'm reckons you'm could be proper krektly right there, me old babber. Come along then girls, let's run with young Kev's plan yeah? See if we catches 'em up wiv their Prawns down, or whatever t'was 'e said?"

"Well I sure as hell ain't runnin' nowhere," said Sarah stubbornly. "And anyway, why the heck would we? It ain't like we's in a hurry or nuffin'!"

"Er, that's not exactly what I meant chickadee," I corrected her politely. "So yeah, don't worry, we won't be going running anywhere today, you're absolutely right, there's no need. Anyway, come on, we'll just go along with what Kevin suggested my dear, okay?"

"Oh, okay then," Sarah capitulated, "which way's Market Place then?"

"Just follow me," I replied, tutting quietly to myself, and turned off to the right instead of heading down past the London.

Market Place was also packed with throngs of people. An eclectic mix of local townsfolk dressed in costume, wearing flowers whilst still tying twigs to lamp posts; a great deal of visitors from other Cornish towns and villages, clearly feeling at one with their Padstonian compatriots; and a multitude of general emmets, some from as far afield as America and Australia, and many accompanied by babies and young children in buggies and pushchairs, all jostling and bustling along in totally different directions to one another in an attempt to snatch a brief glimpse of one of the wildly whirling Osses. Many people carried cameras in the hope of snapping a few shots of a prancing Oss, especially one who may well be in the process of alluring, mesmerising, and finally entrapping a fair young maiden. However, few folks, particularly those of the emmet variety, were aware of the fact that, firstly, Ossin' in itself is a particularly dangerous activity, what with half a ton of highly decorated plywood being slung around at an extremely high rate of knots, and secondly, it was never that easy to get close to an actual Oss in the first place, on account of them being permanently surrounded by their own personal entourage of Mayers and other assorted local supporters.

The local children and teenagers that ran around amongst the crowds appeared to be a law entirely unto themselves, comparable with hoards of young animals recently set free from the entrapment of their cages, and certainly in no way whatsoever under the discipline of any of their parents. Still, I suppose that's effectively what Padstow's May Day festival is ultimately all about; by celebrating the onset of summer one is also acknowledging the final release from the ravages of a cruel, harsh winter, especially such as occurs on the mid-north Cornish coastline. My guess is that King Arthur would have known all about it back in his day, if indeed he were ever actually real, on account of the fact that there's now virtually nothing left of Tintagel Castle, an ancient ruin that nestles near to the end of a headland just a little further up the coast from Padstow, some fifteen miles towards the north-east. Clearly once a fortress to be proud of, but now, sadly, virtually reduced to a crumbling pile of rubble by the ravaging forces of nature. Padstow itself, whilst protected from the powerful winter storms of the Atlantic ocean by being safely tucked away in a hilly little valley just a couple of miles up the Camel estuary, clearly suffers very much from the cold, harsh isolation that it's inevitably forced to endure throughout the lonely months of winter. In many ways, unlike most other Cornish towns, Padstonians appear to wallow in their very own unique brand of tourist-free winter hardship. Hence why, to quote my very own personal words, as I always do on an annual basis; *"Hooray, hooray, the first of May!"* And so too say all of Padstow!

"Come along girls," I called out to Helen and Sarah, "stick close to us blokes, otherwise you're gonna get yaselves lost in the crowds if you ain't a bit more careful."

They pushed past a few people so that they were closer to Kev and myself, then grabbed one of our hands each to reduce the risk of getting separated. It was estimated, back then in 1999, that between forty and fifty thousand people crammed themselves into the narrow, winding streets of the little town of Padstow on Obby Oss day, a mass invasion that wouldn't even come close to being replicated for the remainder of the year, despite the obvious attraction of the little seaside town itself, along with it's beautiful surrounding countryside. Consequently, chaos abounded all around, and we stuck close to each other as we pushed our way through the crowd, seemingly becoming ever-closer to the raucous musical sounds of an Oss procession as we approached the corner of Duke Street. Once we rounded the corner, the music and shouting and laughter grew instantly louder, the crowds grew thicker, and the four of us grew increasingly more determined to push our way to the front. And then we spotted it. Kev was *almost* right! The Blue Oss was gradually being teased along the street, led by it's MC, whilst surrounded by a large crowd of Mayers, supporters and musicians, all of whom were merrily singing the May Day Song. As the Blue Ribbon Oss was steadily prodded on past The Prawn On The Lawn by it's Teaser, dancing, whirling and spinning before it's crowd of Mayers and onlookers, Kevin and I pushed our way a little further towards the front, but we held the girls safely back behind us for fear of one of them being mistaken for a fair young maiden, and entrapped under the magical spell of the Blue Oss himself. *As if such a thing were ever likely to happen!* However, we certainly managed to get close enough to catch a great view of the prancing Oss in all it's mystical glory, and as the Oss and it's merry band of followers continued to get slowly but manically teased along Duke Street, the four of us merrily joined in with the rest of the crowd by singing along with a few of the words that we'd so far managed to pick up to the Padstow May Day Song.

Christopher John Reason

Unite and unite and let us all unite,
For summer is a-come unto day,
And whither we are going we will all unite,
In the merry morning of May.

Arise up Mr. Dyne, I know you well afine,
For summer is a-come unto day,
You have a shilling in your purse and I wish it was in mine,
In the merry morning of May.

All out of your beds,
For summer is a-come unto day,
Your chamber shall be strewed with the white rose and the red,
In the merry morning of May.

Where are the young men that here now should dance,
For summer is a-come unto day,
Some they are in England and some they are in France,
In the merry morning of May.

Where are the maidens that here now should sing,
For summer is a-come unto day,
They are in the meadows the flowers gathering,
In the merry morning of May.

Arise up Mr. Hyde, with your sword by your side,
For summer is a-come unto day,
Your steed is in the stable awaiting for to ride,
In the merry morning of May.

Arise up young Miss Sours, and strew all your flowers,
For summer is a-come unto day,
It is but a while ago since we have strewed ours,
In the merry morning of May.

O! Where is St. George,

May Day Mayhem

O, where is he O?
He is out in his long-boat on the salt sea O.
Up flies the kite and down falls the lark O,
Aunt Ursula Birdhood she had an old ewe,
And she died in her own park O.

With the merry ring, adieu the merry spring,
For summer is a-come unto day,
How happy is the little bird that merrily doth sing,
In the merry morning of May.

The young men of Padstow might if they would,
For summer is a-come unto day,
They might have built a ship and gilded her with gold,
In the merry morning of May.

The young women of Padstow might if they would,
For summer is a-come unto day,
They might have made a garland with the white rose and the red,
In the merry morning of May.

Arise up Mr. Bland and reach me your hand,
For summer is a-come unto day,
And you shall have a lively lass with a thousand pounds in hand,
In the merry morning of May.

Arise up young Miss Wylk all in your cloak of silk,
For summer is a-come unto day,
And all your body under as white as any milk,
In the merry morning of May.

O! Where is St. George,
O, where is he O?
He is out in his long-boat all on the salt sea O.
Up flies the kite and down flies the lark O,
Aunt Ursula Birdhood she had an old ewe,

And she died in her own park O.

With the merry ring, adieu the merry spring,
For summer is a-come unto day,
How happy is the little bird that merrily doth sing,
In the merry morning of May.

Now fare you well and bid you all good cheer,
For summer is a-come unto day,
We call no more unto your house before another year,
In the merry morning of May.

Needless to say, the only words that any of us had realistically learnt to sing were the second and forth line to each verse. *Where's that bloody Jamer when you need him?!!?* That said, if you stick with it for a while, and join in with some of the words that you may happen to have picked up yourself, it's actually a very simple, mesmerising, catchy little tune that very quickly becomes one of those highly annoying earworms! In fact, one year, as I seem to recall, I hummed and sang it to myself incessantly during the entire voyage back to Bristol, much to the extreme annoyance of my crew. That wasn't this particular year though. 1999, as things happened to pan out, turned into an entirely different kind of year altogether, further details of which I won't be divulging until later.

TEASING THE BLUE RIBBON OSS

CHAPTER SIXTEEN

So the four of us danced and sang along merrily to the May Day Song as the bustling crowd gradually made it's way along Duke Street, cheering and shouting as they went, whilst surrounding the protective group of musicians and other assorted supporters of the Blue Ribbon Oss team. The Oss itself whirled and span and bucked in time to the accordions and drums, however, by the time we reached the corner of Mill Square, to the best of my knowledge, the Blue Oss hadn't yet managed to entrap a single fair maiden. Just as the entire noisy entourage rounded the corner into Market Place, Kev looked me straight in the eye and declared;

"I reckon 'tis about time for a lunchtime pint right now Skip, what say we leave this merry old lot to it for a bit and head on down to the Shipwrights for a couple?"

"What a damned fine idea Mister Staines," I agreed with him wholeheartedly. "What's reckon then girls? Fancy a little snifter as an aperitif, along with a spot of lunch?"

"Oh, most definitely," replied Sarah enthusiastically. "After all, it is a party weekend, so I don't mind if I do. I'll have an extra-large gin and tonic please, no ice."

"You certainly hit the nail on the head with the word '*tonic*' young lady," agreed Helen, "that sounds like *just the tonic* for a day like today. I do believe I shall partake of precisely the same!"

"Right then folks," I said positively, "follow me then," and we began heading off towards the harbour, against the flow of the crowds, down the narrow, winding little street which, for some unknown obscure reason, is known as Mill Square.

As we wound our way past Granny's Pasty Bakery and around the corner towards the Harbour Ice Cream Shop, the drums and accordions playing along to the melodic voices of the May Day Song gradually faded into the background, but only, and most unusually, to be steadily replaced by an increasingly louder but different style of music altogether, and very clearly that of a musical genre that was in no way compatible with Padstow's May Day traditions. In fact, as we reached the end of Mill Square, where it meets the adjoining ends of The Strand and North Quay Parade, the music became not only significantly louder, but also what I would describe as distinctly alien to the local culture, especially during that particular weekend. That said, I recognised it in an instant for what it was, and if I'm perfectly honest I have to admit that it brought even more joy to my soul, adding yet another dimension to what was already turning out to be a highly enjoyable weekend. Do we cross the road and join in? Or do we head on to the Shipwrights as agreed? I instantly formulated a cunning plan; *we'd do both!* We hung a left and strolled purposefully down The Parade towards the Shipwrights, leaving the loudly amplified but pleasantly professional sounds of *The Rocky Road To Dublin* by The Dubliners briefly behind us, whilst setting our sights firmly on the pretty little pub at the end of the road.

"Is that really The Dubliners playing beside the harbour?" asked Sarah innocently, as we fought our way through the packed pub towards the bar.

The three of us almost cracked up laughing at that, although thankfully *before* we were served our drinks, and began to force our way back through the crowd towards the exit. Just as well really, because all carry-out drinks were being served in flimsy plastic glasses, which, quite thoughtfully, I always doubled up on. As I shouted our order in across the bar; *'Four pints of Hicks; four double G&Ts, and four warmed pasties please young lady'*, then paid for everything on my card whilst waiting for the microwave to *ping*, I listened whilst Helen patiently explained to Sarah exactly what was going on."

"No, my dear," Helen began, "it's not The Dubliners at all, it's that loveable old rogue, and probably *the* best Irish-Brummie musical comic genius you're ever likely to come across; Chris and Rick's crazy old pirate friend from back in Bristol, Black Jack Davey. By the looks of it, him and his band, Wylde Green, have driven on down here and boarded the Joseph with Rick, and by the *sounds* of it, I wouldn't be at all surprised if they're about to play a full set together."

"Oh dear," I murmured softly to myself as the microwave pinged, *"what on earth could possibly go wrong this time?"*

The young barmaid kindly handed us a couple of trays, and we loaded up our food and drinks, managed to push back through the crowd without spilling a single drop, and stepped back outside into the bright, warm, midday sunshine. Davey was into his next song by then, and as we pushed our way carefully through the swarms of emmets, whilst listening intently to his powerful Irish vocals belting out *The Raggle Taggle Gypsy* to the tune of his own highly talented banjo playing, I could have sworn someone had turned the volume up just a notch or two. *'Yet another inspirational touch of regatta piracy, well done Captain Rick!'* I thought to myself, as we barged our way back towards the harbour, the girls successfully shielding Kev and myself as we protected the precious contents of our trays. Upon reaching the Joseph, still securely moored against the wall at the top end of the North Quay, it was clear that there wasn't sufficient space on deck for all four of us to clamber aboard, so we placed the trays on the ground in between us, then plonked ourselves down on the quay wall right alongside the Joseph's midships. Right next to Davey's amplifier as it so happened, although in no way whatsoever did that detract from Kate's amazing fiddle playing, or indeed Paul's melodic and tuneful pipes. What it clearly did drown out however, much to the disgust of one or two of the townsfolk at the time, was all forms of atmosphere emanating from the local traditional Ossin' festivities. That minor issue, needless to say, was destined to become a far more major issue in the not too distant future. In the meantime, the four of us just sat back and relaxed, got stuck into our delicious pasties and drinks, and listened with great admiration as the band played the soulful and melodic ballad, *Pennies For Your Eyes,* with highly accomplished prowess.

By the time Wylde Green had launched themselves into their own personal adaptation of The Dubliners' *Thirty Foot Trailer,* the audience gathered along the quayside appeared to be growing somewhat, and the volume appeared to have gone up yet another notch. Their performance, however, was simply awesome, as professional as ever, and growing better by the minute. As Paul's pipes echoed around the harbour to the melodies of *Spencil Hill,* followed immediately afterwards by Davey's complex banjo-laced rendition of *The Rhyme Of The Ocean,* the crowds surrounding the Joseph steadily grew larger and larger. It was gradually becoming evident that this was going to be no ordinary occasion; something very, very special was beginning to happen. Somewhere in the distance, in between each of Wylde Green's songs, once our ears had taken a moment to adjust, we could just about make out the faint and distant chanting of the May Day Song away up the backstreets somewhere, as the Ossin' processions continued on their merry old way, each party seemingly oblivious to the other, or at least for the time being anyway. But still the crowd began to grow, and with it the atmosphere too. There could hardly have been a bigger contrast between the two sets of performers; one mystically Cornish, the other blatantly Irish; one delicately acting out their own personal, annual, local ritual, the other raucously blasting out amplified cover songs from halfway across the ocean; one carrying their song and dance to their assorted audiences, the other static whilst encouraging their audience to come to them. For one brief moment I felt as if this wonderful Irish band had achieved nothing other than gatecrashing the poor old Padstonian's unique annual ritual, which quite clearly they had, and during that particular brief moment a random thought ran poignantly through my mind; *'Jeez, thank the Lord that Padstow doesn't actually have it's very own police station!'* However, as it turned out in the end, Wylde Green achieved far more than just gatecrashing someone else's party, they achieved notoriety. *Notoriety, countrywide critical acclaim, a reputation as musicians to be proud of, and an even bigger reputation as pirates to be appalled at!*

By now the remainder of Rick's crew had not necessarily arisen voluntarily, but more than likely been shaken from their beds by the vibrations of the powerful on-deck amplifiers and the sounds blasting out from them, the volume of which, to my own ears particularly, had been turned up still further. Ben and Karen were sat out on the aft deck drinking coffees, as far away from the speakers as possible. Lloyd and Cath were lovingly sat together up for'ard, trying their damnedest not to make any spontaneous honeymoon plans. Little Dave, Shabby and Little Karen had propped themselves comfortably against Rick's somewhat deflated RIB, which was still lashed securely to the mast, and appeared to be chatting incessantly in between songs about the voyage down. And Giles, Derek and Will were wandering around the deck, socialising merrily with one and all, whilst downing countless cans of Thatchers Gold for brunch with big smiles on their faces. As Davey passed his guitar to Kate then picked up his banjo once again, the pair of them expertly played along to Steeleye Span's *The Blacksmith,* Dave's voice now carrying far beyond the reaches of the inner harbour. Whether that was played as a specific request by Will, Bristol Harbour's resident blacksmith, I guess I shall probably never know! However, again the crowd thickened, now completely blocking a good hundred yards of North Quay Parade from shop-front to quayside, as well as surrounding the whole area where the four of us were comfortably sat by at least ten deep. Tom and Catriona pushed their way through the crowd and sat themselves down alongside us, and as I wondered where the other four girls from the Joseph had disappeared to, I peered across the aft deck of the Joseph and clearly spotted not only Rob, Little Kim, Ron and Johnnie all sat out on the deck of the Courageous, marvelling at the obviously pre-planned gig, but also Ray and Jean, Arthur and Sheila, and Dave and Jamer, clapping and cheering along to the music from the comfort of a matching set of folding chairs that they'd neatly set out on the Roehampton's expansive foredeck.

In actual fact, the whole harbour appeared to be enjoying the band's polished performance, as well as the thousand or so people crowded around the quayside, both locals and emmets alike. Clearly this was no impromptu céilidh, this was a well rehearsed, expertly planned and stunningly delivered performance, and as Paul and Kate lovingly accompanied Davey's powerful voice to Emily Smith's *Gypsy Davey*, I suddenly spotted the four missing girls. Nikki, Kim, Mel and Jo all appeared at more or less the same time, although each of them in totally different random places amongst the mesmerised audience, and all four of them carrying brightly-coloured plastic buckets, which they were gaily jingle-jangling up and down whilst the raptured crowd willingly added handfuls of loose change to their ever growing contents. *'Hmmm, busking at it's very best!'*, I immediately thought to myself, as I subtly mentioned to Kev that it was his turn to go buy another round of drinks. Just as Kev stood up with the trays and empties in hand, I heard Nik's inimitable voice directly behind me say; *'Add six pints of scrumpy to that request please Kev, there's a good lad!'* As Davey with his banjo, accompanied by Kate with her amplified acoustic guitar, launched into by far the best rendition of *Duelling Banjos* that I've ever had the pleasure of listening to, Nik courteously added; *'I'll come give you a hand!'* And *still* the music got louder, and *still* the crowd grew larger, and *still* the collection buckets grew heavier! And then, all of a sudden, a minor little problem occurred! Duelling banjos were one thing; duelling *performances* were a whole different proposition altogether!

It was right at that quiet lull in between songs, just as the crowd slowly quietened their clapping and cheering, and Kate took a quick breather, before snatching up her electric fiddle and launching into the intricate intro to *'The Lark In The Morning'*, that a host of voices cheerfully singing; *'Unite and unite and let us all unite,'* became significantly louder, as the Old Red Oss, along with his merry band of Mayers and musicians, was suddenly teased around the corner of Mill Square by his MC, wheeled ceremoniously around to his left, and clearly with no forewarning whatsoever, owing to the gathered multitude surrounding the Joseph, which by now completely blocked the entire street, unfortunately found his pathway ahead totally impassable. An occurrence, as I was later to be made more than fully aware of, that had never, ever happened in the entire history of Ossin', and would certainly never, *ever,* be allowed to happen again! *Oops-a-daisy!* So the poor old Red Oss team had no other option but to wheel themselves back around in the opposite direction and head back towards The Strand, hoping against hope that this unexpectedly enforced detour wouldn't result in them clashing with their sworn enemies, the Blue Oss team, before their duly appointed time when they're both encouraged to come together in front of the Maypole. To the best of my knowledge this accidental clash of opposing colours never actually took place, and both teams were able to adjust and adapt their routes accordingly. In the meantime, *needless to say,* the band played on!

After far too long a wait, Nik and Kev finally returned from the Shipwright's, forcing their way carefully back through the loudly applauding crowd, each with a large, round, heavily laden tray. Two pints of scrumpy for Rue, two for Alan, both of whom were stood applauding directly behind us, and both of whom were forced to cease applauding the second they grabbed their pints. Nik kept two pints for himself and shuffled himself down onto the quayside in between Sarah and Catriona.

"Where's ours then?" asked Tom sarcastically.

"Sorry Tom," replied Kevin with a matching degree of sarcasm, "I'm only a young skivvy apprentice at Rolls Royce, I cant afford to carry that kind of cash around with me."

"Humph!" mused Tom with a grin. "'Spose I'll 'ave to go get me own then! What's want love?"

Tom stood up and trotted off towards the pub to get him and Catriona another couple of pints of scrumpy, and after carefully placing his own overloaded tray down on the ground, Kev took his seat back between Helen and Sarah. I reached across and grabbed my two pints of ale, took the top off both, set one down safely between Helen and myself, then removed my Leatherman from it's belt pouch and uncorked Helen and Sarah's chilled bottle of Mateus Rosé for them. *Well, if you can, then you must, that's my motto!* Just as I finished filling their glasses, Kate grabbed a second microphone, and between her and Davey they sang Ralph McTell's *Streets Of London* as a beautifully harmonised duet together, accompanied once again by the haunting echoes of Paul's flute playing. *And still the crowd grew ever larger, and the buckets ever heavier!* Although, to be fair, the volume remained at a steady half-million decibels for the remainder of the day. And just as well too. Black Jack Davey's voice would've carried right the way across town and all the way up the hill to the park & ride with his raucous rendition of *Johnnie Is The Fairest Man!*

"How long d'you reckon they'll keep on playing for?" Helen shouted in my ear halfway through the chorus.

"At a rough guess," I replied with a broad grin, "I'd say until all four of those plastic buckets are full to the brim."

"Them looks like they's getting' on that ways already," spluttered Rue from somewhere behind me, whilst quite probably spilling half a mouthful of cider into the bargain, "people's chuckin' gert 'andfuls o' shrapnel into 'em!"

"Well good on 'em," I replied positively, "I reckon they deserve it, and clearly so do their beloved audience."

Their beloved audience now appeared to consist of over half the population of Padstow, along with a huge congregation of emmets, pushchairs and all, plus every single sailor and his or her crew moored within the harbour. Come four o'clock in the afternoon the show that the band were putting on aboard the Joseph was certainly more than a serious distraction from what was actually meant to be occurring that particular weekend. *'Oss Oss! Poor Oss!',* I seem to remember thinking to myself at the time. *Oh well, on with the show! And what's more, let's wind it up still further!* As if perfectly on cue, Davey's banjo kicked off at ten to the dozen as he launched himself wildly into *Culchi Lad,* immediately after which he seemed to have well over a thousand onlookers chanting along noisily to the choruses of *The Fields Of Athenry! (Hey baby let the free birds fly!)* This was inevitably followed by rapturous applause from the still-ever-growing audience, which once again echoed satisfyingly off all six solid granite walls of Padstow's inner harbour. At ten past four, precisely two hours before high water, the footbridge was closed off and the barrage gates opened. Both the Jaws and the Thunder speedboats chugged slowly in through the entrance and drifted lazily across what small amount of clear, open water still remained, heading towards the inner slipway to see if there were any potential passengers waiting for a quick blast down the estuary and back. Sadly they were out of luck. No one was in the slightest bit interested in boating just yet, the whole town seemed way too preoccupied with being treated to a fabulous free performance by the trio of musicians that they'd quite obviously deemed '*a highly professional band of infamously acclaimed musical artistes!*' Much to the worsening detriment of the local Obby Oss Festival, it has to be said, as by this time neither the Old Red Oss nor the Blue Ribbon Oss were anywhere remotely to be seen or heard. *Hey ho, their time would come sooner or later!* Little Dave and Will stepped precariously back aboard the Joseph, having both just returned from the pub with trays loaded to the gunwales with cloudy pints of local scrumpy, and were followed very shortly afterwards by Derek and Giles carrying equally well stacked trays crammed with overflowing pints of Guinness. The band took a very brief break, during which they quickly refreshed themselves, clearly grateful for their most welcome gifts of the *ebony nectar!* In fact, Davey managed to down virtually the whole of his first pint in just one single gulp. Immediately after which the three of them launched themselves into yet another Irish classic, *Follow Me Up To Carlow* by The Wolfe Tones. I could definitely see Ron, Johnnie, Rob and Little Kim jigging around merrily out on the deck of the Courageous, and shortly before yet more rapturous applause from the huge crowd I could've sworn I noticed Jean and Jamer dancing a proper Irish jig together on the Roehampton's foredeck, egged on by much hand clapping from Ray, Dave, Arthur and Sheila. I necked what little remained of my first pint of real ale, turned towards Helen and began a brief chat in between songs;

"You do realise this is going to go down disastrously with the local town council, don't you babe?" I stated, beginning to feel somewhat ominous about the potential repercussions of such a massive distraction.

"I don't doubt it for one minute," Helen replied, draining another small plastic cup of Mateus. "They obviously never asked in advance for permission to do this, although I must admit they are playing an awesome gig. Better than I've ever seen at Flanagan's back home. And look at the crowds, they're absolutely loving it!"

"Yeah, that's what's beginning to worry me," I said, starting to fear the worst. "I think after they've finished it'd probably be best if we all go pay a little more attention to the town's poor old Osses. What d'ya reckon?"

"Suits me Hun," Helen replied enthusiastically. "The more fun we can manage to cram into this weekend before I have to leave on Monday, the better as far as I'm concerned."

I was just about to continue with an interesting suggestion for dinner when Davey suddenly started on one of his favourite jokes. Part musician, part comedian, and general all round top class entertainer, he'd always make a point of having the craic in between songs, especially with a bit of ad-libbed banter between himself and his audience. But for the love of Jaysus, don't ever try heckling the man, you'd get shot down in flames before you'd even started! Anyway, regardless of whether he was playing solo or with his band, he'd always had a bit of a penchant for telling jokes. During normal gigs they were generally pretty rude, occasionally bordering on crude even, however today's audience was very much a family affair, so understandably he'd picked one of a considerably toned-down variety.

"Hey, how're all you good folks doin' out there? (cheers and whoops) *Ya know, 'tis really great ta be playin' a spot of fine old Irish music over here in sunny Cornwall today. Bootiful place, bootiful place, dat it is fa sure. And 'specially proud today to be spendin' some time wid our wonderful fellow Celts. Oi mean, after all, de Cornish are all just wannabe Irish folks who couldn't swim!"*

Immediately after which, even before the laughter began, the band started playing *The Irish Rover,* yet another Dubliner's classic, and the whole town began cheering and clapping and merrily jigging along to it. I could tell from the way that the girls were beginning to struggle somewhat with their colourful plastic buckets that the collection was probably going to exceed all expectations, as they kept having to set them down every now and again and join in with the clapping. However, after yet another flippant little quip between songs, Davey suddenly switched the mood entirely, and started on Eric Bogle's politically motivated but beautifully melodic ballad, *The Green Fields Of France*. The crowd hushed, and far above the sounds of pipe, fiddle and guitar, Davey's voice rang out loud, not only throughout the town, but right the way around the Camel estuary. Realistically it was unlikely his powerful voice would've reached quite as far up the river as Wadebridge, however I felt certain that plenty of the residents of Rock would've been listening along their own shoreline, and cheering him along with fervour. *And then another slightly naughty joke!*

"*So dere's dis Cornish fisherman, he foinds 'eeself laid up in Dublin fer de night. So 'e walks into de brothel, chooks five 'undred notes down on de counter, and says ta de Madam; "Oi'l 'ave de ugliest woman ya's got in 'ere, and a cheese butty please." And de Madam says; "Jeez, ya's could 'ave de best lookin' girl in de house and a tree-course meal fer dat much." And de Cornish fisherman, 'e says; "Listen Madam, Oi'm not feckin' horny, Oi'm just feelin' homesick!"*"

That was followed immediately afterwards by *Dirty Old Town* by The Pogues, after which it seemed to me that the time was getting on a bit, as indeed was the tide, and as the water level within the harbour steadily rose ever closer towards our dangling feet, I suddenly realised that all of our glasses had been sat empty for far too long. I checked my watch, and was gobsmacked to find that it was almost six o'clock. It was approaching high water, *but more importantly,* it was also approaching that time of day where both Oss teams would be at their most active. Or should I say *at their most rampant!* I was fairly sure that both Davey *and* Rick were also well aware of that fact, and consequently, whilst also acknowledging that Kim, Nikki, Mel and Jo were now seriously struggling to hold their continually filling buckets aloft, Davey and the band threw themselves wholeheartedly into the final song of their lengthy but highly successful afternoon set. It was yet another very well known old folk-rock song, written originally by The Grateful Dead, subsequently made famous by the likes of The Dubliners and Thin Lizzy, one of my own personal favourites too, but in my opinion always played and sung best by the one and only Black Jack Davey; *Whiskey In The Jar!*

"Tank you's, tank you's, tank you's one 'n' all," roared Davey's voice through the mic afterwards, as the final applause gradually began to settle down, and the crowd slowly began to disperse, *"you's are all too kind, too kind, way too kind be far. Tank you's all from the hearts of our bottoms. May yer Gods go with you's now, and please folks, fer fook's sake, don't none of ya's go fallin' in dat dere watter. G'day ta ya's all."*

I got slowly to my feet, still clapping as I did so, reached across the Joseph's starboard-side handrail, warmly shook Davey's hand, and congratulated him, and Paul and Kate, on their fine performance. I then stretched a little further across and shook Rick's hand, congratulating him on how cleverly he'd managed to orchestrate two exceptionally wonderful shows so far that day.

"So, what's next on the agenda then Skipper?" I asked him expectantly.

"FOOD!" was his straightforward reply. "Ah'm totally Minister'd and Roady'd out right now, and ah'm fookin' starvin'! Six hours solid that bloody Wylde Green's just played for. *Six sodding hours!* God only knows how much those girls have collected in them there buckets, but I do know that at least half of it's gonna go on a damned fine nosh-up fer most of us, *and not a minute too soon neiver!* What's you got in mind then young Chrissy-boy?"

I turned around towards Helen, noticing all of a sudden that Nik, Rue and Alan had disappeared off somewhere, most likely back to the Shipwright's, and asked her, along with Kevin and Sarah, if they fancied the four of us all dining together a little later in Cally's Oyster Bar & Grill, which we'd need to go and book in advance.

"*YUK!*" replied Helen instantly, pretending to choke back the urge to vomit. "You know I can't stand the sight of oysters, don't you, let alone the taste of 'em. *Eeuuch! Definitely not, no thank you!*"

"Well, there you have it then mate, straight from the Oss's mouth," I replied to Rick with a grin, "we're gonna go book a table at Cally's."

"*Seriously?*" queried Helen and Sarah in unison.

"Yes, seriously," I answered calmly. "Although they specialise in oysters, their ordinary range of grills are simply to die for, you'll love 'em, I promise."

"Cross your heart and hope to drown?" asked Helen sceptically.

"Well if you don't, I promise I'll chuck myself straight in the harbour afterwards," I replied with a grin. "And fully clothed into the bargain. Deal?"

"*DEAL!*" shouted Helen, Kevin and Sarah all at the same time.

We each said '*chow for now*' to Rick, to the band, to each and every member of the crew of the Joseph that still happened to remain aboard, as opposed to those that had followed Nik, Rue and Alan up to the Shipwright's, and an extra-special '*CHOW*' to the newly-weds still sat together on the Joseph's prow, empty wine glasses in hand. With the very best intentions at heart for simply walking around the harbourside towards Strand Street, and booking a table for four at Cally's, I turned on my heels, and was immediately accosted by a deep-voiced, bushy-haired, ginger giant, who lovingly wrapped his arms tightly around me in a bear hug, and drawled in his newly-acquired, almost-Cornish accent;

"Well, well, well, what have we got ourselves here then? If it ain't me old buddy, Captain Reason, one of the most infamous pirates on all the high seas! How ya doin' man?"

"Oh my good Gawd, *it's BENNY!*" I exclaimed in mock exasperation. "Jesus Christ, *WHAT ON EARTH COULD POSSIBLY GO WRONG NEXT?!!?*"

WYLDE GREEN PLAYING ABOARD THE JOSEPH

CHAPTER SEVENTEEN

"Benny, me old mucker, how long's it been exactly?" I asked, returning his greeting with an equally powerful hug.

"Well," replied Benny thoughtfully, "the last time we had a beer together was this very same day just a year ago. In fact, if I remember c'rrectly, t'was in the Custom House, and we had a few more than just the one!"

"Ah, no change there then!" I mumbled sardonically. "Last time I remember, it was down in Bristol Marina. You were living aboard a scruffy old wooden motor cruiser that was laid up on the hard, with not a hope in hell of ever floating again. That was probably some ten months ago. And then you disappeared off the face of the planet. What on earth happened there then mate?"

"Haha, you're absolutely right about that old pile of junk never ever floating again," replied Benny with a clearly fake air of innocence about him. "I tried, and it didn't! So I had no choice but to do a runner. I sometimes still wonder to this day whether Davina managed to haul the wreckage of it back up off the bottom of the harbour, or whether she just left it there to rot. The engine never worked anyway, although it wouldn't have been long before that and the other heavy bits sank themselves deep below the mud. Who knows? Shit happens, that's all I can say, and I couldn't afford to hang around and find out, so I just moved down to Cornwall. Anyway buddy, it's great to see you again."

"You too mate, it's been way too long. If I'd've known where you were I'd've made a point of coming down to say hi for a few days," I continued. "So, where exactly in Cornwall are you living now then my friend?"

"I'm afraid I can't say Chris," Benny replied quietly, looking all around him as if he were in fear of being followed, "it's top secret. There's a certain ex-employer of mine that I had a big falling out with, and I can't run the risk of him ever catching up with me again, he's a proper nasty piece of work! No connection whatsoever with Bristol by the way, in fact he doesn't even live in the UK anymore. But it'd be a complete disaster if our paths were ever to cross again, and I'm sure at least one of us would end up in prison for overstepping the mark, so I just prefer to keep my whereabouts low-key these days, if only for the sake of my own sanity. Hence why I no longer own a mobile phone."

"Ah, I did wonder," I said. "I guess that's why you never returned any of my voice messages then. So, who have you come down to Padstow with today then mate, or are you here all on your lonesome?"

"Not at all," beamed Benny. "I'm here with a few mates from Tintagel. We've got a couple of old camper vans up in the park & ride field at the top of the hill. I don't think the council are particularly bothered about us using it as a campsite for the weekend, so long as we're gone by sometime on Monday, which we will be. Gotta get back home then, a couple of the lads gotta go to work on Tuesday. No idea where they are right now mind you, although the Shipwright's would probably be my best guess."

"So is that where you're living these days then Benny, in the ancient slate-built town of Tintagel?" I asked him off the cuff, as I held Shabby's hand to steady her as she stepped ashore from the deck of the Joseph.

"Yes mate," replied Benny thoughtlessly, "and I love it there too. Tough old place during the winter months mind, but it livens up just enough for my liking during the summer. Me and me mates, we all tend to drink in the King Arthur's Arms generally; good ales, great atmosphere. You must come down and stay for a couple days sometime, you and Helen, I'll take you out and show you around."

"It'll be our pleasure matey, we'll make a point of it one day very soon," I replied, grateful for his invite, "although I must say, I already know Tintagel fairly well, including the King Arthur's."

"*OH BOLLOCKS!*" exclaimed Benny, slapping his hand over his mouth whilst suddenly realising his thoughtless mistake.

"Don't you worry for one second my old mate," I comforted him with a laugh, as I threw my arm around his shoulders, "your secret's perfectly safe with me. Er, I mean *us!*"

"*BENNY!*" exclaimed Shabby, throwing herself into his arms unexpectedly.

I interrupted their long-lost greeting for one brief moment, just to explain that I had to go book a table for dinner later that evening at Cally's, but suggested that Benny and Shabbs accompany Helen, Kevin and Sarah to the Custom House, and see if it was possible to fight their way over to the bar, then I'd join them back there just as soon as I was done. All five were in agreement, but before the six of us began wandering back around the waterfront, Shabby shouted back aboard the Joseph to see if anyone else fancied joining us. Kim, Nikki, Mel and Jo appeared to be way too preoccupied with counting out piles of shrapnel scattered across the deck, whilst Davey, Paul and Kate were clearly busy packing up all their musical equipment. Rick, Lloyd, Cathy and Little Dave said they'd do their best to catch up with us a bit later, and Ben and Karen had wandered off to the Shipwright's to join Giles, Derek and Will anyway. Which left just Little Karen with nothing much better to do, and as she stepped towards the Joseph's handrail nodding enthusiastically, I offered my hand to steady her as she clumsily clambered ashore. The seven of us then set off together along North Quay Parade, around The Strand, then, after handing Helen my card and asking her to order me a pint of Hicks, and pay for whatever Benny, Shabbs and Karen fancied too, I walked into Cally's as the others continued on next door and entered the Custom House. Cally's didn't have a table available for eight o'clock, but they said they could just about squeeze the four of us in at eight-thirty, and I said that would be absolutely fine. After confirming that they'd still have plenty of oysters available by then, the manageress wrote my name and phone number in the diary. I then wandered in through the front door of the Custom House, fought my way through the crowd towards the bar, and just as I reached it I was immediately handed a gorgeous looking pint of Hicks by Benny, exactly the same as his own choice of fine ale. Everyone raised their glasses, or should I say *'plastics'*, and all seven of us wished; *'Cheers and good health'* to one another. Following which we searched for seating, but there was none available anywhere, so we took our drinks outside, into what little remained of the evening sunshine.

I asked Benny if he'd managed to catch very much of Wylde Green's performance aboard the Joseph, and he said it was precisely Davey's unmistakeable voice that had drawn him down to the harbour in the first place. So yes, he'd managed to catch most of the show, and what a show it was too; top notch, and bound to get certain people into a whole load of trouble. I pointed across the harbour towards the Marovonne, with the Roehampton moored alongside her, and the wheelhouse of the Dasher which could just about be made out almost hidden behind the bridge of the Vigilant, and explained to him that I'd already got myself into a certain amount of trouble so far that weekend, and that even more trouble was most definitely welcomed, because; *'Isn't that what regattas are supposed to be all about?'* So the more mayhem the better as far as I was concerned. I sensed a certain degree of scheming going on in Benny's mind, knowing him as well as I did, however, no sooner had that begun than he himself noticed Ray, Jean and Jamer step out onto the roof of the Marovonne, and he asked me to hold his pint for him whilst he dashed off down the quayside to dish out more welcoming bear hugs, just as the three of them stepped ashore. Benny had lived in and around Bristol's harbourside for long enough to know just about as many people as Helen and I knew, if not more, and on his way back towards the Custom House, skipping along merrily with his arms wrapped around both Ray and Jamer, he happened to notice Ronnie too, trying to keep his head down as low as possible in a deck chair on the small, lower aft deck of the Courageous, a half-full can of Heineken sat on the deck by his side.

"Yo, Ron," shouted Benny from the quayside directly above, "you gonna come over the road and have a drink with me then matey?"

"Well good grief," Ron called back up, a little shocked to hear Benny's voice, "if it ain't that damned Benny-boy! Where the hell 'ave ya been hidin' yaself all these months matey? Yeah, damned right I'll come 'ave a beer with ya, good to see ya me old mate, good to see ya indeed."

"Where's that number one crew mate of yours Johnnie to then Ron?" Benny asked, as Ron clambered up onto the roof of Courageous's wheelhouse. "He not aboard with ya today then?"

"Off shaggin' somewhere most likely," replied Ron flippantly. "Seems like shaggin''s more interesting to 'im than Ossin' is these days."

Benny held out a hand to steady Ron as he stepped ashore, then followed it up with yet another impressive bear hug, lifting poor Ronnie's feet a good couple of inches off the ground. The five of them then crossed the road, weaving carefully through the crowds, and after greeting Shabby and Karen yet again with even more friendly hugs, I handed Benny back his pint whilst the others headed inside towards the bar. Just then, a large group of people suddenly got up and vacated one of the very few large wooden bench-tables that were situated along Riverside Street immediately opposite the Custom House, and quick as a flash, spilling a good deal of my pint in the process, I dived headlong across the table shouting; 'Reserved for professional pirates only!' Karen laughed her socks off, as indeed did young Shabbatha, and I instructed the two of them to come sit either side of me as quickly as possible, which, once I'd straightened myself out and sat myself down, they immediately did. Helen and Benny took up positions at opposite ends of the other side of the table, leaving room for just four more. Unsurprisingly I actually felt extremely comfortable sat in between Shabby and Karen, however, when Ray, Jean, Jamer and Ronnie returned outside with an extra-large round of drinks balanced precariously on two large trays, I reluctantly gave up my seat for favour of standing alongside Kevin and Sarah. All eleven of us, eight seated

and three standing, then began chatting incessantly amongst ourselves. Partially about how good Wylde Green's performance had
been, partially about how happily married both Lloyd and Cathy
now appeared to be, something that I had to explain in great detail
to poor unwitting young Benny, who'd clearly missed that part
of the day's entertainment. Partially about how much Ossin' we'd
managed to witness so far, and partially simply catching up on
recent times spent apart, as well as reminiscing about many fond
memories spent together over the past.

Just as Kevin and myself turned to walk back inside to order
another round of drinks, our party suddenly grew by another four
as Long Tom and Catriona, along with Rob and Little Kim, accompanied the pair of us as we pushed our way in towards the bar.

"It's coomin', it's coomin'!" shouted Little Kim excitedly.

"What's coming exactly Kim?" I asked inquisitively.

"The Oss, the Oss," she blurted out, "the Oss. It's coomin'
down't road right now! Can ya's not 'ear it fa fook's sake?"

"No my dear, we can't 'ear bugger all inside 'ere, above all this
racket," I replied, trying unsuccessfully to take the mickey out of
her northern accent. "So, which road is it coomin' down exactly?"

"Round t't left like, oop that there road. Coom on, let's 'oory
oop and get back outside."

Kevin paid for a large round of drinks, which he and I carried
back outside on two trays, closely followed by Tom and Catriona,
Little Kim and Rob, the two chaps each carrying trays with a whole
range of assorted beverages carefully balanced upon them; including, much to my dismay, two medium-sized bottles of Evian water.
Sacrilege! Pure sacrilege! I even suggested that both girls try spelling
Evian backwards! And then we slowly began to hear it. The drums,
the accordions, the cheering and loud, merry rejoicing, it was very
steadily approaching us from the direction of Strand Street, just
around the corner. My guess was that they were most likely right
outside Cally's at that point in time, but they were definitely heading in our direction, and with a bit of luck they'd turn right at the
end of the road and carry on along Riverside, passing right by us.
Excitement and anticipation amongst our little group of fifteen was

noticeably growing, and as the drums continued to beat in time to the music, some of the girls began clapping along. And then, as they slowly approached even closer, the music steadily increased in volume, and the singing began in earnest.

"Unite and unite and let us all unite,
For summer is a-come unto day,
And whither we are going we will all unite,
In the merry morning of May."

And before we knew it they were upon us. The Mayers were the first to round the corner, virtually surrounding the whole area that our party was occupying, followed by the MC in his smartly decorated suit and top hat, and then, seemingly out of nowhere, came the Blue Ribbon Oss, dancing, prancing, and whirling somewhat dangerously as he was poked and prodded along by his Teaser. The gaily dressed musicians danced in and out of the Blue Oss's loyal band of followers, laughing and cheering as if they had not a single care in the world, and both adults and children alike all joined in together with the joyful singing of the May Day Song.

"Arise up Mr. Dyne, I know you well afine,
For summer is a-come unto day,
You have a shilling in your purse and I wish it was in mine,
In the merry morning of May."

Oddly enough, by far the loudest voice we could now hear wasn't that of the large troupe of singers, beautifully adorned in their assorted blue and white costumes, but it was, in actual fact, that of Jamer's, as it appeared that he'd managed to learn every single word to the entire song. *Good old Tankman Jamer, he always was by far the best at leading a decent sing-song!* The rest of us did our best to join in too mind you, although none of us had yet managed anything other than the second and forth lines to each verse. Nevertheless, Ray, Ronnie, Tom and myself each gave it our all every time we happened upon a line that we recognised. Even Shabby, Little Kim and Little Karen joined in with the last line to each verse, which, to be perfectly honest, didn't really help an awful lot, but no one cared anyway. The seven of us certainly weren't about to win the choir of the year competition, even with Jamer's more-than-competent accompaniment, however, it mattered not a single jot. It was all about the atmosphere, which was not only happy and buzzing, but also sufficiently stimulating to lift our spirits even higher than they already were, impossible though that may seem. Along with the large gathered crowd of Blue Oss supporters, Jamer began yet another verse, then entirely unexpectedly, the Oss ceased his whirling and prancing and went down on one knee right in front of us. Maybe this was to allow onlookers to take photographs, or maybe it was purely to catch his breathe for a brief moment, none of us will ever know I'm sure, however there was no hesitation with the music, dancing and singing for one single second, and after the briefest of pauses the Blue Oss was up on his feet yet again, whirling and spinning in his never-ending quest to track down the fairest of maidens. None of whom appeared to be putting him to the test at that particular time. There didn't appear to be any young local maidens dancing around him at all, and then suddenly and miraculously making their luckiest of escapes. Nevertheless, it was a wonderful spectacle to behold, and we continued to look on in amazement, whilst singing along to the extremely catchy little May Day Song, as the Blue Ribbon Oss along with his dedicated entourage gradually passed us by.

But we didn't all simply let them pass us by, some of us decided to follow. Benny, Shabby and Helen gave up their seats for Rob, Tom and Catriona, and along with Little Kim, Kevin, Sarah, and myself, the seven of us danced off merrily together down along Riverside, watching the Blue Oss procession with intrigue, and occasionally snapping off the odd photo here and there, in between keeping up with the singing as best we could manage. Then suddenly, just as I was doing my level best to keep a firm grip on Kim to stop her from dancing in front of the Oss herself, a young local maiden, all dressed in silk and fancy finery, made a dash for it. As she laughed and giggled, she danced and twirled provocatively directly in front of the Oss, causing him to buck and spin with double the energy that he'd appeared to have before her sudden arrival. For a brief moment it looked like a simple game of cat and mouse, however the whirling Oss was getting increasingly closer to the clearly carefree young girl, and after what amounted to probably only less than a minute, just as he was about to unwittingly entrap her beneath his shiny black plastic cape, she completed one final dainty little twirl then dashed back off into the safety of the surrounding crowd of Mayers. The drums then began banging even harder, and the accordions played even louder, as the entire procession began singing the May Day Song all over again from the beginning. Not only was the whole spectacle simply mesmerising, but the atmosphere was nothing less than dramatically electrifying.

(Try searching for the Padstow May Day Song on YouTube, and if you can't quite make out the words during the film footage, then listen to the stage version by Steeleye Span!)

THE BLUE RIBBON OSS PASSING THE OLD CUSTOM HOUSE INN

CHAPTER EIGHTEEN

I caught Kim's eye as I attempted to pull her further away from the wildly prancing Oss, and I was about to point out to her the obvious dangers of getting far too close, but to be perfectly honest she was completely away with the fairies by then. Fortunately, just as the MC led the Blue Oss procession down into the narrow little lane that leads around to Avery's Row, all outsiders, onlookers and emmets were squeezed out by the excited band of following Mayers and musicians, and Shabby and I were suddenly forced into rescuing Kim from a certain fate far worse than drowning. To have become a permanent Padstonian for the remainder of her years would've been tantamount to treason, *especially for a yoong lass froom 'Ool!* As we turned to make our way back towards the Custom House to rejoin the others, whilst Little Kim gradually began coming down off her emotional high, Kevin reminded me that we had a table booked for eight-thirty, and it was a little after eight o'clock already. I handed control of the directional momentum of Little Kim's legs over to the more than capable ability of young Shabbatha, snatched the hand of my dearly beloved away from Benny's innocently protective clutches, and subtly suggested that our next alcoholic beverages ought to be one's of champagne, as being, purely in my own considered opinion of course, by far the best accompaniment to oysters.

As we walked back past the Custom House towards Strand Street, as Tom, Catriona and Rob gave up their seats in order that Benny and Shabby could securely wedge Little Kim safely down in between the pair of them, aided deftly by Little Karen alongside,

I said that maybe we'd catch a few of them up by the Maypole in Broad Street after we'd eaten, as it would've gotten dark by that time, and there was a very good chance that somewhere between nine and ten the Red Oss and the Blue Oss would be allowed to meet each other for their first and only time. At this point they'd briefly be encouraged to dance together, whilst both troupes of Mayers ran brightly coloured ribbons around the Maypole, shortly after which both Osses would then be led back to their respective stables by their controlling MC's, before being teased out for yet another resurrection the following year. Obviously, once the Old Red Oss was returned to it's stable at the Golden Lion Inn, and likewise the Blue Ribbon Oss to the Padstow Institute, then clearly copious quantities of both ale and cider would be consumed by one and all, and well into the wee hours without doubt. However, as I pointed out to all of our dear friends gathered together outside one of my very favourite drinking establishments, the culmination of the Obby Oss Festival around the Maypole at the end of a long and tiresome day is most certainly an awesome sight to behold, and one we should all try our very best not to miss. Having all acknowledged my suggestion, Kevin then grabbed Sarah's hand, I kept a tight hold of Helen's, and the four of us strolled around the corner together and walked into Cally's.

A smartly dressed waiter made a note of my name, then showed us to a rather comfortable and well appointed table just inside the front window. The view wasn't up to much, but the smells emanating from the kitchen were simply divine, and I immediately asked the waiter for a wine menu. He brought a large carafe of water over with it, along with a dinner menu for each of us, and I ordered a round of drinks; ale for me, cider for Kev and G&T's for the girls. After briefly perusing the menus, as soon as the waiter delivered our drinks, we ordered our food. Three steaks; a rare ribeye for Helen, a rare rump for Kev, and a medium sirloin for Sarah, each accompanied by thrice-cooked chips; although why the hell they couldn't just cook them properly in the first place completely escaped me. For myself, much to the disgust of both girls it has to be said, I ordered a dozen raw oysters and a side plate of garlic bread. And then to the champagne! *Hmmm, let me see now?* Fifty-five pounds was a little out of my budget for a bottle of Möet, even though Kev and I had agreed to go halves on the entire bill. Sixty-five for a Veuve Clicquot? *Definitely not!* Ninety for a vintage Dom Pérignon? *Not a bloody Hope!* Ah, here we go look; Waitrose Special Cava, £19.99, *just the jobby!* 'We'll take one of those please my good man, nicely chilled over ice in a solid-silver side bucket, if you'd be so kind!' Which, as it so happened, he most certainly was, and moments later he popped the cork, and wedged the bottle firmly amongst the crushed ice in the tall silver-plated bucket that he'd stood on the floor right next to me. I filled four flutes to the brim, and the four of us sat there, raised our glasses together, and noisily drank a heart-felt toast;

"Here's to May Day in Padstow, to both the Red AND the Blue Oss teams, and to mayhem and misadventure continuing for evermore – CHEERS!"

All four of us downed our flutes in one huge gulp, and if I remember rightly, all four of us damn nearly choked ourselves half to death on the bubbles. *'Hmmm,'* I immediately thought to myself, *'must order myself another bottle of that!'* And so I did. And then the food arrived, and all praise to Cally's, it all looked absolutely amazing. Apparently the steaks most definitely were, very much so as I was led to believe afterwards, however both Helen and Sarah clearly had a big problem watching me tackle my delicious oysters, because every single time I lifted my head and glouped one directly from it's shell into my mouth, they both looked away and shuddered. *Twelve times in a row!* Having said that, each one was washed down with a gorgeous mouthful of cheap Cava, poured generously from the second bottle, and I can honestly say, hand on heart, they truly were simply divine. Needless to say that after all twelve I felt absolutely stuffed, and four portions of garlic bread on top didn't help the situation much either. However, after a brief inter-course respite, all four of us made sure we'd left *just* enough room for a small portion of billionaire's cheesecake with cream. *And what better way to finish off a meal that I do believe I'd been looking forward to for exactly a whole year!* Once we were done, Kevin and I went halves on the relatively hefty bill that we were presented with, although as I believe I probably came off considerably the better out of the two of us, I simply swept all thoughts of debate under the mat, thanked the staff for their exquisite food and excellent hospitality, grabbed Helen's hand and headed for the door.

"Come along guys 'n' gals," I said enthusiastically, once we'd pushed our way out into the bustling street, "we're gonna miss them Osses meetin' up around the Maypole if we ain't a bit sharpish."

"Well I ain't rushin' nowheres," stated Kev defiantly. "I'm absolutely stuffed, I is! So if ee wants to go on ahead, you'm carry on mucker, but I'm gonna take me time ploddin' along slowly fer now."

As both girls were in full agreement with Kev I decided to hang back with them, and we therefore plodded along very slowly together towards the top end of Strand Street, then around the corner to the bottom end of Broad Street. Fighting our way that far through the crowds wasn't overly easy, but once we reached the bottom end of Broad Street progressing any further was clearly going to prove impossible. The only thing I could clearly see towering above the heads of the enormous crowd was the highly decorated top of the Maypole itself, and the brightly coloured bunting that gaily flowed out from it in all directions, and gently fluttered in the cool evening breeze. Looking skywards was a picture of tranquility. Looking directly ahead was a picture of pure mayhem. *May Day Mayhem, and we were all exceptionally proud to be mixed up in it!* We pushed further forwards through the tightly packed crowd, and as we steadily became more and more entrapped amongst the jostling deluge of bodies, Sarah gradually began to feel ever so slightly claustrophobic. I could just about make out the occasional clashing of two extremely heavy sheets of plywood, accompanied each time with extra-loud shrieks and cheers, even above the raucousness of the crowd's normal song and dance.

Every now and then a tall, black, pointed hat, with either red and white or blue and white streamers trailing from it's top, would briefly flash high up above the crowd, and then instantly disappear back down below again, as the Old Red Oss and the Blue Ribbon Oss continued to dance, spin and whirl themselves excitedly around one another, occasionally clashing with each other, whilst trying their best to avoid injuring any of their excited supporters that closely surrounded them. As they did so, we could clearly see the alternate red and blue ribbons dangling from the very top of the Maypole gradually becoming evermore entwined around one another. Just about see it, we *almost* could. Hear it, we most *certainly* could, for on occasion it was bordering on deafening. But get any closer to it we most definitely couldn't, the crowd was way too dense. The only one of our close circle of friends that I briefly managed to spot was Long Tom, happily jigging away directly across the other side of the square. Then suddenly, shortly before ten o'clock, the unmistakeable shrill of old-fashioned tin whistles, way over and above the banging of drums and squeezing of accordions, and not just two of them either, but a great many. Not that the music altered tone in any way, shape or form, and the singing of the May Day Song continued with as much gusto as ever, but the loud shrill of the whistles was clearly a sign for each of the Osses to cease with their over-exuberant merriment and allow themselves to be teased back towards their stables. Ever so slowly the huge crowd gathered before us began to divide into two, reminiscent in many ways to Moses' parting of the waves, and as the music, dancing and singing continued as joyfully as ever, those dressed in red and white slowly began teasing their Oss back off down Lanadwell Street towards the Golden Lion, whist those dressed in blue and white danced and sang their way back along Market Place in the general direction of the Padstow Institute.

"Now fare you well and bid you all good cheer,
For summer is a-come unto day,
We call no more unto your house before another year,
In the merry morning of May."

The music, along with the catchy words to the song, gradually faded into nothingness as the Blue Oss team disappeared off into the night, however I couldn't get that damned tune out of my head!

It had now become a seriously bloody annoying earworm, and the fact that we were still following the tail end of the Red Oss parade along Lanadwell Street certainly didn't help the fact. We stopped when we reached the front door of the London Inn, although sadly my annoying little earworm didn't. In fact, the truth is, it stayed with me for the remainder of the night, the only thing finally rendering it harmless being sleep, much, *MUCH* later on. However, at least it made me appear to be a cheerful little soul, as I sang it quietly to myself everywhere I went, or at least up until people started telling me to shut the hell up. *'How bloody rude!'* I thought to myself with a considerable degree of mirth.

Coincidentally we'd arrived at the front door of the London just as Tom and Catriona had too, so the six of us decided to dive in and have ourselves a pint together. No sooner had we stepped through the doorway than I was accosted once again by dear old Benny, who threw his arms around me and told me in no uncertain terms, typically I might add, that it was my round. And Benny wasn't alone either. He and his small handful of playmates from Tintagel had managed to drag Rob, Little Kim, Little Karen and the Shabster along with them, and they'd all just happened to have met up with Nik, Alan and Rue, as well as Derek, Giles and Will, all of whom were reluctantly admitting that they'd somehow managed to avoid the majority of *that noisy old Ossin!* By my best observation I'd've said their were around fifteen of our Bristol contingent in there altogether, all hogging one end of the long narrow bar, so I politely refused Benny's kind offer to buy a round, and opted to buy just the six of us one instead. We each said a warm and friendly *'Hi'* to everyone in turn, following which it seemed to take me forever to get served, which I wasn't in the slightest bit surprised about as I'd never seen the London quite so busy as that in all my life. Even Rick Stein was stood over in the far corner, swilling a pint of Cornish real ale whilst merrily chatting away to what could well have been a small BBC TV production team. Eventually I managed to pass drinks over the heads of the crowd in the general direction of Helen, Kevin, Sarah, Tom and Catriona, and simply kept my fingers crossed that each of them had found their rightful owners. I then chatted briefly with Nik, Alan and Rue, just double-checking that everything was all shipshape and Bristol fashion back aboard the Marovonne, which, thankfully, all three of them were happy to confirm that indeed it was. *'Good, good,'* I mouthed above the din. Next I had a quick chat with Derek, Giles and Will, asked them how they'd enjoyed their day so far, and how things were coming along aboard the Joseph.

"I think you'd best go talk to Rick about stuff like that," replied Derek, with what appeared to be a kind of tongue-in-cheek half smile.

"Oh, I see, like that is it?" I replied jokingly, before asking about the whereabouts of the band.

"Like that it most certainly would appear!" replied Will, winking at both Giles and Derek together. "As for that crazy Irish-Brummie, Black Jack Davey, and his wonderful band of excellent musicians, I do believe they've holed themselves up for the night in the Metropole, having made more than enough cash to cover at least five-star accommodation for the three of them, as well as getting themselves as wasted as they fancy for the rest of the night, if indeed that is what they fancy. That said, I reckon they'll most likely be back off to Bristol come the crack of dawn, quite possibly before breakfast even. Or at least they will be if they know what's best for them!"

"Oh dear," I said, trying unsuccessfully to look a little glum, "things gone a little awry have they?"

"Like Derek said," replied Giles, straight and to the point as always, "best go talk it through with Rick, he's the one in trou, trou, er, *charge!*"

"Okey dokey, I shall do just that then," I said positively. "Any idea where he might be this evening?"

"He said he was off to have a chat with Raymondo," offered Derek thoughtfully, "so my best guess would be the Custom House, it's a little quieter than most other pubs in town. Meanwhile, I'm pretty sure that Ben and Karen are still drinking down at the Shipwright's with Little Dave and Jo, Nikki and Mel. Either way, the interior of the Joseph is sure as hell gonna reek of a pretty bloody disgusting mixture of smells come this time tomorrow morning!"

"Hmmm, nice!" I replied, turning my nose up at him in mock disgust. "Okay then mate, thanks for the info, I think we'll sup up here and head on down to the Custom House, see if we can catch up with the young skipper down there."

I put the idea to Helen, and she quickly and willingly agreed, I guessed wanting to escape from the tight squeeze and din of the London rather than stop for another. Kevin and Sarah said they were going to stay on for a bit in an attempt to get young Nik to put his hand in his pocket for once, and Tom and Catriona politely said thank you for the drinks, have a pleasant evening and we'll catch you on the flip side. Before we left I took Benny to one side for a quiet, private little chat.

"Listen Benny," I began secretively, "I've got a cunning little plan for tomorrow, and I'm hoping that you'll come in on it with me."

"Sounds intriguing my dear friend," he replied, seemingly hooked, "please, tell me more, I'm all ears."

I briefly outlined my cunning little plan to him, and after almost falling flat on his face with laughter, knowing me as well as he did, he simply replied;

"Fucking brilliant mate, what could possibly go wrong?"

So together we agreed, 10am meet aboard the Marovonne for breakfast, and then we set off with the worst of intentions in mind, and put our ridiculous little plan into action. We shook hands on it, then Helen and I warmly wished everyone a pleasant rest of the evening together. I subtly winked at Benny just before the two of us stepped out into the cool, refreshing night breeze together, then began heading hand in hand back down to the Custom House, unsurprisingly with both of us still humming and singing the May Day Song.

The walk back along Strand Street towards the harbour wasn't quite as simple as I was expecting. In fact I'd go as far as to say it was chaotic, with groups of locals stood around chatting and drinking together, young children running around everywhere and generally misbehaving, whilst at the same time countless thousands of emmets, many pushing buggies carrying either sleeping or crying babies aboard, battled through the crowd in opposing directions in a struggle to reach their assorted holiday accommodations. I lost count of the number of times I said sorry to people for bumping into them. Finally, after a two minute stroll became a ten minute battle, we walked in through the front door of the Old Custom House. Again, it was probably busier than I'd ever seen it before, but being a relatively large, spacious establishment, we found it fairly easy to force our way through the crowd towards the bar. As I ordered myself yet another pint of Hicks, and a large orange juice and lemonade for Helen, who was struggling somewhat to keep up with most of us pirates' levels of alcohol consumption, I spotted Rick and Kim sat at a large table over in the far back corner with an as yet unknown group of compatriots. We managed to push our way through the jovial milling throng that we're all crowded around the three-sided bar, without spilling too much of our drinks, and were immediately both invited to pull up seats in order to join none other than whom I'd been expecting all along.

Sat to the right of Rick and Kim were Ray, Jean and Jamer, and sat opposite them, right by the window, were Ron and an unremarkably tipsy Johnnie. At the left hand end of the large, old pine table sat Lloyd and Cathy, although I can honestly vouch for the fact that they most definitely weren't holding hands, so Helen and I pulled two small stools out from around the corner by the fruit machines and took our positions at the table, just to Rick and Kim's left. A great deal of initial friendly greetings were immediately followed by much general laughter and small talk, mainly revolving around the Obby Ossin', and who'd managed to see what. As it turned out, Rick and Kim, together with Lloyd and Cath, had met up with Ron and Johnnie just a few meters from where we'd been stood with Kev and Sarah up by the Maypole about an hour previous, and had witnessed pretty much the same as we had, although we'd clearly all missed each other. After the Osses and their supporters had been led away to their respective stables, they'd then opted for the spacious comfort of the Custom House, as opposed to the rowdiness of the London. So now here we all were, all sat together, just as I'd predicted earlier during the day. The four most determined and responsible skippers around, along with their loyal and trustworthy crew. Well, I suppose that's one way of putting it, and certainly the best, as well as the politest, although if I were to add other factors into the equation, *such as Nik for example,* then I guess I could think of countless other ways of putting it. However, the fact remained that Ray, Rick, Ronnie and myself had stuck to our guns, as we always did, and achieved precisely whatever it was we'd set our minds to achieving. No hesitations, no going back, we simply do what we say we're going to do, and that's it, full stop. And then suffer the consequences, either along the way or afterwards *(All four of us know precisely where I'm coming from with that, however, maybe that's just the very nature of the sea itself!)* So I turned to Rick, and as suggested by some of his other, quite possibly slightly more drunken by now crew, asked him outright whether there were any potentially interesting, or dire even, consequences resulting from the afternoon's shindigs aboard the Joseph.

"Well Chris, it kind of panned out something like this," Rick began sheepishly, as everyone else sat around the table, Kim included, clearly tried their best to stifle their sniggers. "Shortly after the band packed all their equipment back into their illegally-parked van and shot off up the hill towards the Metropole, I was accosted from the quayside by a rather shaken looking young Steve. He told me, in no uncertain terms, that Malcolm was demanding to see me in his office at my earliest available opportunity. To which I replied; *'Hey ho, let's go get it over and done with right now then!'* So I immediately hopped ashore and followed Steve around to the Harbourmaster's office, walked in, said a pleasant *'good evening'* to Malcolm, then pulled up a chair and asked him how I could help."

Rick took a breather before continuing, along with a long swig on his ale, which coincidentally, everyone else, including myself, subconsciously copied. He then placed his glass back on the table and continued;

"HELP? HELP? WHAT D'YOU BLOODY WELL MEAN BY HELP, SONNY?', were the first words he threw at me, followed

immediately afterwards by; *'YOU'RE NO BLOODY HELP TO ME WHATSOEVER, NOR TO THE WHOLE OF THIS TOWN! IN FACT, YOU'RE MORE OF A BLOODY EMBARRASSMENT, THAT'S WHAT YOU ARE!'* 'Ooohh,' I replied, sucking in my breathe, *'that's a bit harsh, don't ya think? I mean, come on Malcolm, it wasn't exactly me that turned the volume up, I wasn't in charge of the band, it was that bloody Irish lad, that what's 'is name, Davey-something-or-the-other, he's the one what was in charge of it all.'* To which he replied, with his voice still raised towards me; *'IT'S YOUR SHIP SKIPPER, IT'S YOUR PROBLEM!'* I kept my cool and calmly informed him that, not only had there *been* no problem whatsoever, but on top of that we'd kept a couple of thousand people well entertained for the whole of the afternoon, and judging by their reactions they absolutely loved it. *'So where exactly lies the problem, sir?'* *'YOU STILL DON'T GET IT, DO YOU RICK? MAY DAY IN PADSTOW IS A TRADITIONAL LOCAL'S RITUAL, NOT A BLOODY ROCK FESTIVAL! I CAN ASSURE YOU I HAD MORE COMPLAINTS FROM THE LOCALS THAN YOU HAD CHEERS FROM THE TOURISTS! WHEN EXACTLY ARE YOU LEAVING?'* Hmm, blunt and to the point, I thought, as well as a little bit rude. I still think we put on a good show regardless. Anyway, he seemed to calm down a little after having let off steam at me, which, to be fair, I guess he'd probably been ordered to do by his superiors within the town council anyway, many of whom would've been actively taking part in the Obby Oss Festival. So I guess poor old Malcolm was caught between a rock and a hard place if the truth be known. I answered his question as thoughtfully as I could. *'Well to be honest Malcolm, we haven't actually decided when we're leaving yet, I haven't looked at a weather forecast or put a passage plan or anything together yet, so I can't really say. However, one thing I can assure you of, those noisy Irish rapscallions, they've already gone. Cleared off immediately after the show, so you've nothing to stress about there.'* Malcolm kept his voice raised for one last moment, as he shouted at me; *'THANK GOODNESS FOR THAT. IF YOU HAPPEN TO SEE THEM AGAIN PLEASE INFORM THEM, WITH THE FULL AUTHORITY OF THIS TOWN, THAT*

THEY'RE MOST DEFINITELY NOT WELCOME BACK HERE AGAIN. NOT FOR MAY DAY, IN FACT, NOT EVER!' He then lowered his voice and began speaking to me in a far more civilised manner."

Another breather, during which Rick finished his pint, and good old Ronnie, who clearly already knew the end result of Rick's story, offered to go buy another round for whoever raised a hand. I counted the hands as they shot up; Lloyd, Johnnie *(no surprise there then!)*, Ray, Rick and myself. The others all refrained, siting the fact that they'd already had enough for one day. To be honest, virtually the whole town had downed considerably more than their fair share. Rick continued with his portrayal of events whilst Ron waited patiently at the bar.

"*'I need you to move the Joseph please Rick, and the sooner you do the better.'* Malcolm said bluntly. I asked him why exactly, whereupon he informed me that, firstly, we're still moored to the quay that's generally reserved for *'late arrivals and emergency vessels only'*, so he needs to move us anyway. And secondly, sometime before high water tomorrow, after the barrage gates have opened at precisely 17.24hrs, the Jubilee Queen will be docking right in the corner of the inner harbour, right where we're currently moored ourselves, in order to allow a couple of coach loads of pre-booked OAP's to board, and as they've all paid a tenner each for a two hour coastal seal-watching trip, we need to vacate the area to allow them access. Ordinarily the Jubilee Queen would've loaded from the Ferry Slip along the outer harbour wall during this particular weekend, but as many of this particular party are partially disabled they won't be able to manage the walk, so the JQ's berthing in the inner harbour to make it easier for them. So there we have it folks, we've gotta move the ship. I asked him where best to move to, and he told me alongside the Roehampton please, but having chatted to Ray about it, now I know that he's aiming to leave for St Mary's shortly before eight o'clock Monday morning, I thought it best if we just slide in between the Roehampton and the Marovonne. We'll probably need a spot of help with the ropework, having just the one single engine the same as you Chris, but does that sound good with you me old mucker?"

"All good with me matey," I confirmed obligingly. "I've only got the one question for ya; what sort of time tomorrow are you thinking of moving her?"

"Well," said Rick thoughtfully, "if it's gotta be done, which clearly it has, and there's no arguing with that fact, so I guess the sooner we do it the better, then we can crack on with enjoying ourselves. So, what say around ten o'clock in the morning, how does that suit?"

"Suits me just fine Skipper," I agreed. "I'm meeting Benny aboard at ten anyway, and I'm sure everyone else will be up and about too, so there'll be plenty of hands on deck to help slot you in. All good with you Raymondo?" I asked, just double checking.

"Already cleared my friend," Ray replied, sticking his thumbs up.

"Cool, so no worries then Rick, me old mate," I said willingly "whenever you're ready, we'll be stood by waiting for ya."

"Thanks a lot guys," Rick said gratefully. "It shouldn't take too long, we'll have everything all set up and ready well before ten anyway. And that's precisely what I told Malcolm too. So there was no quibbling at all, I simply agreed to his demand, apologised if we'd upset as many people as he said we had, which I don't actually believe for one minute anyway, and just before I turned to leave we shook hands together quite amicably. So I don't think there's actually any major problem there anymore, not really, not given that I'm fully complying with his instructions."

"Well thank the Lord for that then," I said, breathing a sigh of relief. "At least all's well that ends well. Apart from one minor little point that is . . . "

"Being what exactly?" queried Ron, as he set another round of drinks carefully down on the table.

"It hasn't ended yet!" I replied, with a wicked grin on my face, and a massive twinkle in my eye.

"Oh sweet Jesus," muttered Jamer nervously, *"whatever next?!!?"*

Some twenty minutes later, after most of us had supped up, we decided to turn in for the night. Well, all apart from Johnnie that was, who decided it best he go pay a quick visit to the London and catch up with some of the other wannabe drunkards. I wished him *'bon chance'*, took Helen by the hand, and headed for the door. Closely followed by Jamer, who was even more eager to get his head down than any of the rest of us, then Ray and Jean, who stepped hand in hand gracefully across the road immediately behind Helen and myself. Rick and Kim followed on immediately afterwards, closely accompanied by Lloyd and Cathy, and paused briefly before heading off around the waterfront towards the Joseph. Finally, Ron stepped out onto the narrow pavement, fully supporting Johnnie with just the one arm, whilst evidently whispering certain meaningful words of wisdom directly into his right ear hole, both of which were no mean feats in themselves. Not that I could blame him, after all, they were due to sail on the same tide as the Roehampton, albeit to entirely different destinations. Heartfelt *'good nights'* and *'sweet dreams'* and *'see you all first thing in the mornings'*, amongst various other pleasantries, were acknowledged all round, after which we each headed off to our respective ships. Ron packed Johnnie off up the lane towards the London, desperately requesting him to go easy on the local gentry, then crossed the road and stepped aboard the Courageous. Helen took Jamer by the arm and escorted him safely and sedately back aboard the Marovonne, and once Ray and Jean eventually made it back down through our saloon they carefully helped Jamer negotiate the relatively simple step across the handrails from one ship to the other. Helen and I blessed them for their genuine consideration towards everyone that they clearly cared for, then bid them all a peaceful night's sleep. *(As if!)*

It wasn't only me that took a comfy folding chair out onto the roof of my ship that night. Ray joined me in one of his own atop the Roehampton, and I'm pretty sure that Ronnie sat outside on the deck of the Courageous for a bit too. Not only that, but if I wasn't very much mistaken, there was a certain female Lieutenant, accompanied by a rather distinguished looking male commander, both relaxing comfortably together in the shelter of the Vigilant's upper flybridge. Doubtless there were countless other skippers and crew sat out on the decks of their yachts as the clocks steadily approached midnight, however, regardless of how many folks were sat peacefully relaxing aboard ship around the harbour, the over-whelming sense was one of complete stillness and perfect silence. Perfect silence around the harbour that was, however, there was a sound that was coming from somewhere towards the middle of the town, and a most pleasant sound it was at that. Had it been windy then it may well have been drowned out altogether. However, the cool night air was as still as the stars that twinkled brightly way above the black, moonless, cloudless sky, and the sounds contin-ued to pierce the silence within the inner harbour as if they were as near to us as the closed down fairground was on the adjacent quayside. No one had their radios on, all TV's and stereos remained entirely silent, and every sailor aboard their yachts listened intently in a combination of pleasure, disbelief and awe, as the locals of the town, regardless of whether they wore blue or red, all banded together around the Maypole at the top of Broad Street and sang their hearts out one final time to the May Day Song. As the town clock struck midnight, and I headed off to join my loved one in our comfy little cabin down below, the very last thing I remember from that exceptionally special night was not the crash, bang, wallop of my seriously pissed-up crew returning noisily aboard halfway through the night, but simply those beautiful words to the catchiest of tunes that I swear shall remain indelibly stamped upon my heart forever;

Unite and unite and let us all unite,
For summer is a-come unto day,
And whither we are going we will all unite,
In the merry morning of May.

ESCAPING THE CLUTCHES OF THE OLD RED OSS

CHAPTER NINETEEN

Sunday the 2nd of May 1999 – officially Hangover Day! I woke up early enough, bright as a button, with no signs whatsoever of any hangover. As indeed did Helen, and so did Sarah. I don't think the relatively silent closing of the barrage gates at around 9.00am had woken us, so much as the clatter of the footbridge handrails and subsequent crossing, passing and chattering of countless emmets with their whinging youngsters at such an unnecessary hour of the day. Still, at least the opening of the footbridge had made it far easier to access the shower block, and by 9.20am I was back in the Marovonne's galley with a brew on the go, whilst waiting for the girls also to return. Number one plan of action for the day; move the Joseph! What hope of any practical assistance from my entirely incompetent and most likely incapable crew I wondered? The girls returned to two steaming-hot mugs of tea awaiting them, just as Kevin climbed the for'ard stairwell into the wheelhouse and slumped himself down in the skipper's chair with his head in his hands. *'Ouch!'* was literally the only word he could manage.

"Go get yaself a hot shower Kev," I told him, with what I considered to be a reasonable lack of sympathy, "then get ya ass back over here, get some coffee down ya neck, and get yaself ready to lend a hand please."

Quietly and obediently, Kev slumped off ashore with his washbag and towel, whilst I stepped out on deck to say good morning to Ray. Jamer and Dave who were sat in the Roehampton's wheelhouse drinking coffees, whilst Ray and Arthur were wandering around the decks doing a fender check. We exchanged pleasantries together, commenting on how magically the previous night appeared to have ended, and noting that once again the sun appeared to have risen into a virtually cloudless bright-blue sky. I wasn't entirely sure quite how magically the night had ended for all those that had stayed behind late in the London Inn, although I'm sure we'd all find out sooner or later when we got the opportunity to examine their bruises. Still, just like the Padstonian locals, they were entitled to their day of laziness, as indeed we all were. After all, being a Sunday it was truly meant to be a day of rest anyway, so, grateful for the fact that I had at least one crew member still alive and vaguely *compos mentis,* I decided not to disturb my remaining crew's well-needed beauty sleep. Two of us aboard each vessel would be perfectly adequate to assist Rick with slotting the Joseph in between the Marovonne and the Roehampton. Especially considering that Rick, as it turned out I had correctly anticipated, was landed with precisely the same crew issues aboard as I was. Still, I knew that Lloyd would be up and at it bright and early, plus Kim was a pretty competent deck hand too, crewing as she did at the time for the Bristol Ferryboat Company. So all in all there'd be plenty of capable hands around to help with the operation, regardless of those that were best left sleeping their hangovers off. Oh, and plus Kevin of course!

Kev stepped back aboard fifteen minutes later looking marginally livelier than he had when he'd first appeared from his pit, and I immediately handed him a hot mug of strong black coffee. I told him that he'd have to take specific instructions with regard to rope handling from either Rick or Lloyd aboard the Joseph, or Ray or Arthur aboard the Roehampton, because I wasn't going to be available myself. Fortunately there was very little wind in the inner harbour that morning. Other than what reeked from some of the portholes of both the Joseph *and* the Marovonne, there was just the lightest of breezes, but for safety's sake I was going to be standing by in the RIB, just in case I was needed to help out with manoeuvres, which I was pretty sure I would be. Plus, as things stood, the RIB was in the way where we'd left it, so I'd have to move it anyway. Kev acknowledged the fact, finished his coffee, and thankfully looked as if he was slowly coming back to life again. And talking of coming back to life again, who should suddenly appear on the quayside at a quarter to ten, but dear old Benny.

"Blimey mate," I exclaimed with mild surprise, "it's not like you to be early for an appointment!"

"The guys up top the hill in their little camper vans, they've only gone and run out of coffee,' Benny beamed at me, "bloody useless little shavers. So I figured the easiest thing was just to come and nick some of yours. I assume that's okay? Permission to come aboard Skipper?"

"Permission dutifully granted," I replied sarcastically. "Did you get the bus down into town?"

"No, I'm not even sure if it's running today," Benny replied, "so I ran all the way. Couldn't help it! I tried walking, but the hill's too damned steep, so I had no choice but to simply follow what my legs insisted on doing. Morning Kev, milk and four sugars please. So, what are we up to then my man?"

"Well buddy," I began slowly, "it's a bit like this ya see. Rick's gone and got himself into a tiny bit of bother with the harbour authorities for allowing illegally amplified music aboard ship yesterday, so they've told him he's got to move the Joseph. Not only that, but the Jubilee Queen wants to load a large party of partially disabled folks aboard directly from North Quay Parade a bit later today, so they need to move the Joseph because it's in the way."

"What utter bollocks," exclaimed Benny in disgust. "Firstly, the band were awesome, and everyone around the harbour loved them to bits. And secondly, the Jubilee Queen has a bow-mounted passerelle, she loads from the front, so the Joseph's not in anyone's way in the slightest. The JQ can simply pull up alongside her, drop her forward ramp, and on they all walk. *Simples!*"

"Well maybe that depends on just how *partially* disabled some of this party actually are," I replied, trying my best to sound sympathetic. "Maybe she does need to moor starboard-side-to for some reason, I've no idea. But I do know that Rick has considerably upset one or two of the hierarchy within the town's council, so who knows, maybe the Harbourmaster's just trying to kill two birds with one stone."

I think Benny was about to climb up on his high horse about small town political peer pressure, and all that kind of malarkey, when fortunately I heard the deep thumping *BOOM* of an old Gardner engine firing up with it's exhaust port very close indeed to the harbour wall, the echo from which softly reverberated all around the harbour's early morning tranquility. I told Benny that regardless of the rights, wrongs, whys and wherefores, Rick had already been through all of that whilst receiving the *'naughty little boy'* lecture from Malcolm, which he'd taken perfectly reasonably upon his adequately broad shoulders. So, moving indeed he was, and right there and then was when it was happening. I outlined the plan to Benny for the Joseph's tight little manoeuvre, along with the reasoning behind it, then asked him if he would simply work with Kev, as, when and if his help might be needed. Nodding his head in agreement, he and Kev finished their coffees, and as I grabbed the kill-cord off the chart table and swung myself down into the RIB, Arthur passed a couple of giant orange ball-fenders across to Kev and Benny from the clear port side of the Roehampton. I fired up the RIB, untied the painter, and backed it out into clear water, taking great care not to scrape any part of it along the hull of the Vigilant, which was directly astern of me. In fact, it was actually the position of the stern of HMCC Vigilant that was going to make this normally simple manoeuvre considerably more complicated than it otherwise would have been. Still, it was what it was, and between us we'd deal with it.

From where I was now sat at the wheel of the RIB, drifting almost motionlessly right in the centre of the harbour, I was able to see both Rick stood in the wheelhouse of the Joseph, and Lloyd stood out on her aft deck, as well as Ray on the Roehampton's foredeck and Arthur standing astern. I was now in a position to signal instructions to both should they be required, however, as the plan had already been pre-discussed and agreed, then hopefully I wouldn't need to. Rick had already cast off the Joseph's bow and stern lines, leaving both springs still attached, and at just a few minutes past ten o'clock he gave Lloyd the command to pull aboard the stern spring, then wound the engine into forward gear on just tick-over revs. Very steadily and gracefully the stern of the Joseph sprang itself away from the quayside, and continued rotating the ship's port beam forwards out into clear water. Once the ship had reached the fullest extent of it's spring motion, Rick engaged neutral and Lloyd released and slipped the bow spring. Rick then engaged reverse thrust, and with the wheel hard over to port, he very, very carefully manoeuvred the stern of the Joseph as far back as it was possible to go, almost touching the West Quay wall, as well as the array of little day yachts moored to the floating pontoons. Quick stop, wheel hard over to starboard, engage forward gear, then run around in a clockwise circle towards the starboard-side stern of the Vigilant. Whilst Rick was expertly carrying out this manoeuvre Ray had released and retrieved the bow line connecting the Roehampton to the Marovonne, and Arthur had released the stern line, but kept it attached between the two ships, simply letting it run loose. Once the two ships were free from each other, Kevin and Benny gently pushed the Roehampton slowly away from the Marovonne with two long boat hooks, then I very carefully ran the RIB in between the two ships, nudged the bow into the beam of the Roehampton amidships, and pushed her still further away, until there was roughly a thirty-foot-wide gap right down between the two hulls. I quickly spun around to the port side of the Roehampton, bumped her hull amidships once again, and stopped her dead in the water. *Phase one completed!*

Now to deal with the part that we knew from the start would be the biggest problem, that being the Joseph's turning circle. There's no way that Rick could have simply driven the Joseph directly between our other two ships, even with a good hard thrust on full starboard lock, as her turning circle was simply too wide. However, with a good old nudge under her bow from the RIB, coupled with the safety of heaving lines thrown from the Joseph's bow to Ray whilst he stood on the bow of the Roehampton, and Kevin as he stood on the aft deck of the Marovonne, then between the four boats I reckoned we'd got this pretty much covered. As the Joseph's bow inched ever closer to the flat stern transom of the Vigilant, Rick having already pulled her back into neutral whilst keeping her gradual forward momentum still swinging around to port, I ran the RIB directly under the port side of the Joseph's bow, pushed the rounded front of it's Hypalon tubes firmly against the Joseph's turquoise planking, and opened the throttle. The front end of the Joseph moved sideways a lot easier than I'd expected, and missed the starboard rear end of the Vigilant by more than I'd initially anticipated. I would imagine that not only us, but also the entire crew of the Vigilant, would've been eternally grateful for small mercies at that particular moment, and I immediately eased back on the throttle. Once the Joseph was perfectly lined up with the centre of the gap between the other two ships, I then pulled my gear shift back into neutral. Rick straightened the wheel, nudged her into forward gear, and whilst I repositioned the RIB alongside the Vigilant's starboard quarter, just to ensure that the canoe-stern of the Joseph didn't side-swipe her at the very last second, Lloyd heaved the safety lines across to Ray and Kevin. Rick then slowly steered the twenty-foot-wide Joseph straight down through the middle of the thirty-foot gap and pulled her to a dead stop perfectly in line with the other two ships. Arthur and Benny suddenly became rather busy, carefully repositioning fenders in the most appropriate positions, whilst Kevin and Lloyd pulled, attached, then secured the bow and stern lines between the Joseph and the Marovonne. Lloyd and Ray then worked together to use the Roehampton's own bow and stern lines to draw the Roehampton back securely against the Joseph, then made her off fast too. For additional security Ray and Arthur heaved two additional warps across the Joseph's bow and stern, and Kev and Benny fastened them to a couple of unused cleats on the Marovonne's fore and aft decks. The whole process from start to finish had taken no more than fifteen minutes, with not a single bump or scrape anywhere along the way, and the only other people that had awoken and risen aboard the Joseph were Ben and Karen, who were now sat comfortably together out on deck watching what was going on. *'Excellent,'* I thought cheekily to myself, *'fresh olives for breakfast!'*

Clearly my own services were no longer required, so I drove the RIB right out into the centre of the harbour, fully opened the throttle with the wheel hard around to starboard, and performed a perfect little almost-vertical pirouette in celebration of the three of us making what was ultimately a very difficult manoeuvre seemingly look like a piece of cake. Not wanting to create too much wash within the harbour itself, I respectfully kept my high speed pirouette to just the one revolution, immediately after which I noticed the beady, piercing eyes of the Commander of the Vigilant intensely drilling holes directly through my own. Unperturbed as I generally am by authority, I ran the RIB alongside the Vigilant amidships and shouted loudly up at the Commander;

"Is there some kind of problem I can help you with sir?"

"No, no, no, er, not at all really," he replied, a little surprised that I'd made the first move. "No, in actual fact, I'd just like to compliment you on your handling of what was clearly a very tricky and difficult manoeuvre in such an expert manner."

I thought for one brief moment about twisting his comment to my advantage by letting him know that I was perfectly capable of pulling far more *cunning stunts* than that with my powerful little RIB, however, the second I noticed the three gold stripes on the cuffs of his immaculately-pressed uniform, along with the two gold stripes on those of his second in command, who by now was stood right next to him up on the flybridge, I thought better of it and simply responded to him with genuine sincerity;

"It's not me that deserves the compliments sir, it's young Rick, the skipper of the Joseph. He put the plan together, essentially on the basis that the Roehampton will be sailing before we do, and it was him that executed it to perfection. Raymond and myself simply complied with Rick's instructions, it was as simple as that."

"Very well, if you say so, although from where I'm standing it looked very much like a joint effort to me," he continued. "Nevertheless, please extend my compliments to young Rick as well, if you'd be so kind."

"Indeed I will sir," I replied politely.

"Not that I feel inclined to compliment him in any way on his flag etiquette mind you," he added in a slightly derogatory tone.

I looked across at the Joseph, ran my eyes up her foremast, and immediately understood exactly what he meant.

"Oh that," I replied with a haughty laugh. "That's not meant as any kind of flag etiquette sir, that's just Lloyd's old stripy underpants hanging out to air. I'm fairly sure they've gone past their sell-by date, if you know where I'm coming from."

"Very well, carry on," he curtly ended the brief conversation with.

'Oh indeed I will sir!' I thought wickedly, *'Most definitely I will! Where's that there Benny then?'*

I pushed myself away from the Vigilant, clunked the RIB into gear, then wedged it neatly between the canoe-sterns of both the fully converted Marovonne and her sister ship, the unconverted Joseph. It was a pleasure to have the two ships moored side by side once again, something that we'd not done since a rather noisy joint party that we'd orchestrated together back in Bristol the previous year. I disengaged the RIB's kill-cord and climbed back up onto the aft deck of the Marovonne. Rick had shut the Joseph's engine down by then, and by way of a thank you he offered to buy us all breakfast over in the Quayside Café. Well, not exactly all of us, but those that had helped with the relocation of his ship, plus their partners, if they should happen to be sufficiently awake by then. At a little before eleven o'clock ten of us walked back around the harbour, stepped into the caff, and were lucky enough to find two small tables available, which we pulled together to make into one. Ronnie, Tom and Catriona were already sat in there, just finishing up. I commented on Rick's skilful manoeuvres with the Joseph, which they all acknowledged with admiration, saying that they'd watched the whole thing through the café's front window, however; *'too many cooks, etc, etc!'* I couldn't have agreed more. Folks tripping over one another whilst manoeuvring three ships each weighing close on seventy tons is a potential recipe for disaster. Helen, Sarah and Kim had all taken the opportunity to use the shower block during proceedings, but were all sat with us now, as were Kev and Benny, along with Lloyd, Ben and Karen. Ray and his crew had politely declined Rick's offer on the basis that Jean and Shiela were already preparing a late breakfast for all of them down in the Roehampton's lower galley, hence why we'd not seen them as yet. And everyone else aboard the Joseph, and indeed the Marovonne, were all still snoring their heads off, on account of the fact that they'd all not long returned from an exceptionally late-night lock-in in the London. Ron confirmed that Johnnie had woken him up once again at something like four-thirty in the morning, hence why Helen and I had also awoken briefly when presumably Nik, Alan and Rue had stumbled back aboard, if indeed all three of them had made it. One never knew with young Nik!

No matter, although we still decided to make a point of inspecting them all for bruises a little later anyway. Evidently Benny hadn't stayed out for much longer after we'd left the London, hence why he was as fresh as a daisy, and Cathy had gone for an early breakfast on her own, then set off on a lengthy trek along the picturesque coastal path. And no one had a clue as to the whereabouts of Rob and Little Kim, or whether they were both still aboard the Clair de Lune or not. Again, no matter, they'd all show up again sooner or later. So the ten of us ordered full English breakfasts, some small, some large, *Rick's absolutely massive,* and sat with large pots of tea scattered amongst us whilst we waited for them to be served. And that's when Ronnie decided to make a public announcement. He stood up, waved a copy of what was clearly a local newspaper in the air, which he'd grabbed off a side table on his way into the caff, and proudly shouted across the room;

"Hey guys 'n' gals, take a look at this then. WE'RE ALL BLOODY FAMOUS!"

"What the hell are you talking about Ronnie?" Rick asked sceptically.

Ron passed Rick the copy of Sunday's *Cornish Daily Independent* that he'd held aloft, then Rick laid it flat on the table in front of him, *unopened,* and exclaimed in horror;

"Oh shit, I don't believe it, we've only gone and made the front page news!"

Rick held the newspaper aloft so that everyone could clearly read the extra-bold headline, which to be perfectly honest was pretty unmistakeable, and then proceeded to read the small print out loud, so that everyone else in the café, many locals included, could hear him, and consequently, *they all immediately realised it was all about us*!

MAY DAY MAYHEM! PADSTOW'S ANNUAL OBBY OSS FESTIVAL GATECRASHED BY PIRATES AND MUSICIANS FROM BRISTOL

The annual May Day parade through the streets of Padstow yesterday was hijacked by a pirate fishing vessel arriving from Bristol, accompanied aboard by a live, noisily-amplified Irish band. According to the Commissionaires Office, the level of decibels pumping out from the giant array of speakers positioned all around the ship's deck was not only way too loud, but also highly illegal. The ship itself, apparently named the 'Joseph', had sailed down from Bristol the previous night via Ilfracombe, but had failed to provide a written application in advance to stage a live event. Said application would undoubtedly have been refused anyway, regardless of the fact that some fifteen hundred or so tourists surrounding the northern corner of the inner harbour seemed to have very much enjoyed the show, which was performed extremely professionally, or so I've been led to believe, by an unknown group of Irish musicians.

In an official statement, the Harbourmaster has confirmed that the captain of the Joseph, who's name currently remains unknown to the writer, was suitably reprimanded afterwards for his actions, as indeed would the musicians also have been, had they been anywhere to be found. It's now presumed that they returned to Bristol by vehicle first thing this morning, although it's unclear just yet as to when the Joseph might be leaving. This unauthorised disturbance down by the harbour caused a whole array of problems for the local townsfolk. The music itself, deemed by the town's Commissionaires to be way too loud, continued for the entire afternoon, commencing at midday and terminating at six o'clock. Not only did this drown out all semblance of gaiety accompanying the two Oss parades whenever they drew close to the waterfront during the course of the afternoon, but at one point the Red Oss team was forced to reverse it's direction of travel when confronted with the band's audience, who were mostly of tourist origin, and were apparently blocking the entire width of the waterfront road for a good two hundred yards of it's length. This was something that has never happened before in the entire two-hundred-year history of the town's May Day celebrations, however it has also been confirmed by the Master of Ceremonies that it will most definitely never be allowed to happen again.

On a much lighter note, we are pleased to announce that the Obby Oss Festival finished entirely successfully in it's usual manner, around the Maypole on Broad Street, and ultimately no harm whatsoever was caused to either beast or maiden. Additionally, in a comment made to the Independent late yesterday evening by the landlord of the Rock Inn across the water, he said, and I quote; "Both myself, my staff, and my huge crowd of customers, all of whom danced the afternoon away up on our first floor balcony, making the pub a far higher daily profit than usual, would like to thank all those involved in Padstow Harbour for putting on such a wonderful, first-class, musical performance. We'd certainly be more than happy to welcome that very same Irish band back to our own pub garden at some point during the summer, so should you be able to provide us with their contact details at some point we would be most grateful." To the best of my knowledge these comments have yet to be passed on to the Padstow Commissionaires Office.

In other matters around the region . . .

TS ROEHAMPTON, MV JOSEPH AND MV MAROVONNE

CHAPTER TWENTY

"Bravo! Bravo!" came the cheers from approximately fifty percent of the café's customers, although mostly from various sailors and their assorted crew it has to be said, the majority of whom comprised of just our lot anyway. The other fifty percent appeared to simply look away in mild disgust. Hey ho, no one got crushed or mashed on our account, so in our opinion it was most definitely worth it. *Bravo indeed!*

"Looks like they may have got themselves another gig at some point then," I ventured to Rick, whom I could tell by now was both inwardly feeling proud, whilst outwardly looking mildly sheepish.

"I don't think they'll be venturing back down this way anytime soon," Rick replied sullenly, quite possibly for the benefit of the locals amongst us. "I'm pretty sure they'll just stick to their regular stomping grounds for the rest of the summer. But don't you worry matey, I'll catch up with 'em sooner or later. That Black Jack Davey lad, he still owes me a slap-up meal for yesterday's shenanigans, that was supposed to be the deal. Trust me, we'll even up the score between us one of these days. For example, maybe I'll ask him to play some kind of *'Benefit For Rick'* gig at some point in the future. I mean, you never know, I might just end up getting married myself one of these fine days. After all, *worse things happen at sea!"*

"Talking of which," I winked at Benny, as he wiped his plate clean with a freshly buttered slice of crusty white bread.

"I know, I know," he replied, stuffing the whole slice in his mouth in one go, "low tide one o'clock. Don't worry buddy, I'm on the case."

"Oh yes, and what type of mischief are you two scheming little rascals planning for the rest of the day then?" demanded Helen inquisitively. "Clearly it doesn't involve the RIB, 'cos that's locked inside the harbour, moored astern the Marovonne. So come on fellas, give! What's going on? I wanna know?"

"Don't worry babe," I replied innocently, "I'll tell you, it's no secret. At least, not from you or any of the rest of us in here anyway. Well, apart from the locals that is, we need to keep it low-key at the moment as far as they're concerned. But essentially we've come up with a cunning little plan to wind the emmets up, and I reckon if we pull it off properly it's gonna go down a storm. I'll tell you about it when we get back aboard ship, and then, as and when you see some of our friends over the course of the day, you can subtly let each of them know what we're up to. We won't be gone for too long mind, we'll be back ashore in plenty of time for tea."

Very generously, Rick asked the waitress for the bill, then covered the cost of everyone's breakfasts in full; all ten of us! Ron, Tom and Catriona had already left, wishing us a pleasant day as they went, then sarcastically suggesting that we try our best not to wind the local town council up still further by causing yet more *disturbances in the equilibrium.* Benny and I simply kept our heads down at that point. Then, one by one, we all got up and filed back out onto the waterfront. I thanked Rick for his generosity, handed Benny a tenner, which he knew precisely what to do with, bid Lloyd, Kim, Ben and Karen a peaceful, relaxing and entirely uneventful day. I took Helen by the hand, and along with Kev and Sarah we began pushing our way through the bustling waterfront street back towards the Marovonne. It was rapidly approaching midday, and whilst I noted just how crowded the entire town still appeared to be, albeit mainly with countless emmets and their annoying little brats that kept running into me, I wondered to myself whether any of my remaining crew had managed to shake themselves awake as yet. There was clearly good reason for 'Hangover Day' being aptly named so, especially given that none of the townsfolk who had taken part in the previous day's *Festival Of The Obby Oss* were anywhere to be seen that morning either. As we rounded the corner onto *Car Park Quay*, after checking that Helen's car was still safely parked up, without a ticket on the windscreen, Kevin shouted a question at me over and above the noise of the fairground music that was just beginning to start up;

"Hey Skipper, what are you and Benny up to then? I know you've got something up your sleeve."

The four of us stepped aboard the Marovonne together and hopped down the stairs into the saloon, where it instantly became a whole lot quieter than it was up on the quayside. Rick, Kim and Lloyd followed us aboard not long after, then stepped out through our starboard-side saloon door and climbed easily over our hand-rails, hopping down onto the Joseph's port-side walkway. Rue was sat quietly in the corner of the saloon holding a steaming mug of coffee in his hands, and in a slightly hoarse voice he quietly informed us that Alan had gone to use the shower block, and Nik was still away with the fairies in the land of nod. *No surprise there then!*

"Okay Helen, Kev, Sarah, Rue," I began with a smirk, "feel free to point out to as many emmets as you possibly can the crazy, stupid futility of our forthcoming actions. As well you all know, low water today is shortly after one o'clock, at which time the Town Bar will be high and dry, it's golden-yellow sand glowing beckoningly below this beautiful, bright-blue, cloudless sky, right out in the middle of the Camel estuary. So, just for fun, just for a good old-fashioned wind up, Benny and myself are going to pitch a tent right in the middle of the sandbank, have ourselves a few beers together, and give the whole town the impression that we fully intend on camping there for the night."

"Have you completely lost the plot mate?" asked Rue, almost choking on his coffee.

"Yep!" I proudly replied. "I certainly hope so!"

"You're crazy," said Helen, a sad look of disappointment slowly creeping across her face. "The pair of you, you're totally stark raving bonkers."

"Yep!" I replied again. "You've just about got the measure of it there babe."

"Nice one Skip," sniggered Kev, "what could possibly go wrong? *Again!* Anyway, how are you both plannin' on gettin' out there?"

"I'll get the skipper of the Black Tor to drop us off," I replied.

"And how are you planning on getting back again?" asked Helen, her look of disappointment gradually turning to one of mild concern.

"I'll get the skipper of the Black Tor to pick us up again," I replied confidently.

"You're all bloody mad, you lot are," said Sarah, as she tutted and headed off down below to her cabin for something, "totally shot away in the head, all of you."

"Yep, well that's the way it'll hopefully look, so that's the plan," I agreed with her. "Anyway Helen, you know where my camera is don't you? Next to the bed down in our cabin. Could you and a few others take a little stroll around to the outer harbour wall, and once we've got the tent all set up, just fire off a few snaps for me please. Use the telephoto lens if it looks like we're too far away. That okay with you sweet pea?"

"Yes, I suppose so," Helen replied a little begrudgingly, "if I really must show some kind of interest in your idiotic lunacy. But then we're going shopping! There's a couple of nice little things that Sarah and I spotted in one of the little gift shops on the waterfront, so we're going to go and browse together for a while. Don't worry though, we won't be too far away, and I'll make a point of getting the photos taken first."

"Thank you sweetie," I replied, giving her a quick little cuddle, "you're a diamond."

There was a series of thuds across the Marovonne's coachroof as Benny returned back aboard, and after noisily jumping back down into the wheelhouse he set eight cans of Tribute down on the chart table, and loudly exclaimed;

"Ready when you are Cap'n Pugwash!"

"Arrrrrrrr, come along then me hearty, let's go search for them there hidden pieces of eight!" I replied enthusiastically.

I jumped down the aft stairwell and grabbed an old four-man tent that I'd owned since long before I'd bought the Marovonne, one that Alex and Tori, my two youngest, had shared with me on many an expedition together. It was neatly packed away, still with none of the poles or pegs missing, in a rather anonymous-looking zip-up grey bag. At the same time I grabbed a small, black, empty rucksack, just large enough to fit the eight cans of ale in, and once back in the wheelhouse I handed it over to Benny.

"Assuming this all goes according to plan," I said to Benny, "one of us will be carrying a full bag back here later, and one of us an empty one."

"Bagsy you the full bag, bagsy me the empty bag," bagsied Benny the bagsy-boy.

"If I must!" I replied flippantly. "Come along matey, let's go do it!"

I kissed Helen cheerio, the two of us said chow to the others, then we grabbed a bag apiece, hopped up onto the ship's roof, and stepped ashore into the delightful midday sunshine. After crossing the securely shut barrage gates, with deep water immediately to our left, and nothing but a long drop down into boggy grey mud over to our right, I made an eminently intelligent decision. On the basis that what we were about to attempt was going to be in full view of thousands of people, many of whom would undoubtedly be staring directly at us looking somewhat dumbfounded, I figured it best we utilise the facilities in the shower block before setting off on our way. Thankfully, I might add, it was an extremely wise decision indeed. Following which, I shouldered the relatively lightweight tent, Benny strapped the rucksack to his back, and the two of us set off together, up across the fields and down past the memorial benches towards St Saviour's Point. It was twelve-thirty, and whilst I wondered to myself which one of the two skippers that I'd already had the pleasure of meeting might be piloting the Black Tor across the Camel, I chatted away merrily to Benny about the phases of the moon. Most importantly we were just a few days past the half-way point between a new moon and a full moon, which meant that the tides would still be reasonably neap. Spring tides occur around the times when the moon is either new or full, and on low water springs the Black Tor Ferry drops off on Daymer Bay beach, immediately opposite St Saviour's Point, because the water is too shallow to run all the way up to Rock Ferry Slip. Fortunately, low tide that day still provided adequate depth of water for the Black Tor to safely make it to Rock, and by the same token, providing we were lucky enough to be graced with the same friendly skipper that had gladly returned the drunken trio of us to our home shores a few days previous, without demanding any payment, then he should easily be able to drop us off on the downstream leading edge of the Town Bar along the way. *Fingers crossed!*

As it turned out, we were indeed lucky. If I remember rightly, which, in all honesty, I probably don't, his name was Robbie. When we arrived at St Saviour's Point, some fifteen minutes after leaving the noise of the harbour behind us, the Black Tor was just rounding the northern tip of the Town Bar, on it's way back towards us with around twenty passengers aboard. It arrived approximately two minutes later, and we stood aside and waited patiently whilst all the passengers slowly disembarked via the ferry's lowered forward ramp. We were amongst a dozen or so new passengers waiting to board, and once it was our turn to do so Robbie immediately recognised me, said a very polite good day to me, then, with a wicked grin, he asked me if we were off to the pub again. I was as polite back to him as he was to me, complimented him on his manoeuvring ability with the nine-ton ferry, and simply said we probably wouldn't be going to the pub until much later that evening. It was only once Robbie had raised the ferry's ramp, backed her away from the beach, spun her around to face the opposite direction and engaged forward gear, that I left Benny sat with the two bags on the starboard-side wooden bench-seat, and approached him with a broad, friendly smile on my face whilst he stood concentrating at the helmsman's station. I'd already handed Benny a poorly octopus *(six quid!)* to chuck in Robbie's young nipper's bag when he came around collecting everyone's fares for the crossing, but I sidled up to Robbie himself with an extra fiver in my hand and set it down in front of him. I asked him very nicely, using the politest pleading tone that I could manage without laughing, if he'd kindly drop us off on the Town Bar on the way across to Rock. I said not to bother dropping the forward ramp all the way down, just lower it slightly above the sand and we'd be happy to jump.

In no uncertain terms Robbie pointed out that, firstly, MCA Regs dictated that the forward ramp must be fully lowered before disembarking passengers, and secondly, he wasn't in the slightest bit interested in the fiver that I had on offer. He was, however, more than happy to oblige with my request, and halfway across the estuary he gently nudged the flat-bottomed bow of the Black Tor onto the soft, golden-yellow sand at the northernmost tip of the expansive sandbank. Whilst the remaining passengers' jaws dropped in stunned silence, Benny and I grabbed the two bags, and leaving the five pound note precisely where I'd placed it in front of Robbie, the two of us jumped down onto the sand before the front ramp was even halfway down.

"Cheers Skipper," I shouted back at Robbie, as we began plodding steadily towards the centre of the roughly forty acre sandbank, "catch you again in a couple of hours or so."

I didn't quite catch his reply, but it seemed friendly enough as we waved each other off. We turned and surveyed our surroundings. The visible sand on a shortly-after-neap low tide is roughly a quarter of a mile square, equating to the forty acres mentioned, and at that particular time it's highest point was about one meter above sea level, just a hundred meters due south of drop-off point, as in upstream towards Wadebridge. We marked our spot, dropped our bags and began to unpack the tent. I have to say that, during the setting up process, Benny wasn't actually a whole load of help. For the most part he just moaned that the wire pegs wouldn't hold firm in the soft, dry sand, they kept pulling out every time he attached a guy rope to them. I told him to stamp them in hard with his foot, then leave the guy rope slack. We were only putting it up for show, it wasn't as if it needed to withstand a force eight gale or anything. In fact, we weren't even going to stay in it, but it did have to look the part. Plus, out in the middle of the estuary there was a considerably stronger breeze than there was around the inner harbour; 'So *stamp them there pegs in good 'n' hard me old mate!*'

Some ten minutes later, shortly after low water, we had the tent looking pretty much perfect. It was unlikely it was going to stay that way for very long, and to a certain extent we daren't even breathe anywhere near it, but providing it didn't simply collapse altogether it would suffice for the time being, at least hopefully for long enough to serve it's purpose. I stuffed the empty tent bag inside the rucksack, including the separate zip-in ground sheet, which I hadn't bothered zipping in, and the pair of us very gingerly crawled inside together. I didn't dare zip the front flaps together for fear of pulling the whole thing down on top of us, so I just left the front open, but for the time being all appeared well in the whimsical, esoteric, make-believe world of Chris and Benny. *'Time for a little celebration me thinks,'* me thought. I pulled a four-pack of Tribute out of the rucksack, passed one to Benny, and cracked one open myself. *'Ahhh, a well-deserved amber nectar indeed!'*

"So, when was the last time you put a tent up then young Benny?" I asked after downing the initial half of my first ale rather quickly.

"Ohhh, at a rough guess, I'd say approximately two days ago. Up in the park & ride field at the top of the hill, remember? Right behind me mates' two old camper vans. Yeah, I guess you were a little squiffy when I told you about it, so hardly surprising you don't remember. Anyway, it's tiny, only just about room for one, but a lot easier to put up than this big old thing. Having said that, I still found it a struggle, and I wouldn't be at all surprised if it's blown halfway across the hillside by the time I get back up there. *If I ever get back up there!* And the time before that, well I guess it would've been back in the good old days of the Cubs, so that would've been what, some twenty-seven years ago? Shit, no wonder I'm no bloody good at it, I'm well out of practice!"

"Never mind matey," I said, cracking open another can of ale, "between the two of us we got this one up okay, so all good. And you're more than welcome to crash aboard the Marovonne if you don't fancy the walk back up that steep old hill yet again, I'm sure you know that. You can use the sofa in the saloon if you like, and I'm sure I can find a spare sleeping bag kicking around somewhere."

"Okay, well just so long as it's not a sleeping bag that Nik's been using," Benny replied, turning his nose up in mock disgust, "then I may well take you up on that offer, that's very kind, thank you."

"No problem at all my friend," I replied warmly, "you're more than welcome anytime, it'd be my pleasure. Anyway, I do hope Helen's managed to snap off a few decent photos of what we're up to, I told her to take a walk out onto the outer harbour wall where she'd get the best possible view."

"Oh I'm sure she has," replied Benny positively, laughing at the same time, whilst also pulling the second four-pack of cans out of the rucksack. "Not only that, but I bet you a pound to a penny there's a whole load more people stood alongside her wondering what the bloody hell's going on. Just before we left I heard Kev saying he was off to inform the others what we were up to, so I wouldn't be at all surprised if it's all over the whole of town by now."

"I wonder if we should go take a peek just to find out?" I suggested nervously.

"Good idea," replied Benny. "Let's just walk around the back of the tent and dig a hole in the sand. Don't even look over towards the harbour, just dig for a while for no reason, and then crawl back inside again. That'll give the old emmets something else to ponder over, and we're bound to notice if anything's amiss out of the corners of our eyes."

"Okay, let's do it," I said positively, although I sat there first for another couple of minutes whilst I polished off my third can of Tribute.

We'd been out there altogether for well over an hour by then, which meant well over an hour after low water. I checked my watch; just after two-thirty. I needed to keep a close eye on the tide height too, because I was well aware of the fact that flow rates weren't always necessarily a precise science. I was also well aware of the fact that the incoming tide would eventually cover the last remaining spot of dry, golden-yellow sand at more or less exactly the same time that the barrage gates to the inner harbour were due to open, in other words two hours before high water, which I knew was predicted at 19.24hrs that evening. So at the very, *VERY* latest we needed to be gone by five o'clock. *Ahhh, plenty of time yet!* I crawled out of the tent first, squinting my eyes against the brightness of the sun, stood up and walked clockwise around to the back of the tent. Benny followed me out immediately afterwards, then walked around the back in an anti-clockwise direction. We both fell to our knees together in a position that we guessed couldn't be seen by nosy parkers with binoculars staring our way from the shoreline, and began to dig down deep into the sand with our hands. To anyone that had been able to clock our activity, such us those across the way in Rock, I suppose it would've kind of looked as if we were trying to bury something. '*A couple of rough-necked old pirates burying a tatty old cloth bag stuffed full of ancient gold doubloons*' went briefly through my mind, '*and X marks the spot!*' Realistically however, we were simply taking the piss. Having said that, when we stood back up and began to walk back around to the tent's front entrance again, I immediately noticed, out of the corner of one eye, that there was a considerably larger crowd than I'd anticipated gathered along *all* of the harbour walls, many of them pointing in our direction, and out of the corner of the other eye, I briefly clocked the fact that the forty-acre sandbank had now reduced in size to approximately thirty acres. '*Hey ho, still plenty more time for a good old wind-up, let's go drink some more ale!*' The pair of us crawled back inside the tent and sat there thoughtfully together.

"How many people d'you reckon are stood around watching us then?" I asked Benny, pulling the ring on my forth and final can of Tribute. "I'd take a guess at around five hundred or so."

"Nah," replied Benny, who'd only just cracked open his third, "there's gotta be at least a coupla thousand!"

I stared at him in disbelief, but as my eyes gradually adjusted once again to the gloom inside the tent, I began to notice the quietly sniggering grin that had slowly spread across his face, and took it to mean that he was simply allowing me my moment of glory, albeit taking the piss in return at the same time. But I was happy with that, and happy with the fact that we'd at least created some kind of audience, even if the majority of them were just queuing for the fairground rides. I slowed down on the ale a little in an attempt to let Benny catch up. I think my over-exuberance at setting the whole thing up in the first place had got the better of me somewhat, so I lay back and relaxed for a bit. Not that that helped particularly, I think I was still too excited about seeing the looks on people's faces once we got back into town. Benny opened his forth can of ale just as I was finishing mine, and at a little after three o'clock I took another quick peek outside the front flaps of the tent. That's when I decided that enough was enough, there was little point in trying to milk it any further, and on the basis that I was dying for a piss, plus there was a good chance that the thirty acres of sand had now become just twenty, I figured it would be a good time to pack up and hitch a ride home. I unhurriedly raised the issue with Benny, who, after giving it a brief moment's thought, concurred with me entirely, and proceeded to down the remainder of his ale at a significantly faster rate. Once finished, we both looked each other straight in the eye, simultaneously cracked up laughing, then admitted that we were both dying for a piss!

Thank God that particular tent didn't have a built-in groundsheet! Having said that, it was way too small inside to stand upright, so for fear of pissing all over each other I crawled out of the tent so that Benny could go first. I took the rucksack along with me, mostly full of empty, crushed beer cans, then pulled out the tent bag and laid it flat on the warm sand whilst I waited for him. Then Benny crawled out and jovially shouted; *'Your turn,'* and I crawled back in again, taking great care as to exactly where I knelt. Worryingly, Benny immediately began pulling pegs out of the sand before I was finished, and an image of me wandering around the sandbank looking like a bright-blue ghost suddenly sprang to mind. Fortunately though, I just managed to finish in time, and I crawled back outside and quickly grabbed a firm hold of the poles, then lifted the entire thing well away from the damp patch.

"Arrr, good thinking Cap'n Pugwash," said Benny in his best pirate accent.

"Hmmm!" was all I could manage by way of reply.

I pulled all the poles out from inside the tent, then together we rolled it tightly back up, then slid the whole lot neatly back into it's bag and zipped it back shut. Job done! We stood up and surveyed our surroundings; 3.45pm, the incoming tide was approaching it's maximum flow rate, and the Town Bar had indeed reduced in size to less than twenty acres. In actual fact, *significantly* less! As we stood at it's highest point, which by now was probably a little under half a meter above sea level, we both spotted the Black Tor at the same time, just as it was about to leave St Saviour's Point bound for Rock. We picked up our bags and slowly began to walk the fifty paces between ourselves and the water's edge, then plonked ourselves down again and waited. I used the tent as a seat and made myself comfortable, whilst Benny removed his tee shirt, rolled it up to use as a pillow, and stretched himself out under the glorious sunshine. As the Black Tor chugged past us some hundred meters or so away, heading towards Rock, we remained seated whilst we waved lazily at everyone aboard as they sailed by. I could clearly see that Robbie was no longer skippering the ferry, there was a different guy in charge now, someone that I didn't recognise, but he merrily waved back at us, just as the other fifteen or so passengers did. That was cool, all nice and friendly, and we didn't want to go to Rock anyway, we just wanted to go back to Padstow, so we'd just sit and wait for the right bus, so to speak. We watched as the passengers disembarked at Rock Ferry Slip, and another eight passengers stepped aboard. The skipper then spun the ship around and began heading back towards us. We immediately stood back up, Benny pulled his tee shirt back on and slung the rucksack around his back, and I shouldered the tent once again. As the Black Tor steadily approached we both held our arms out as if to stop the bus, but the ferry failed to slow down. It came a little closer, and as Benny began waving his thumb, as if to hitch a ride, I desperately waved my one free hand in a beckoning motion, as if to say; *'Come over here and pick us up please.'* Sadly though, despite the fact that our intentions were both clear and obvious, the Black Tor failed to alter either speed or course, and as it sailed on by just a hundred meters north of where we were stood, whilst we gradually retreated backwards an inch at a time as the tide steadily continued to consume what remained of our little island, I could quite clearly see the skipper of the ferry reaching over the port handrail, laughing at our predicament, and vigorously giving us the V's!

"OH SHIT, THAT'S GONE AND BLOODY TORN IT THEN!" I said to Benny, chucking the tent down on the sand in anger.

"Yeah man," agreed Benny jovially, "looks like someone's deliberately gone and pissed on our picnic."

"It ain't fuckin' funny buddy!" I said, becoming somewhat annoyed with myself. "We ain't gonna be able to swim back, not against *that* current, not fully clothed, and not carrying all *this* bloody lot!"

"I'd already figured that one out mate," Benny agreed, his expression gradually turning rather solemn. "So what's we gonna do then my friend? Surely you've got a Plan B up your sleeve?"

"There's only one Plan B I can think of right now," I said, plonking my ass back down on the tent once again.

"And what would that be exactly Cap'n Pugwash?" Benny asked, clearly hoping that I might actually have one.

"Panic!" was unfortunately all I could come up with.

I sat there with my head in my hands looking as glum as a glum thing on a glum day. It was 4.15pm, and the tide was rushing in at such a rate that I estimated the Town Bar would most likely be completely covered within the hour. And the harbour gates wouldn't open until 5.24pm! What to do, what to do? I got up and walked to the edge of the sand nearest the outer harbour, taking a step back as my feet began to sink into it where the seawater was beginning to soak in, and considered the swim once again. However, despite the fact that we were just a few days after neaps, I estimated the rate of flow to be somewhere around four knots, and the ever-increasing distance to be about a quarter of a mile. Even if we irresponsibly discarded the tent, the rucksack full of rubbish, *and* half our clothes, including our footwear, then began swimming at a decent pace directly towards the outer harbour's north wall, I estimated we'd probably end up suffering from exhaustion somewhere around the start of the Camel Cycle Trail, about a mile further upstream. Not only that, but although I've personally always been a strong swimmer, Benny certainly wasn't! In fact, I'd never actually seen him attempt to swim, but he reliably informed me that he was pretty bloody useless. Which meant that, in reality, we'd probably find ourselves floating underneath the cycle-track bridge and halfway up Little Petherick Creek before some kind, sympathetic old soul wandered down through the stinging nettles, then the reeds, then waded out through the waist-deep mud and dragged the pair of us back to safety. *'Not gonna happen!'* I determinedly told myself.

Having walked back to the safety of the centre of the one remaining acre of sand, which stood about a foot above sea level at that point, we sat there in silence together for a good fifteen minutes, staring back at the crowds that had lined the harbour wall and were staring directly out at us. The Black Tor passed us once again, heading across to Rock, but this time the skipper gave two quick blasts on the ferry's horn before leaning across the starboard handrail and once again vigorously giving us the V's. *'How bloody rude!'* I thought to myself, as we both sat there half heartedly giving the V sign back to him. The half dozen passengers he had aboard all appeared to be laughing in our general direction too. *'Even more bloody rude!'* I thought. Benny was beginning to look quite seriously worried by now, so I figured it best I give him a small degree of comfort.

"Listen mate," I began in earnest, "I've done the maths, calculated the tide versus the time versus the depth of water, and I've reached a positive defining conclusion."

"Oh yeah," queried Benny, seemingly clutching at straws, "and what would that be then?"

"We're both gonna drown." I answered him bluntly.

"Oh, fucking great," he muttered, "is that seriously the best you can come up with?"

I thought about it for a bit longer, as I watched the big hand on my watch pass the quarter-to mark whilst we sat there huddled together on half an acre of gorgeous soft sand, which by now was just nine inches above sea level. I leant back over the tent and stared dreamily up into the bright-blue, cloudless sky, watching the wheeling seagulls way up high whilst clearly deep in thought. The tidal flow rate was beginning to ease off just a little, and despite the misleading bullshit that I'd just cruelly fed Benny with, I actually felt reasonably confident with my mathematical calculations.

"Eh oop lad," I suddenly exclaimed, "I feel a lightbulb moment coomin' on!"

"Go on then Einstein," said Benny sarcastically, *"enlighten me!"*

"Well, it kinda goes like this," I replied, pulling my phone out of my pocket. "I reckon it's about time we went to Plan B."

"I thought you said there wasn't a Plan B?" asked Benny angrily.

"Every good sailor *always* has a Plan B," I replied in a matter-of-fact tone.

"Wanker!" said Benny bluntly.

I hit Helen's number on speed dial, and she answered immediately. Her voice on the other end of the phone sounded extremely panicky, and she told me that there were hundreds of people standing all around the harbour walls, worried to death about us and taking loads of photos. I told her to calm down, not to be alarmed, and that I had the situation perfectly under control.

"Now listen carefully babe," I said, using my very best calming air of authority. "I want you to walk back around to the inner slipway please, then just in front of Tom and Catriona's boat, the Kathleen B, you'll see two young guys preparing a couple of Dorys. They're small, open, white fibreglass boats with wooden bench-seats and black, fifty horsepower, Mercury outboards on the back. The lads are probably refuelling them as we speak. You can't really miss them, they're moored directly below the large black and yellow sign that says; *'Get Your WATER TAXI From Here',* and they've both got *'WATER TAXI'* written along their sides. If I had their number I'd call them myself, only I've never had any need for it, I've always had my own water taxi available. Sadly, today I don't! Anyway, speak to Paul, explain our predicament to him, offer to pay him double whatever he wants, and tell him from me, nicely but firmly mind, to please get his ass out here the second the harbour gates open! All understood hun?"

"Loud and clear Skipper," replied Helen obediently.

"Wanker!" said Benny even more bluntly.

I checked my watch again; a few minutes after five o'clock. We still had twenty minutes to wait, and although our colourful little island had now shrunk to just a quarter of an acre, leaving us just seven inches above sea level, the rate of flow of the incoming tide still continued to slow, and I felt increasingly more confident about our pending rescue. The Black Tor sailed past us once again, this time without a single passenger aboard, the skipper not even bothering to give us a single glance, although it was now significantly more than a hundred meters away from where we were sat. Not that we were sat for very much longer! By quarter past five we were down to just four hundred square meters, and the dry, powdery, golden-yellow sand was gradually turning a pale brown colour as it began to soak up the salt water. As we stood up and picked up our gear, we gradually began to feel our trainers sinking slowly into the wet sand. At twenty past five what remained of the Town Bar was roughly about the size of a cricket pitch, four inches high in the centre at most, and our trainers were soaked right through. Precisely four minutes later the barrage gates to the inner harbour, about a third of a mile away from where we were now stood, gave an audible little shudder, then slowly but steadily began to open. Before they were fully open, just as soon as there was sufficient gap in between them, the welcoming sight of a fifteen-foot Dory came speeding out of the harbour, shot quickly towards us, then, with it's engine's power-tilt raised, skidded to a halt on the edge of what little remained of Padstow's Town Bar. Benny unsquelched his feet from the sodden sand and climbed aboard, and after saying a polite *'good afternoon'* to young Paul, and thanking him for so generously offering to take us for a spin in his pretty little speedboat, I threw the tent aboard, shoved the bow back off the sand, and climbed aboard myself. Paul lowered the outboard, spun the Dory around, and headed back towards the harbour.

"Well," I exclaimed joyfully, "that was a whole load of fun, wasn't it Benny-boy!"

"Wanker!" was all he could come up with by way of reply.

"Oh come on buddy," I said, trying to get him to look on the bright side. "I mean, we achieved our goal, didn't we? We wound up the local townsfolk good 'n' proper, as well you can see from the surrounding crowds, who've clearly been stunned into abject silence, and we got ourselves safely back ashore again. Surely that's gotta be *'mission accomplished',* has it not?"

"Yeah, by the skin of our bloody teeth!" he replied morosely.

Then suddenly, upon seeing a fairly large crowd of people gathered around the top of the slipway as we slowly approached it, half of them friends of ours that we knew well anyway, but all of them giving us a rapturous round of applause, Benny lightened up. As Paul pulled the Dory up alongside the slipway I asked him how much he wanted for his little excursion. When he said; *'Oh, just give me a tenner please mate,'* I looked him in the eye, said; *'Sorry buddy, I don't have a tenner on me,'* pulled *two* ten pound notes out of my pocket, thrust them firmly into his hand, and thanked him genuinely for his excellent rapid response to Helen's request, along with his immaculate last-minute timing. I then grabbed the tent and stepped ashore, followed immediately by Benny with his clattering lightweight rucksack attached to his back. Once we reached pavement level, having nodded and smiled appreciatively at the still-applauding crowd, I turned and looked back out through the open harbour gates. There was no sign whatsoever of a single square inch of the yellow-sanded Town Bar, it simply looked as if it had never existed in the first place. I turned to face the crowd, most of who's applause had now turned into lighthearted jeers of sarcasm, and with a beaming smile I proudly announced above the noise;

"Timed to absolute perfection, *as always,* even if I do say so myself!"

To which Benny immediately replied;

"That last half an hour or so scared the living pants off of me!"

"Campers one, emmets nil," I declared, raising another cheer from our diminishing crowd.

And then I noticed Steve, the Harbourmaster's weary young assistant. He was stood directly behind Rob and Little Kim, waiting patiently for the fuss to die down. And moments later, once it very quickly had, he stepped forward, and with a blank look on his face and an emotionless tone to his voice, he looked me in the eye and bluntly announced;

"Malcolm wants to see you in his office Chris, RIGHT NOW!"

Christopher John Reason

PITCHING OUR TENT ON THE TOWN BAR

CHAPTER
TWENTY-ONE

"Oh dear," I said jokingly to no one in particular, "upset one or two of the locals have we?"

"It's no laughing matter," replied Steve sternly. "Follow me immediately!"

I handed the tent to Benny, told him and Helen that I'd meet them back aboard the Marovonne just as soon as Malcolm had finished giving me a bollocking, and set off with Steve towards the Harbourmaster's plush little office alongside the waterfront. Two minutes later I walked in and plonked myself firmly down on an old swivel chair right in front of Malcolm's rather large and considerably cluttered desk. He was sat motionless directly opposite me, and quite clearly appeared to be fuming. He immediately looked me straight in the eye and began shouting;

"WHAT THE BLOODY HELL D'YOU THINK YOU'RE PLAYING AT SONNY JIM?"

"Chris," I calmly corrected him.

"WHAT?" he stormed

"My name's Chris, not Jim, as well you know Malcolm," I cockily replied.

"DON'T YOU GET FUNNY WITH ME SUNSHINE! WHAT THE BLOODY HELL D'YOU THINK YOU'RE PLAYING AT BY PITCHING A TENT OUT ON THE BAR? D'YOU HAVE ANY IDEA JUST HOW MUCH TROUBLE YOU'VE CAUSED? WHAT

231

EXACTLY WAS THE PURPOSE OF THAT POINTLESS LITTLE EXERCISE?"

"A piss-take sir," I replied, calmly and to the point.

"WHAT?" he stormed again.

"Your average common or garden piss-take sir, designed to cause shock and consternation amongst the emmets, and to generate a scary reaction from anyone stupid enough to believe for one minute that we were serious. It would appear that I underestimated the level of success of our little venture." I offered with a mixed degree of pride and sarcasm.

"SUCCESS? SUCCESS? YOU CALL THAT BLOODY SUCCESS? YOU'VE GOT THE WHOLE BLOODY TOWN UP IN ARMS ABOUT IT. FROM THE SECOND MY OFFICE OPENED THIS AFTERNOON I'VE BEEN INUNDATED WITH BOTH LOCALS AND TOURISTS ALIKE, EVERY SINGLE ONE OF THEM PANICKING, WHILST NOT ONLY IN GENUINE CONCERN FOR YOUR SAFETY, BUT QUITE OBVIOUSLY FEARFUL FOR YOUR LIVES AS WELL!" he hollered at me.

"Oh come on Malcolm, it's me your talking to now, Chris Reason," I began, sticking up for myself and my reputation. "You know me, you know full well what I'm capable of, and you also know that I fully understand these waters, possibly almost as much as the local fishermen do. There's no way that I would put anyone's lives at risk, not ever. I'm far too cautious and calculating for that to happen. But that's not to say that I don't mind playing my little jokes now and again, just to cause a bit of a stir. So that's all it was, a little *'harbour regatta'* joke, carefully designed to cause a bit of consternation amongst the misunderstanding emmets of this world, and clearly it worked better than I'd imagined it would."

"WORKED? WORKED? YOU HAVE NO BLOODY IDEA CHRIS! GOD ALONE KNOWS JUST HOW MANY 999 CALLS WERE MADE BY THE DUMBFOUNDED CROWDS WATCHING WITH CONCERN ALONG THE OUTER HARBOUR WALLS. NOT ONLY WERE BOTH OF PADSTOW'S LIFEBOAT CREWS SCRAMBLED, AWAITING MY DECISION TO LAUNCH, BUT I EVEN TOOK A CALL FROM THE

COASTGUARD STATION AT RNAS CULDROSE TO INFORM ME THAT THEY'D ORDERED A SEA KING SEARCH AND RESCUE HELICOPTER TO BE PUT ON STANDBY, AND MADE AIRBORNE AT A MOMENT'S NOTICE!"

"Well they'd've had a bit of a wasted trip, now wouldn't they sir! And why the hell the local lifeboats got scrambled I've *no* idea! All of our mates from Bristol, the skippers *and* crew from all six boats, they all knew we were going to play a practical joke before we even started. Robbie and the other skipper of the Black Tor, they both knew exactly what we were up to as well. Not that the second guy, who's name I don't actually know, was any bloody help to us. In fact, if anything, he made the situation appear ten times worse than it needed to have looked, so maybe you should haul *him* over the coals too! But the fact of the matter is, even before we set off, enough people in town already knew what our intentions were, and there should've been no need in the slightest for *anyone* to go to panic stations," I offered by way of my considered defence.

"I HAVE NO CONTROL WHATSOEVER OVER THE RESULT OF 999 CALLS, YOU SHOULD KNOW THAT! AND THE CREW OF THE BLACK TOR ARE ONLY ALLOWED TO OPERATE TO STRICT MCA REGULATIONS, SO DON'T YOU DARE GO IMPLICATING THEM IN THIS STUPID LITTLE CHARADE OF YOURS. IN FACT, DON'T YOU DARE TRY BLAMING ANY OF THE LOCALS DOWN HERE FOR ANYTHING, IT'S YOU BLOODY LOT FROM BRISTOL, YOUR'E THE BLOODY TROUBLEMAKERS AROUND HERE, AND I SHALL BE GLAD TO SEE THE BACK OF YOU. ALL OF YOU, THE WHOLE BLOODY LOT," he continued.

"Oohh, I bet you say that to all the sailors after May Day's over and done with," I said flippantly.

"I BLOODY WELL FEEL LIKE IT SOMETIMES!" he shouted back at me.

"Well stop crying over milk that never even got spilt please Malcolm. All you needed to say when people came running to you screaming in panic was; *"Oh that! Don't worry about that! That's just Chris Reason, he's one of our regular visitors. He thinks he's a bit of a pirate, likes to play practical jokes on people all the time. Just ignore him, he's perfectly capable of looking after himself, and with any luck he'll be sailing himself and his crew back out of here any day now."* That would've done the trick, and nothing more would've needed to have been said about it. *Simples!"* I told him with a grin.

"IT'S NOT THAT BLOODY SIMPLES CHRIS!" he continued to shout at me. *"I'VE HAD COMPLAINTS FROM LEFT, RIGHT AND CENTRE ABOUT VIRTUALLY ALL OF YOU, AND NOT JUST FROM THE LOCAL TOWNSFOLK EITHER, BUT ALSO IN WRITING FROM A SENIOR COMMANDER IN HER MAJESTY'S FORCES. EVEN THE LOCAL PAPERS HAVE GOT YOU DOWN IN WRITING. NOW DO ME A FAVOUR PLEASE AND GIVE ME A LEAVING DATE?"*

"Well sir," I carefully began my considered reply, "the Roehampton and the Courageous 2 are both leaving on tomorrow's early morning tide, the Roehampton bound for St Mary's, and to the best of my knowledge the Courageous bound for Falmouth."

"I'm well aware of that thank you Chris," Malcolm replied, having seemingly now calmed himself down somewhat. "And furthermore, I've had no complaints whatsoever regarding Raymond or Ron, it's not them I'm concerned about. Although it's entirely possible I might get a couple of minor moans at some point in the future with regard to a certain crew member of Ron's, as is not uncommon at this time of the year, although as yet that remains to be seen. No, it's not them I'm interested in Chris. When exactly is the Joseph leaving?"

"I've no idea Malcolm, you'll have to ask Rick himself about that," I replied in all honesty, "although I suppose I could take a rough guess and say Tuesday. After all, it is a bank holiday tomorrow, so most of us are just gonna laze around and relax. However, I believe high water Tuesday morning is around 07.50hrs, so I wouldn't be at all surprised if he leaves just as soon as the gates open, punches the tide all the way up to Hartland, then runs straight into Bristol shortly after dark the same evening. That's what I'd probably do. Plus I'd imagine the Kathleen B and the Clare de

Lune will follow his lead; not that they'll be able to match his pace of course."

"Logical thinking Chris, makes eminent sense to me, so I'll keep my fingers crossed," replied Malcolm calmly. "And what about you, when exactly were you and your delightful crew thinking of lowering that Scull & Crossbones and running the Marovonne back out of here?"

"Well, you see, it's kinda like this sir," I began sheepishly, "we've got a once-in-a-lifetime total solar eclipse coming up later this summer, and it can't be seen properly as far north as Bristol, the only part of the UK in which it'll be perfectly visible from is Cornwall and a tiny bit of South Devon. So, seeing as Padstow Harbour is legally a maritime *'Safe Haven'* and all that kinda stuff, as clearly listed in the Reed's Nautical Almanac, then I figured that, rather than sail all the way back to Bristol, and then sail all the way back down again, I might as well leave the Marovonne down here for the rest of the summer."

"WHAT?" he screamed at me.

"Yeah, and just to be on the safe side," I continued calmly, "I figured I'd leave young Nik aboard too, just to keep an eye on things for me whilst I go back to work. He'll be fine, he'll get himself a job somewhere, and obviously I shall pop down most weekends to ensure that all is well."

"OH LORD JESUS HELP US!" Malcolm exclaimed in exasperation. *"GET THE HELL OUT OF MY OFFICE RIGHT NOW!"*

"Well thank you kind sir," I replied calmly, as I stood and headed for the door, "I'll keep you updated just as soon as I know anything definite."

'Well, that went extremely well then!' I immediately thought to myself, once I was stood back outside in what little remained of the evening sunshine. I acknowledged young Steve, who was leant against the wall in the shade, smoking a cigarette whilst clearly keeping very tight-lipped about things, then I turned on my heels and began strolling slowly back towards the Marovonne. *'Hey ho, just another day in paradise!'*

I bumped into Ray and Jean, Arthur and Sheila, and Jamer and Dave on my way back to the Marovonne. I asked Jamer if he fancied coming up on the Wipe Out with me one more time, but his answer was brief and to the point; *'Don't you think one cunning stunt is sufficient for the day young laddie?'* Yeah, I guessed he was right, I couldn't really argue with that one. I asked him where they were going, and he said they were all meeting up with Ron and Johnnie in the Custom House to discuss their plan of action for leaving early the following morning. After letting them know that Malcolm was more than happy for me to leave the Marovonne moored in Padstow for however long I felt like it, I said I'd leave them in peace to discuss their plans together, and maybe catch up with them for a farewell drink or two a little later on that evening. Before walking the final few paces, stepping aboard ship and hopping down into the wheelhouse, I opened the Lucy box and checked the electricity meter inside once again. *How very odd!* The dial was spinning at the usual rate, but the meter still read *'FULL'.* I wondered for a brief moment if someone else was either purposefully or accidentally feeding it for me, but then I kicked myself and told myself not to be so stupidly naïve. I heard chattering voices ahead of me, and I peeked through into the saloon to see who was there. Helen and Sarah were flicking through the photos on the screen of my digital camera, whilst Alan was listening intently to the significantly embellished picture that Benny was painting with regard to our afternoon's escapades, which apparently included; *'How we only just about managed to evade a certain horrific death by the width of an Oss's hair!'* *'Hmmm,'* I thought to myself for the hundredth time that weekend.

One of the reasons why Benny was waxing lyrical was because Giles, Will, Derek and Shabby had heard the rumours kicking around town, and had stepped aboard off the Joseph in order to hear the true version first hand. I'm not entirely sure that Benny's highly enthusiastic elaboration was a hundred percent accurate, but it didn't matter in the slightest to me. Providing it made for good story telling, then that's essentially what it was all about. Benny stopped talking the moment I stepped down into the saloon, and asked me outright how I'd got on at the Harbourmaster's office. *'Like a house on fire!'* I lied, although, putting that into some kind of realistic context, maybe it wasn't altogether a lie.

"We've been cordially invited to remain in port for the entire duration of the summer," I proudly announced, whilst thinking to myself; *'That was a far more positive lie!'*

"Bloody liar!" said Giles with a wicked grin on his face.

"Yeah, well, I guess he wasn't exactly best pleased," I reluctantly admitted, "but I can't really blame him I suppose. I mean, how was I to know they'd put a Coastguard Sea King rescue helicopter on emergency standby? Not exactly my doing. Malcolm knows me well enough, he should've know we were only having a laugh. Wait 'til I get my hands on that skipper of the Tor!"

"You can't exactly blame him, now can you Chris," said Will sympathetically. "Poor young Robbie, he would've got himself into some serious trouble with his boss for dropping you off there in the first place, and his later replacement would've been under strict instructions not to get involved."

"I can't see any need for him to give us the V's in such a sarcastic way though, can you?" I queried, staring vacantly at Benny whilst not really expecting an answer.

"You'd've got far worse from me if I'd been the skipper of the Tor," interjected Derek. "I'd've persuaded all the passengers aboard to give you the V's whilst I dropped me pants and mooned at you."

"Now that I could've coped with," I replied with a cackle. "It's not as if I haven't given others similar treatment myself. Ask Kev about the time we went conger fishing out of Lyme Regis if you ever get the chance. Talking of Kev, where is he? Where's Nik and Rue? Where's Rick and Kim? Where's the newlyweds, Lloyd and his dearly beloved wife Cathy? Where is everyone?"

"I know Kev, Nik and Rue went off to the Shipwright's with Rob and Little Kim," replied Sarah.

"And Rick and Kim, Lloyd and Cath, Little Dave and Jo, and Ben and Karen, they've all headed into town together in search of something to eat," volunteered Shabby, then added; "quite probably in a curry house somewhere, knowing Rick, if indeed there is such a thing in town."

"How about Mel, Nikki and Little Karen?" I asked, not wanting to leave anyone out.

"Can you not hear their screams?" queried Helen, as she took me by the hand, led me out onto the aft deck, and pointed up at the Wipe Out, just as it was about to drop from the highest point of it's high-speed, vomit-enducing revolution.

"Eeuww, good luck to them with that!" I said, suddenly grateful for the fact that Jamer had turned my latest offer down. I then took a quick peek over the Marovonne's stern, just to ensure that my RIB was still securely moored and fully inflated, and more to the point hadn't been purloined for dubious purposes by young Nik yet again, which it clearly hadn't. I then called Benny outside to join me, and once he was stood next to me, I put my arm around his shoulder, pointed down at the RIB, and stated in no uncertain terms;

"Next time I come up with one of my cunning little plans that can't possibly fail, my dear old friend, try ya best to make sure I take one of those with me!"

"Oh, indeed I will Cap'n Pugwash," came Benny's sarcastic reply, "you can count on it!"

Shabby and Sarah joined the three of us out on the aft deck, and just as they did so the Jubilee Queen came steaming in through the harbour gates. It was approaching seven o'clock, around half an hour before high water, and as the JQ settled her bow into the deep, still water and drifted slowly across to the far side of the inner harbour, we suddenly noticed two luxury coaches parked one behind the other halfway along North Quay Parade, along with a rather large crowd of elderly folks slowly milling around along the quayside. Unsurprisingly, the JQ headed directly towards them, then, when her bow was about four feet from the quay wall, her well-practiced skipper briefly ran both her engines astern and brought her to a perfect dead stop. He then gently lowered her bow-mounted passerelle directly down onto the pavement.

"See, what did I tell you?" said Benny angrily. "She's not gonna moor starboard-side-to at all, nothing like it! Because she's got both bow and stern thrusters, the skipper has no problem keeping her perfectly stationary wherever he likes. So every single one of that group are simply gonna walk directly up the gangplank, straight onto her bow, then around to their seats, just like I said they would. So you know what that means then, don't you my old boy?"

"Indeed I do matey," I replied with an air of disappointment. "That means there was absolutely no need whatsoever for Rick to move the Joseph first thing this morning."

"Exactly!" replied Benny.

"To be perfectly honest mate," I continued, "now that I've had a bit of time to think about it, I'm not entirely sure that Malcolm was overly angry with me earlier. He let it go all too easily. I'm not so sure he was altogether that angry with Rick either. In fact, I've come to the conclusion that he's probably just having his strings pulled by some unseen person at a higher level than him. In exactly the same way that Geoff has his strings pulled by Richard back in Bristol. I mean, after all, this little *'leisure amenity'* down here in sunny Padstow is owned and operated by the local authority in exactly the same way that Bristol City Council runs it's own depart-ment of leisure services. So essentially, although Malcolm is the *face* of authority, I think he's basically just a puppet, albeit a highly qualified one. D'you know, I wouldn't even be at all surprised if he'd secretly taken a liking to Wylde Green's music yesterday too."

"I wouldn't be at all surprised if you were right Mister Chris," said Benny, slowly stroking his long ginger beard, "that's the way hierarchy works within local authorities. The ones with the real power, the ones that hold the purse strings, for the most part they're the unseen untouchables that spend most of their time larging it up in their ivory towers. With one or two exceptions it's pretty much the same everywhere."

"Indeed it is Benny-boy, indeed it is," I agreed with him. "Still, let's not let local politics get in the way of good old-fashioned piracy, eh? After all, this whole weekend was put together by those very politicians for the sake of others having fun, so fun is precisely what we shall have. How does that old motto of ours go exactly matey? '*Fun In The Sun, Drink All The Rum, No Harm Ever Done!*'"

"I can think of others too," said Shabby with a grin, "such as that old anchor tattoo you had done on your leg for example; '*Live Without Fear, Laugh Without Caution, Love Without Regret*', that one always made me giggle."

"Indeed Shabbs, in fact I seem to remember that one stemming from some kind of '*Momentary Lapse Of Reason*,'" I replied, as I pictured the irony of that particular episode in my life.

"Hey ho; '*What Doesn't Kill You Makes You Stronger,*' said Helen sarcastically. "Come on guys, enough of this nonsense, I'm hungry. Can I suggest we go get fish and chips over by the harbourside again please?"

"Good move princess," I agreed, "lead on, I'm sure most of us will follow, I don't think any of us have eaten much since breakfast."

"Yippee, Padstow's finest fish and chips," said Sarah excitedly. "Yummy, I can't wait!"

Helen led the way back through the saloon, up into the wheelhouse, then once again up onto the ship's roof amidst the noisy racket of the clattering fairground rides. And everyone followed. Me, Benny, Shabby, Sarah, Alan, Giles, Will *and* Derek, apparently all nine of us had consumed nothing but alcohol for the most part of the day, and we all agreed that a good, classic, old-fashioned fish and chip nosh-up on a wooden bench-seat alongside the harbour should prove just the token for soaking it all up. Just as we stepped ashore, one by one, line astern, we stumbled across Mel, Nikki and Little Karen as they staggered unsteadily off the Wipe Out's checkerplate walkway. Or should I say, a little more accurately, they stumbled into all of us. Just as well really; better that than stumbling directly into the harbour! I asked the three lovely young ladies if they fancied joining us at Padstow's finest fish and chip café, but all three of them simply looked goggle-eyed at us whilst giving me the distinct impression they were all about to throw up. I honestly thought Sarah was going to wet herself laughing, and I told Helen to lead her away for fear of embarrassing the three poor girls. Fortunately, help was immediately at hand. Derek put his arm around Mel's waist, Will did exactly the same to Little Karen, Giles grabbed a steadying hold of Nikki, and between Benny and myself we managed to persuade all three of them that, at least for the sake of their own safety, they'd be far better off just coming along with us and sitting down, even if they couldn't stomach the thought of eating anything just yet. I felt pretty confident that all of them would after not too long.

So now there were twelve of us, and whilst we all ambled our way along the quayside towards the Courageous 2, and the fish and chip café immediately opposite on the other side of the street, I wondered just how difficult it was possibly going to be to find seating that would accommodate every one of us, especially given how crowded the little town still was. That thought was intensified after passing the Courageous, when Tom and Catriona alighted from the Kathleen B and decided to join us, however my concerns proved unfounded once we reached the right plaice *(sorry, place!),* as there were more than sufficient vacant bench-seats on the waterfront along The Strand. Derek, Will and Giles carefully ensured that the three girls were safely seated, then asked them once again if they fancied anything to eat, and as they all appeared to have suddenly made miraculous recoveries, they each asked for small portions of fish and chips. The remainder of us all wanted extra large portions of the same, with the exception of Giles and Alan, who both fancied one of Granny's delicious pasties, *yet again!* Of the fourteen of us all now feeling considerably ravenous, seven queued inside the caff for the food and drinks, whilst the other seven spread themselves out along three of the vacant benches in order to safely reserve places for all of us. Some fifteen minutes later, each and every one of us having coughed up the cash to pay for our own food for a pleasant change, we took up every square inch of available space on all three six-seater bench-seats situated along the waterfront, whilst we all got stuck into our superlative meals. Every one of us had a neat wad of three or four large sheets of plain-white greasy paper sat on our laps, on which sat beautifully battered portions of freshly caught cod, along with countless hundreds of golden-brown chips, and each of us also had a can of some type of non-alcoholic fizzy drink sat on the pavement down by his or her feet. To any outsiders we must've looked a picture of perfection, potentially worthy of a local picture postcard even, although sadly, the majority of us knew better than that. Sometimes however, the truth is easily hidden. Easily, that is, until one of the local *bastarding* seagulls tried yet again to fly off with a beakful of Giles's pasty, and another one of the not-so-little shits managed to get away with a decent sized portion of Helen's delicious battered cod. *That's* when you begin to realise that we're nowhere even remotely close to being picture postcard material. Haha, that was a fun evening; Giles two, seagulls nil, although sadly Helen didn't fare quite so well in her little tussle, and for all my best defensive efforts I simply ended up with a half-decent collection of lightly-bleeding claw marks all up my right arm. Much to my dismay, all that achieved was to set everyone else off laughing. Oh well, it was mine and Helen's decisions to eat outdoors I suppose, what else did we expect exactly?!!

We all finished eating a little before nine o'clock, just after the street lights surrounding the harbour gradually began one by one to automatically illuminate themselves, and shortly after the Jubilee Queen had steamed back into the harbour to disembark her aged party of seal watchers. High water had occurred at around 19.35hrs, so the harbour gates would be closing once again in about forty minutes. I wondered to myself whether they'd moor the JQ up for the night inside the inner harbour, most likely alongside the North Quay where the Joseph had been, or whether they'd run her back out to her anchorage out in The Pool like they normally did. On the basis that many ships were leaving on the following morning's early tide, including the Vigilant, the Dasher, the Roehampton, the Courageous, plus more than likely a hundred or so other yachts and motorboats bound for various ports along the Welsh coast, then I guessed it'd make more sense to run her back outside, well out of harm's way. Still, by the time we'd all deposited our empty food wrappers and crushed drinks cans in the conveniently provided council waste bins, then began walking slowly together along the waterfront towards the Shipwright's for a couple or three nightcaps, the two luxury coaches with their full-to-capacity loads of semi-disabled passengers had left the scene, but the JQ was still sat there motionless in the eerily black water, her twin engines still ticking over quietly, and her vast array of interior, exterior and navigation lights beautifully reflected in the stillness of the harbour. As we all walked on past, stepping carefully over the front edge of the JQ's passerelle, there's one image that still sticks in my mind to this very day that reminds me so poignantly of that particular night. Stuck right in the middle of the JQ's central wheelhouse window, clearly illuminated by her bow's bright deck lights, was a large poster, one that I'd seen dotted all around the town on many an occasion that weekend. The poster was wonderfully enigmatic in it's simplicity, having no need whatsoever for information other than the three basic words that it displayed, along with the image that summarises, for myself at least, the spirit of what Obby Oss Day is all about. I stared with passionate intrigue at that highly familiar poster, proudly displayed in the front of the JQ's wheelhouse, for as long as it took for Helen to grab a tight hold of my arm, then yank me firmly away from the water's edge for fear of me toppling in. Only then did I turn, and with a renewed thirst in my throat, and my eyes fixed firmly on the new target directly ahead of me, I took Helen by the hand and followed our other twelve friendly companions in through the front door of the Shipwright's.

Christopher John Reason

THE INFAMOUS OBBY OSS POSTER

CHAPTER
TWENTY~TWO

As Helen and I shuffled our way along to the far end of the bar, after we'd been served with our drinks, I suddenly realised that everyone was in there. And I mean *everyone!* Although, to be fair, they weren't just *in* there, they were scattered around all over the place; some stood at the bar, namely Giles, Will, Derek and Benny, some sat at inside tables. Some stood chatting together just outside the bottom entrance, where they had a clear view across the outer harbour wall towards Rock, and the rest just milling around in the pretty little beer garden out the back. I left Helen merrily chatting away to Shabby, Mel, Nikki and Little Karen at the bar, then Tom, Catriona and I followed Sarah down a couple of steps and over to a table that Nik, Kev, Alan, Rue, Rob and Little Kim were all sat at, Tom trying his best not to spill his ale as he carefully ducked underneath each of the old oak ceiling beams that hung low over-head. Sarah grabbed a seat next to Kev, then I asked Rob if he and Little Kim were stopping down for the bank holiday the following day, and when they were considering sailing back. Just as I suspected, Rob said they were going to leave at the same time as Rick on the Tuesday morning tide, but they'd probably anchor off Lundy overnight again on the way home, seeing as the Clare de Lune had nowhere near the cruising speed of the Joseph. Suddenly, upon noticing just how totally wasted Nik appeared to be, his eyes resembling piss-holes in the snow once again whilst he stared blankly into the far distance at precisely nothing, seemingly entirely oblivious to our presence, I wisely chose to take my leave, and bid all seven of them a pleasant evening together. Tom and Catriona did exactly the same thing to the other five that were seated, however, whereas they turned right at the far end of the inn, and stepped outside onto the paved dead-end street to join Ray, Jean, Arthur, Sheila, Jamer, Dave, Ron and Johnnie, who were all still chatting excitedly together about where their further exploits the following day were going to land them up, I decided to hang a sharp left, and stepped out into the rear beer garden to have a quick conflab with young Rick.

I immediately spotted both Lloyd and Cathy, happily chatting away to each other whilst sat romantically together in a two-person swing-seat underneath a rather beautiful pink-blossomed rose arch. After offering them my sincere congratulations once again on their perfect, albeit somewhat *unexpected* wedding, I politely asked them if they'd decided on any specific honeymoon location as yet. In perfect harmony together, they both politely suggested I go talk to someone else, and preferably about something entirely different altogether. I laughed as I headed off across the patio towards where Rick and Kim were stood, deep in conversation with Ben and Karen. Not wanting to interrupt for the time being, I sat myself down on an old wrought iron bench-seat, and struck up a conversation with Little Dave and Jo, who both appeared to be sat there simply enjoying the coolness of the pleasant night air, whilst stargazing at the myriad of pin-pricks of light way up above the clear, cloudless sky. I commented on the fact that there was almost a three-quarter moon low down on the far horizon, meaning that we were almost halfway between neaps and springs, which in itself ought to give the Joseph a good old helping hand whilst sailing back up the Bristol Channel towards home in a couple night's time, however, both Jo *and* Little Dave appeared to be in somewhat of a quandary, so instead of harping on about tidal flows I politely asked them what it was about.

"Well it's kind of like this," began Jo slowly. "Dave's got some business that he'd like to go and take care of down in Falmouth, so he's wondering if maybe he should hop aboard the Courageous and sail around Land's End with Ronnie tomorrow, particularly given that the marine inshore forecast is pretty good for tomorrow. The trouble is, his van's parked up in Ilfracombe, and Rick would prefer not to stop off anywhere on the way back, partially due to the tight time constraints in reaching Bristol in one hit, and partially because he'd be passing Ilfracombe at low water anyway, making it rather difficult to stop off there."

"It's a little more complex than that too," said Dave, nodding towards Rick, Kim, Ben and Karen. "That's precisely why they're all deep in conversation right now. Rick doesn't particularly want to sail until Tuesday, partially because he needs to take on more fuel before leaving, and Ben wants to sail back with Rick anyway, as do Giles, Will, Derek and the three girls; they're all happy to take the Tuesday off work. But Karen's not, she wants to open up The Olive Shed back in Bristol on Tuesday lunchtime, as well as Tuesday evening. It's a cracking little business they've got themselves going there, and she doesn't want to let any of it go, not even for a single day. Not that I can blame her mind you. Having said that, given how many of us there are down here this weekend, in actual fact, thirty-four of us in total, or at least so it would appear, we figured that one way or another we'd be able to sort something out. Got any helpful suggestions mate?"

"Me?" I asked, pretending to look a little shocked. "Come on Dave, you know me, I'm *always* full of helpful suggestions. Let me ask one simple little question first though, before I pull my rabbit out of it's hat. Jo, do you drive?"

"Yes, I most certainly do," replied Jo confidently.

"Well there we have it then, *simples!*" I confirmed without elaboration.

"There we have what exactly Chris?" Dave asked, looking a little puzzled.

"Right then mate," I began, having suddenly donned my organisational cap, "you go let Ron know that you'll be crewing with him and Johnnie round to Falmouth tomorrow, and I'll go interrupt these guys over here and tell Ben it's fine for him to sail back with Rick on Tuesday. In the meantime, Helen's got her little Astra down here with her, because she's not actually allowed to take Tuesday off work, and so far she's only got the one passenger with her, that being Sarah, who also has to work on Tuesday. So therefore Jo, Helen can drop you off in Ilfracombe on her way home tomorrow afternoon, then you can go get Dave's van and drive on down to Falmouth to meet up with him. Then Helen can drop both Karen and Sarah back to Bristol by Monday teatime, so all sorted. How does that sound?"

"Absolutely bloody marvellous mate, you're a star," Dave replied. "Well done, and thank you."

"No problem mate," I said, "only too glad to help. Not only that, but it saves a whole lot of faffing about with taxis and trains, etcetera. What a nightmare that would be."

"You see darling?" said Dave to Jo with a broad grin across his face. "I told you one or two of our lot were bound to have their vehicles down here, I just knew it."

"Sadly it's only the one though," I said thoughtfully, "which means that, come some point before next weekend, Me, Kev, Alan and Rue are all gonna have to catch the train back to Temple Meads anyway."

"Why's that then Chris?" queried Dave. "Why aren't you sailing the Marovonne back to Bristol?"

"I've decided to leave her down here until the total eclipse on August the 11th," I replied with a smile. "I'll sail her back on the next half-decent opportunity I get after that."

"But I thought the Harbourmaster had thrown you out, told you to leave?" asked Dave quizzically. "At least, that's what I'd heard anyway."

"Well if he did, he certainly didn't make a very good job of it!" I replied sarcastically.

"And what about young Nik?" asked Jo sympathetically. "Right now he doesn't even look fit to drop, let alone fit to travel anywhere."

"Yeah," I replied, weighing up the pros and cons in my mind once again, "I'm leaving him down here as well. I'd rather have some kind of security aboard at the very least, whilst I'm away from here working, although I must admit, I certainly got the impression it was that part of my plan that the Harbourmaster seemed most perturbed about. Still, I've told Nik he'll have to find himself a job whilst he's down here, and I've told Malcolm as much too, so hopefully, fingers crossed, nothing should go too much awry."

"Hahaha," replied Dave haughtily. "Famous last words Chris. Keep me posted as to how much trouble he gets himself into please buddy."

I acknowledged that with a friendly laugh as I stepped in between Rick and Ben in a subtle attempt, firstly to interrupt their conversation, and secondly to put forward my proposal. And once I had, I was most pleased when it went down a storm with all parties, especially Karen. All I had to do now was run the idea past Helen, but that could wait for the time being. Having just successfully organised everyone's onward journeys for them, regardless of the fact that in reality, all I'd actually done was to volunteer someone else's services for the task in hand, I fancied a little small talk for a change. I was still feeling proud as hell with mine and Benny's camping endeavours, although I was more than happy to listen to other people's reactions to Benny's far more embellished accounts of what actually happened, rather than my own over-simplified version. So I turned to Rick and asked him, purely off the cuff, if he'd managed to locate a decent curry house anywhere in town.

"Well, surprisingly enough, that was much easier than I thought it'd be," replied Rick, clearly relieved with the fact that I'd managed to help sort out Ben and Karen's little dilemma for them. "I always thought the Prawn On The Lawn around in Duke Street was just another seafood restaurant, but in actual fact they cook their own freshly caught fish in many different styles; Thai, Chinese, Indian or even just plain old English. We all chose totally different dishes to each other's , but I personally had the Sri Lankan black curried cod with baby gem, truffle oil and Grana Padano sauce, and bloody delicious it was too. Their prices weren't too bad either, although to be perfectly honest we weren't overly bothered about that. I had a call from Black Jack Davey earlier during the day. He apologised for running off with the collection buckets after their gig yesterday, but he somehow knew he was going to get caught out by the town council one way or another, so he'd felt it best they make an early exit from the scene of the crime. Anyway, true to his word, he told me to take a few close friends with me, go grab a good old nosh-up somewhere, and stick the bill on his credit card. So we did, and it was fab, and so indeed was the wine, *all eight bottles of it!* Anyway, I called Davey when we'd finished and he never even flinched when I mentioned how much the total bill came to, he simply paid for it over the phone and said; *'No problem moy friend, tanks fer helpin' te make de day sooch a success fer de lot of us all!'* I hate to think how much cash they must've finished up with altogether in them there plastic buckets, but our pretty hefty slice of it never fazed him in the slightest."

"Ah, so all's well that ends well then?" I asked him, not wanting for there to be any loose ends left hanging around as a result of our *almost-perfectly-orchestrated* weekend of mayhem together.

"Definitely seems that way me old *matey-buoy*," he replied, patting me on the back ever so slightly harder than I would've preferred.

"Cool," I said coolly, "I always did prefer a happy ending."

"Oi don't reckon you'll be foindin' one o' they down yer matey," interjected Benny, who'd quietly sneaked up behind me unnoticed, "oi reckon you'll 'ave to be sailin' back up Brizzle fer one o' they!"

"Fool!" I answered him back with a friendly laugh.

I left Benny with Rick, in order that he could recount his own version of our little camping expedition together in it's far better embellished format than mine. Apparently, as I'd found out from Rick at some point the following day, we were both as drunk as lords before we'd even started, and the water was almost up to our necks by the time we were finished. *Good old Benny!* Ben and Karen both said thank you to me as I turned to walk back into the pub, and Jo threw her arms around me and gave me a quick peck on the cheek. Feeling a little warm glow of pride inside, I then opened the back door to the pub, and almost knocked Little Karen's drink out of her hand as I stepped through into the dimly-lit lounge area. We had a quick *'oops-a-daisy'* giggle together, then I held the door open and allowed her, Nikki and Mel to pass by into the beer garden. Once my eyes had become accustomed to the dimness, I stared up through the crowded pub just to make sure everyone appeared to be okay. Helen and Shabby had managed to find a couple of bar-stools, and were merrily chatting away to each other, the pair of them right down at the far end of the bar. Giles and Derek had joined Rob and Little Kim, and along with Kev and Sarah were sat at the table just over to my right, although Giles was now sat on the little stool that Nik had been sat on earlier. Nik himself was securely wedged into the corner of a window seat, his head lolled over to one side against the partially-glazed, half-height oak parti-tion, seemingly away with the fairies *(yet again!)*. I asked if Nik was actually okay, my concern for him quite clearly genuine, however, when Kev told me he was fine really, and said; *'Just leave him to me mate,'* I said; *'Fine,'* and just left him to Kev. *Always the best way!* Apparently Rue had stepped outside for a breathe of fresh air, fol-lowing Will as he did so, and Alan was using the gents. I followed Rue and Will's example and stepped outside into the street myself. It was dark, the sky was crystal clear, twinkling brightly with a thousand trillion tiny little lights, each one over a hundred-million light years away, and it had gone off considerably chilly. The only person wearing a nice warm jacket was Jean, so I stepped up beside her, wrapped my arms around her waist inside her open-fronted woolly jacket, and laid my head on her shoulder, as if to make like I was trying to warm myself up.

"Get off, ya daft old bugger!" she jokingly laughed at me.

Reluctantly I removed my arms from around her waist, gave her a quick peck on the cheek, and turned to face Ronnie. He was leant alone against the low slate-capped dry-stone wall that ran along the rough-paved edge of the dead-end street at the far end of the Shipwright's solid granite walls. He was staring thoughtfully across the outer harbour wall at the almost three-quarter moon, which was steadily rising higher and higher above the horizon, arcing it's way slowly southwards in the direction of Wadebridge.

"Penny for ya thoughts my friend?" I asked, suddenly interrupt-ing his train of thought.

"Oh, just considering that rugged old monster down at the end of the line mate, that's all," he replied in his usual relaxed manner.

"Land's End?" I said knowingly, "she ain't gonna be nowhere near as wicked as she usually is come tomorrow lunchtime buddy. You'll more than likely be rounding her pretty much on slack water with a mere south-westerly force two to three forecast, should be a walk in the park for a salty old sea dog like you."

"Yeah," replied Ronnie thoughtfully, "a salty old sea dog like me, plus that salty old sea dog of a crew mate stood over there for company, the one that's gonna have the world's biggest-ever hangover from hell to keep *himself* company with. Look at the state of him Chrissy-boy."

Ron pointed across the street towards Johnnie, who was stood chatting, albeit better described as slurring, to Jamer, Dave, Rue and Will, and just to add a minor alteration to Ron's own turn of phrase, I would've opted for the word *slumped* as opposed to *stood!* However, I'd seen poor old Johnnie in far worse states than that on many a previous occasion, plus I had news for Ron too, news which I felt sure he'd fully appreciate, so I simply smiled and handed over my knowledge, which I hoped would be sufficient to lift his enthusiasm. After all, enthusiasm was never something that good old Ronnie was generally short of.

"I'll tell you one thing for starters me old mate," I began positively, "your Johnnie and my Nik, two bloody peas in a pod those two are. I've never known anything quite like 'em, and certainly couldn't be like 'em meself. Drunk as a pair o' skunks one minute, then up, ready and rarin' t' go the next. I've watched our Nik steer a true compass course for four hours solid with his eyes firmly shut, and I guarantee you that your Johnnie could navigate you safely around Land's End and straight into the tightest space available in Penzance Harbour no matter what kind of state he got himself into the night before. Plus I reckon you know that full well anyway, just as much as I do. They're a pair of true legends them two, they genuinely are, and I take my hat off to the both of them."

"What hat's that then Chris?" asked Raymondo, earwigging from the sidelines whilst noticing that I wasn't actually wearing a hat. I ignored him and continued with imparting my news to Ronnie.

"Anyway mate, it's not only Johnnie and his stonking great hangover that you'll have to keep you company whilst rounding the End tomorrow, Little Dave said he'd like to tag along with you too, providing that's okay of course? Apparently he has some business to take care of down in Falmouth, and seeing as that's where you're headed, he thought maybe he could hitch a ride with you. I know he'd much rather sail than drive. And I don't mean just tomorrow either, I mean *always!* I honestly think that lad must've been *born* at sea! Anyway Ronnie, I know he'd make a great crew mate aboard anyone's ship, maybe you should go have a chat with him, he's sat out back in the beer garden."

"Indeed I will Chris my boy," said Ron, suddenly looking a little brighter. "I know exactly how good a sailor Little Dave is, so it'll be my pleasure to welcome him aboard. Thanks for the heads-up matey, I'll go let him know right now."

With a slightly refreshed level of enthusiasm, Ronnie stepped back into the pub, then headed out into the rear garden to confirm his arrangements with Little Dave. I then stepped up alongside Raymondo, put my arm around his shoulders, and asked him subtly why he was burbling on at me about hats.

"You started it," he said with a smirk, "you said you take your hat off to both of them. But you ain't wearin' no hat, so how could you?"

"That's 'cos I already took it off to 'em me ol' mate," I replied jovially. "Anyways-up, you'll be the one wearing the skipper's hat tomorrow morning my friend, how are you feeling about leaving this here pretty little town behind."

"Well, much as we all love a bit of Ossin' down 'ere for May Day my son," said Ray, now wearing his slightly more serious hat, "to be perfectly honest it'll make a nice change for the six of us to just go and find some peace and quiet somewhere. And what better place to find it than anchored off St Mary's for a few days."

"I couldn't agree with you more my friend," I replied knowingly. "I've done the same myself a couple of times in the past, once with Bettola and once with the Marovonne. Bettola was only thirty-eight feet long, and had a relatively shallow draft too, so we were able to moor her right alongside the harbour wall, well ahead of the Scillonian's berthing area and well away from where the fishing boats land their catches, and the inter-island water taxis pick up and drop off. But with the Marovonne being so much bigger, plus having a draft of almost two meters, that time we had to lay at anchor out in the bay, then continually run back and forth with the RIB to the Town Beach whenever we wanted to go into Hugh Town. Not that that ever proved a problem mind you, in fact for the most part it was great fun, especially when we went off wildlife spotting around the islands. Both the flora *and* fauna on and around the Scillies are simply spectacular, I can honestly recommend absolutely *everyone* go visit the place at least once during their lifetime. The only one minor issue we did have though, when we were anchored down there a couple of years back with the Marovonne, was when it blew up one of those unusual north-westerlies. It was probably only about a force three at the time, but that still created quite a swell across the bay, and when she's laid to anchor in a half-decent swell the Marovonne tends to roll like a pig. Which, needless to say, makes sleeping through the night somewhat uncomfortable, to say the least. I know we could've swung around to the other side of Hugh Town and anchored off Porthcressa Beach, but we didn't bother, we just rode it out for the couple of days that it lasted. And after that, when the north-westerly ceased altogether, everywhere became totally still, silent and fogbound. It was really eerie, although I have to say that was the perfect time to go dive the kelp forests and swim with the giant basking sharks. Stunning wildlife, spectacular scenery, I love the place to bits."

"It certainly is Chris," agreed Ray, "so are you gonna come sail with us then my friend?"

"No mate," I replied firmly, "I'm gonna stay here with me mates and get drunk! Haha, no, I'm only kidding. After all the mayhem that's gone on over the last few days, I'm just gonna hang around here and chill for the rest of the week. I have to be back in work next Monday mind you, but to be perfectly honest, I'm kind of missing Tori and Alex quite a lot already, so there's a good chance I'll catch the train back to Bristol sometime on Friday so that I can take them out with me over the weekend. I promised them both that the next time we spend a weekend together I'd take them swimming at The Oasis Centre in Swindon, and I'm actually really looking forward to it. Anyway, you and Jean go take your friends over to St Mary's for a few days peace and quiet me old mucker, keep a close eye on that there Jamer, especially when 'e's getting' on 'n' off the ship, t'ain't quite the same out there as 'tis in 'ere. Oh, and keep a close eye on the weather too, 'cos it's gonna turn soon."

"Yeah, tell me about it!" replied Ray, "I went and got a five-day marine forecast from the harbour office earlier. Tomorrow's gonna be fine, south-westerly two to three, visibility good, sea state slight, just perfect for us, and perfect for Ronnie's hundred-odd mile trip around to Falmouth too. But then there's a low heading our way in a few days time. It's currently centred some way south of Iceland, but if it does what it's predicted to do we're gonna have one hell of a rock 'n' roll ride on our way back towards Lundy, and probably all the way up the Bristol Channel too. If Rick's leaving Tuesday morning, along with Tom and Rob, then they're all gonna be fine. But come next weekend we'll have a full moon once again, so we'll be back up onto big spring tides, and as per usual the weather's steadily worsening in the lead up to them."

"Ah, I see," I said to Ray, as I looked once again towards the bright, ever-rising moon, "I haven't actually looked at a medium range forecast myself, as I wasn't planning on leaving just yet. In actual fact, I'm planning on leaving the Marovonne down here for the eclipse, so all I'm really hoping is that it doesn't rain for the rest of this week, and after that I'm not really bothered. But that aside Ray, tell me please, what exactly is predicted with this next incoming low?"

"Well, come Thursday night, possibly into Friday morning," Ray began, seemingly without worry, "the wind's supposed to be backing north-westerly, force four at first, increasing to five, possibly six during Friday daytime, and occasionally force seven in exposed areas. Visibility remains good throughout, however, the sea state, which is obviously gonna be right on our port beam with a north-westerly, is predicted to turn from moderate to rough throughout sea area Lundy, occasionally very rough to the west. We were thinking of staying Thursday night and leaving Friday morning, but having just scanned through that little lot I think we'll aim to leave Thursday morning instead, and see if we can't just run home ahead of it all."

"Would you consider running into Swansea if it catches you up the ass before you're back through the Holmes?" I asked with genuine concern.

"Not a chance me old mate," he replied confidently. "I've sailed the Roehampton through way worse than that before, she's a great old girl. Yeah, she rolls a bit, especially in a good beam sea, just as we all do. But she's got a really good turn of speed if ever I need to wind her right up, and that wonderfully flared bow forces her through the waves with an unbelievable degree of comfort. I remember one time we were heading from Dartmouth to Penzance in a south-westerly force eight, just me, Arthur and Dave aboard, and she was dancin' around all over the place through the twenty-foot white-caps, fire extinguishers and all sorts flying loose around the saloon, but she took us straight through it solid and true, just as if it was exactly what she was built for, although I'm not entirely sure she was. Still, I even managed to push her all the way up to eighteen knots at one point, and that's fast enough to force any amount of water out of the way with that perfectly-shaped flare that she carries under her bow."

"I don't doubt it for one minute my friend," I said, acknowledging his vast experience behind the wheel. "I'd put my entire trust in the Roehampton too, in exactly the same way that I know the strengths and limitations of my own ship, the Marovonne. To be honest though, my concern was more for Jean and Shiela. I'm not entirely sure they'd feel particularly happy if you decided to sail back home from St Mary's through a north-westerly five stroke six. Keep a close eye on it Ray, weigh anchor and run well ahead of it please, even if only for the sake of the ladies aboard. Better to cut your holiday short by a day or two than to make the poor girls ill for the rest of the week."

"I will do buddy, don't you worry," Ray agreed with me. "There's one thing that always comes to mind on occasions such as this though, one image that'll always stay with me for as long as I live."

"What image is that exactly me old mucker?" I asked with intrigue.

"It's that poster that you've got securely attached to your saloon's for'ard bulkhead aboard the Marovonne. Ultimately it's that standard that we all tend to live by nowadays. Do me a favour Chris, remind Jean and Sheila exactly what it says please."

"Oh *that* old poster," I replied nonchalantly. "That kinda stuff is for the likes of you and me matey. The likes of Rick and Ronnie, Tom and Rob, and possibly certain other dedicated crew members that we each have. It's most certainly not for the likes of everyone though. Never forget my friend, to your average landlubber, which often includes our various assortment of fair-weather passengers, *a rough sea is nothing but a horrible, massive, scary monster, and for the sake of their own sanity, generally best avoided like the plague!*"

Christopher John Reason

THE FRAMED POSTER ON THE MAROVONNE'S
SALOON WALL

CHAPTER
TWENTY~THREE

It was getting on towards closing time in the Shipwright's, and the majority of us, me included, wanted to get off to bed pretty soon, on account of some of us folks having an early start the following morning. I warmly shook Raymondo's hand, then Arthur's, then gave Jean and Shiela each an affectionate little hug. I wished them all a safe onward passage, bid them goodnight, then stepped across the road to wish Johnnie the same. He was sat on the cappings of another low dry-stone wall, still trying his damnedest to make conversation with Will about rounding Land's End the following morning. I shook Dave's hand, then gave old Jamer a big hug, and wished them 'bon voyage' for the following day. I asked Will if Johnnie was going to be okay, but Johnnie immediately looked up at me himself and asserted positively;

"A'sh ish goon bisht roit ash a good'un blahsh!"

"Ah, I'll take that to be a 'yes' then buddy," I laughed, Will laughing alongside me too.

"He'll be absolutely fine Chris," said Will, "this is pretty standard practice for our Johnnie. I guess it kinda makes up for the fact that he never drinks whilst at sea, just like the rest of us."

"Yeah, I'm well aware of that me old mate," I continued jovially. "'Yo ho ho and a bottle of rum, and then the funny old fat fucker's done!' Isn't that how our Ronnie usually puts it? Anyway, I just wanted to let him know that he's gonna have some extra company on the way round to Falmouth, 'cos Little Dave's tagging along for the ride too."

"That doesn't surprise me," said Will, "he was bangin' on about it all the way down here. He's got something going on down in Falmouth that he seems pretty excited about, but he's keeping very tight-lipped about it at the moment. Hey ho, time will tell, eh."

I reached down and grabbed Johnnies limp right hand, shook it gently, and wished him a *'bon voyage mon ami'* for his forthcoming sailing adventure."

"A'sh a gluuden dunnit bud, ch(hic!)," he replied, entirely incoherently.

I laughed again, patted him firmly on the shoulder, then walked straight through the bottom end of the pub and out into the beer garden. Lloyd and Cathy were now sat at a round wooden table underneath a large white parasol chatting to Rick and Kim, whilst Ben and Karen were happily swinging away together in the double seat underneath the rose arch. Giles, Derek and Benny were sat at another table, taking it in turns to tell rude jokes to the three girls, who clearly weren't particularly impressed by any of them. I walked over to Little Dave and Jo, who were both still sat on the little wrought iron bench, Ronnie stood right beside them firmly clutching a fresh pint of orange juice and lemonade, and asked them if the plan was acceptable to everyone.

"The plan works brilliantly Chris," confirmed Ronnie. "It'll be just great having Dave here come along for the ride. In fact, better than that, he's offered to take first watch for me, if and when I fail to wake that daft old sod outside up when it comes time to leave. And I wouldn't be at all surprised if that watch didn't last all the bloody way to St Ives, what d'ya reckon Dave?"

"That's fine by me Ronnie," replied Dave with a smile that exuded nothing but confidence. "In fact, I'd be more than happy to sail the Courageous around Land's End and all the way up to Falmouth single handed if you both want to get your heads down, it makes no odds to me at all."

"Oh, come on guys," I said positively, "credit where credit's due. I know you'd be more than happy to take that task on Dave, and more than capable of it too. And I know you'd be more than happy to put your trust in Dave's ability too Ron. But Johnnie ain't really *that* bad, we all know him a little better than that. He may be in a bit of a mess right now, but I guarantee you he'll be up and at it, raring to go and ready for anything, even before you get the Courageous anywhere near that dastardly Doom Bar in the mouth of the Camel."

"Yeah, I guess we all know you're right there me old mate," admitted Ronnie. "Just like you said, him and your Nik, two peas in a pod them two are. So I guess the only thing I have to worry about right now is how the hell I'm gonna get the lumpy old sod back aboard the Courageous this evening."

"Same as!" I replied, peering towards Nik through an open rear window. "Although Nik's obviously just a tad lighter than your Johnnie. Still, I'm sure you'll find plenty of comrades willing to give a hand me old mate. Meantime, I s'pose I'd best go impart our news to my dearly beloved, she's still sat at the bar chatting to Shabby and has no idea what I'm going to put to her yet."

Not that it was going to take her hugely out of her way on her drive back to Bristol the following day, but it was only fair I go and discuss it with her anyway. I shook Little Dave's hand, and wished him a safe and fair weather rounding of the *'rugged monster'*, then gave Ronnie a quick friendly hug, wished him all the best, and intimated that there may well be a good chance I'd see him and Johnnie back in Padstow once again on their return voyage back to Bristol, on account of the fact that we'd probably still be there. I left them to it, stepped back inside, and walked across to the table that my own crew were sat at. Rob and Little Kim were deep in conversation with Rue about computers, whilst Alan earwigged as best he could, although clearly most of the technical jargon flew way over his head anyway. Kevin was acting all lovey-dovey with Sarah, almost embarrassingly so I might add, whilst poor young Nik appeared to be entirely comatose, still wedged firmly in the corner by the window. All good there then! I left them chatting and walked through the long narrow lounge towards the bar. Helen and Shabby had been joined by Long Tom and Catriona, and were still all having a good old chin-wag together. Tom asked me if I fancied one last beer, to which I gratefully replied; *'Yes please buddy, I'll have another HSD please.'* The four of them were halfway through their final drinks of the night anyway, and once I'd been handed mine by the barman I made a decent effort to catch up with them. During a brief lull in the conversation I turned to Helen and asked her if she'd mind taking two more passengers with her during her drive home. She said that was absolutely fine, then asked me who and why. I ran through the whole scenario with her, including the bit where she'd need to make a slight detour in order to drop Jo off in Ilfracombe, and fortunately she seemed perfectly happy to oblige, which was great. I then asked Tom how he felt about giving Ron a hand to hoist Johnnie back aboard the Courageous without risking a life-threatening dunking in the harbour.

"I've seen the state Johnnie's got himself into," replied Tom, looking a little uneasy about the idea, "I reckon it's gonna take at least four of us to carry that operation out successfully."

"Okay matey," I said, finishing the last of my ale, "I volunteer Alan and Rue to give both of you a hand then. They're both relatively sober themselves, so between the four of you I'm sure you'll manage, plus I'd lend a hand myself too if it was really needed, although it looks like Kev and I are gonna have our hands full getting Nik back aboard the Marovonne without dropping him in the drink."

"Okay, cool," agreed Tom willingly, "'tis getting on a bit, let's go get it done then."

So we did, and that's basically how *Hangover Day* ended for the majority of us. Between Ron, Tom, Rue and Alan, they managed to scrape Johnnie's almost dead-weight up off the dry-stone wall, then, followed closely behind by Catriona, they frogmarched him back around to the Courageous and, with only the *mildest* of struggles, safely managed to escort him back aboard. Tom and Catriona then said goodnight and climbed back down onto the Kathleen B. In the meantime, Kev literally picked Nik up and threw him over his shoulder in a well-practiced fireman's lift, and with Helen, Sarah and myself following along behind, we all marched briskly back towards the Marovonne. I was pleased to note along the way that they'd run the Jubilee Queen back out to The Pool, thus allowing adequate manoeuvring space for the vessels that were going to be leaving early the following morning. Kev stepped aboard first, and managed to hump Nik all the way down into the saloon without spilling him, then laid him out on the sofa-bench, shoved a life jacket under his head for a pillow, pulled a blanket out from the under-seat cupboard and threw it over him. After thanking Alan and Rue for their help with Johnnie, everyone said goodnight to each other and headed off to their respective cabins. Moments later, Jean and Sheila stepped aboard, and I helped them down the steps, out onto the starboard-side walkway, and over the handrails onto the Joseph. Ray, Jamer, Arthur and Dave followed immediately after, we all said goodnight to one another, then the gents assisted the ladies on their way across the Joseph's foredeck and onto the Roehampton. Just before I headed off to bed myself, Little Dave and Jo stepped back aboard, then hopped over onto the Joseph with yet another polite goodnight. So the only people left in the Shipwright's late that night were Benny, Rob and Little Kim, plus Rick with his remaining crew of the Joseph. I was away with the fairies myself whenever most of them finally returned aboard, and failed to hear a single peek from any of them.

06.30hrs, 3rd May, 1999 – Bank Holiday Monday. I was awoken by the very slight movement of the ship's hull as the harbour barrage gates powered themselves open two hours before high water. As I stepped up into the wheelhouse, wash-bag in hand, the first thing I did was to trip over young Benny, fast asleep and still snoring right where he'd landed after seemingly falling through the doorway that led in from the ship's roof up above. My foot in his ribs failed to stir him, so I continued on my way, stepped ashore, then began to walk the long way around the harbour towards the shower block. All around me was eerily silent; no one anywhere appeared to be awake as yet. I opened the Lucy box and checked the electricity meter; still on *'FULL'*. I checked Helen's car; I couldn't even see the little parking meter ticket sat on the dash for seagull shit. Half the bonnet, most of the front windscreen, and at least half the roof were plastered in a thick layer of guano. *What a ridiculous place to park! Who's bloody stupid idea was that then?!!?* I crept past the Courageous 2, no signs of life on her as yet, and neither was there on the Kathleen B, or the Clare de Lune either. The sun was just beginning to creep up above the top of the hills behind Rock across the other side of the Camel, and it's early morning orange glow shimmered beautifully off the still waters of the inner harbour. As I rounded the end of the West Quay and headed towards the shower block, I couldn't help but consider the contrast between the perfect tranquility of how things were right then, and how it was all going to become complete mayhem once again in an hour or two's time. I punched in the 1 2 3 4 code to the shower block entrance door, seemingly the very first on the scene at the time, or so I thought, stepped inside and bumped straight into Ray and Arthur.

"Ah, top of the mornin' to ya's both," I greeted them, in the friendliest fake-Irish accent I could manage at the time, "and what a bootiful mornin' it is fer sailin' too, dat it is."

"Morning youngster," replied Ray cheerfully, "everyone still alive after last night then my friend?"

"Ooooh, extremely unlikely!" I said, sucking in a deep breath beforehand. "Anyways, you all set to go matey? What time are you setting off exactly? Smack on high water I would guess?"

"Your guess would be correct my friend. All of us that are heading south-west will be leaving around eight-thirty, then we'll run down towards St Ives with the outgoing tide giving us a helping hand along the way. Those running across to Wales will probably leave it until the last minute so that they can catch a bit of slack water halfway over, but I've got a feeling that the Vigilant and the Dasher are heading in the same direction as Ron and myself, so I expect all four of us will be leaving at the same time."

"Oooh," I exclaimed, "now that's gonna be interesting to watch. I'm not sure the entrance gate's quite wide enough for all four of you together!"

"Not *exactly* the same time, you silly sod," said Ray, laughing at my weak attempt at stupidity.

I winked at him, told both him and Arthur that I'd be around to help them with their mooring warps when the time came, then stepped into one of the half dozen well-appointed shower cubicles. Fifteen minutes later, fully abluted and thoroughly refreshed, I stepped back out of the shower block to the softly booming rumble of HMCC Vigilant's powerful twin Caterpillar engines as they slowly began to warm themselves up. Once I'd walked halfway back around the harbourside, I heard a slight spluttering sound, followed by another deep boom, and the considerably smaller, but relatively just as powerful, twin Caterpillars aboard HMS Dasher also fired up, then set themselves quietly to idle whilst they took their time to reach their optimum operation temperature. Simple logic I suppose; the larger the engines, the longer they take to warm up. Even I liked to give the Marovonne's wonderful old Gardner 8L3 a good twenty minutes or so to do the same. As I ambled back past the Courageous, Ron stuck his head out through the cabin door and said; *'Morning Chris,'* and as I stepped back aboard the Marovonne I bumped into Little Dave, his own wash-bag in hand, who muttered something along the lines of; *'What's all that bloody noise about? Haven't you lot got the hang of rags 'n' sticks yet?'* All I could think of by way of reply was; *'Morning Dave.'* I managed to avoid the still-snoring Benny as I stepped carefully back into the wheelhouse, grabbed the kill-cord off the chart table and clipped it securely around my waist, left my wash-bag on the side and stepped down into the saloon. Nik was more or less in exactly the same position that Kevin had laid him in, but he was gradually beginning to stir, so I gave him a quick shove on the shoulder before stepping out onto the aft deck.

The early morning air was no longer quite as fresh as it had been initially, there was now a distinct smell of diesel fumes wafting gently in my direction. As I stood there in the shadows, waving it away with my hand whilst waiting for the first rays of sunshine to appear over the top of the harbour wall, a soft young female voice called out to me from somewhere further aft;

"Good morning Mister Chris Reason," said the voice in both a friendly *and* familiar manner, "would you happen to be sailing along with us today by any chance?"

"Ah, morning Sue," I replied with equal familiarity, suddenly spotting Lieutenant Moore stood close to the forepeak of the Dasher. "No ma'am, we're staying down here for the summer. The Roehampton's leaving today, bound for St Mary's, and the Courageous 2's heading on around the corner to Falmouth. I think the Joseph and our other friends are all gonna leave it 'til tomorrow now, then they'll just head back towards Bristol. I know you're leaving on the top of the tide today Sue, d'you mind me asking what your destination is?"

"Not at all Chris," replied the skipper of the Dasher politely, "we're heading back to our base in Gosport, all of these cadets we have aboard are due back in college come nine o'clock tomorrow morning."

"Fortunately for you, you've got a significantly better turn of speed than these ancient navy MFV's of ours then," I said, clearly drawing a comparison between old and new, the relevance of which I'm quite sure she made a mental note of. "And the Vigilant? Where would her next destination be ma'am?"

"Ah, now that I definitely can't tell you I'm afraid," she replied, lightly tapping the side of her nose. "Top secret, or at least so I'm informed. From today onwards she's back on official duties, and her manoeuvres are a closely guarded secret known only to those way above my pay grade, so unfortunately I don't even know myself. In fact, once we leave here, I couldn't even tell you whether she's heading south-west, north-west, or north-east."

"Oh well, let's just keep our fingers crossed she ain't headin' south-east then!" I joked.

Lieutenant Moore laughed aloud at my little quip, then politely said;

"Enjoy the rest of your holiday Chris."

To which I replied, equally as politely;

"Safe passage Skipper, may the Gods of the ocean sail peacefully with you, and go steady with the parking once you reach Gosport."

She laughed and threw me a friendly wave as she turned and headed back towards her command post. It was almost eight o'clock, and the harbour had come alive by now. I heard two more low growls, followed by a light vibration that filtered gently across the Marovonne's decks. Two puffs of black smoke climbed lazily into the air from astern of the Roehampton as her twin Gardner's began to settle then purr on tick-over. Ray, Dave and Arthur stepped out onto her starboard-side decks just as the Vigilant cast off her mooring lines, her well-disciplined crew pulling them efficiently back aboard and coiling them neatly onto their fully automated drums. After three short blasts on her extremely loud ship's horn, her skipper then expertly reversed her directly back into the open space that had been occupied not too many hours previously by the Jubilee Queen. *Just as well she'd vacated the inner harbour then!* The Vigilant then engaged forward drive with her starboard engine only, and very slowly sailed out through the outer harbour, spun around to the north, and headed off down the deep water channel, past the JQ as she lay peacefully at anchor out in The Pool, and on towards the Channel Buoy. Rick and Derek came out on deck aboard the Joseph, as did Kev and Rue aboard the Marovonne, and between them they released two of the four mooring lines that kept the Roehampton firmly secured alongside our two ex-navy MFV's. As Dave and Arthur slowly began dragging the warps back aboard and neatly coiling them up, the Dasher also gave three short blasts on her horn, reversed skilfully back into clear water, then followed the Vigilant out into the Camel *without bumping into anything!* The last thing I noticed as she disappeared through the open barrage gates was one small piece of black gaffer tape limply trailing from the base of her transom.

I swung down into the RIB next, attached the kill-cord, fired up the outboard, then asked Nik to release the painter for me just as he popped his groggy head over the ship's stern. I told him to go grab a quick shower, then I'd pick him up off the outer floating pontoon *in just five minutes!* He hopped ashore immediately and began a slow jog all the way around the harbour towards the showers. Meanwhile, I backed the RIB away from between the Marovonne and the Joseph, and when Ray shouted from the Roehampton's wheelhouse; *'Cast off fore'ard, cast off aft,'* Rick and Derek assisted Dave and Arthur with releasing and retrieving the two remaining warps that held the Roehampton alongside the Joseph. Once she was free from her ties, just her fenders still lightly touching the Joseph's hull, I gently pushed the bow of the RIB in between the two ships until they were separated from each other by a good six feet. Raymondo then clunked the Roehampton's starboard engine into forward gear, and at dead slow ahead she chugged majestically back out of the harbour and followed the two warships off down the Camel just a few minutes behind them. Okay, so now to help Ronnie with his struggle in attempting to extract the Courageous 2 from the tight little corner that it was wedged into. I pushed the RIB away from the side of the Joseph, spun it around so that I was facing the slipway, and ... *WOW! How the heck did he manage that?* The Courageous was already away, clear of all other vessels, Ronnie stood up near the prow coiling up her bow lines, Little Dave skilfully manoeuvring her at the wheel, whilst Long Tom and a few other skippers wrestled with countless other warps, including those of the Kathleen B, as they ran back and forth along the quayside. Well fair play to Ron and Dave. And guess what? Yep, *no sign of young Johnnie as yet!* I ran the RIB alongside the Courageous and shouted up; *'Well done guys, have a good trip, sail safe!'* Ron was way too busy with the ropes to acknowledge me, but Dave gave me a quick wave. I followed close behind her until she exited the inner harbour, and just as I noticed Rick, Derek, Jo and Rue all stood at the far end of the inner harbour wall, waving farewell to those aboard the Courageous, I spun the RIB around to port, pulled it alongside the floating pontoon, and told Nik and Kev to jump aboard.

Once we were all seated I backed the RIB around in the outer harbour, clunked it into forward gear, and chugged slowly out between the outer harbour walls. I then opened the throttle up, gave her a bit of welly, and ran up onto the Courageous's wake just as she passed the Channel Buoy. Ron was at the wheel now, although there was no sign of Little Dave anywhere. My guess was that he was probably down below in the galley. We followed the Courageous for a good two or three minutes, then suddenly, just as Ron steered her neatly past the Brea Hill Spit Buoy, a rather familiar face peered joyfully over the stern handrail, laughed audibly at the three of us, then waved a mug of steaming hot coffee high in the air, spilling not just a small amount of it over himself, the resulting scald inevitably going unnoticed. We cheerfully waved back at dear old Johnnie, all three of us pleased to see that he was both awake and smiling, then with a positive thumbs-up we sped on past the Courageous and caught up with the Roehampton just as she was approaching the Greenaway. It was an hour and a half before high water, a day beyond halfway between neaps and springs, and there was no sign whatsoever of the Doom Bar, it was already covered. Fortunately though, there was no real sign of any waves anywhere either. The light south-westerly breeze was blowing gently over the inflowing tide, and for as far as we could see across Padstow Bay, underneath yet another glorious, cloudless, bright-blue sunny sky, the sea was as flat as a pancake. I ran the bow of the RIB right up underneath the Roehampton's tender, slung and securely fastened underneath her stern-mounted davits, and shouted up to Jamer, who was stood out on the aft deck admiring the view along with Dave, Jean and Sheila. Ray was pushing his ship through the water at somewhere around ten knots, and I guessed that Arthur was probably sat next to him programming waypoints into the GPS.

"Hey Jamer," I shouted from my seat tucked low beneath the wheel, "why don't you stop off here again on your way back from St Mary's? I promise we'll take good care of you when we take you back up on the Wipe Out again."

For all the gentleman that old Tankman genuinely was, I'm afraid his reply back to me remains entirely unprintable, even to this very day. The three of us laughed our socks off, wished the four of them a safe trip and a pleasant holiday in the Scillies, then sped on past them in an attempt to catch up with HMS Dasher. As we shot past Stepper Point and out towards the open Atlantic at somewhere in the region of thirty knots we just spotted the tail end of the Dasher rounding the seaward side of Gulland Rock. Judging by the wake that she was leaving behind her I estimated her speed at in excess of twenty knots, so it was unlikely we'd catch up with her before she rounded Trevose Head, which frankly would've been nothing other than reckless on our part had we attempted it, so we headed towards Gulland, against the incoming tide, then slowed and drifted for a while. There was a good chance that the Vigilant had already rounded Trevose Head by then, and was well on her way towards Newquay, if in fact that was the direction she'd taken. She certainly hadn't headed north though, otherwise we'd still be able to see her, but just as we spotted the Dasher again, way off in the distance approaching Trevose Head Lighthouse, the Roehampton steadily crept up behind us. We all waved again as she passed us at around twelve knots following the same path as the Dasher, and then sat there waiting for the Courageous to pass us, which took another seven or eight minutes at her much slower cruising speed of just over six-and-a-half knots. As the Courageous passed us by, Johnnie was sat at the wheel, concentrating hard on the small illuminated screen of the GPS that Little Dave had pre-programmed before leaving port, and Dave and Ronnie were lazing comfortably in a couple of deckchairs out on deck, simply enjoying the early morning sunshine. They all threw us another friendly wave as they chugged on by, leaving us gently bobbing around in their wake.

As we turned to head slowly back towards Padstow Bay, the next ship to leave the mouth of the Camel was the Jubilee Queen, and she steamed towards us at around fifteen knots, heading roughly in the direction of Harlyn Bay, no doubt on yet another highly profitable two-hour seal-spotting expedition. We passed the JQ doing roughly the same speed as her, but in the opposite direction, bouncing turbulently over her huge bow wave just as a hundred or so emmets waved cheerfully towards us, whilst desperately trying to stop their wailing youngsters from trying to climb up on the ship's handrails. As we rocked from side to side in the wake of the JQ I pushed the throttle all the way forward again, and at high speed we shot through the mile-wide gap between Pentire Point and Newland Island and headed onwards towards The Rumps. It wasn't far off high water by then, and the flow rate of the incoming tide had slowed significantly, however the eddy that it still created around the back of The Mouls, another series of little islands and rocky outcrops just to the east of The Rumps, looked as dangerous as ever, the sound of the waves crashing against the rocks almost as noisy as the huge flock of seagulls that were cackling overhead. So I spun the little inflatable around and drove us back towards the lee of Newland Island once again. Halfway there I slowed to a halt, killed the engine, and sat there listening to the sudden and almost-deafening sounds of silence again. The sea was dead-flat-calm, the cliffs of Pentire Headland masked out all sound of the waves swashing around The Mouls, and even the seagulls had disappeared way off into the distance. *'Wow, silence is certainly golden,'* I thought to myself. Immediately after which, Kevin started shouting with rather an exaggerated degree of excitement.

"Skipper, skipper, look over there to our right," he shouted, nudging me hard on the shoulder, *"there's a shark, a MASSIVE shark, right there, about a hundred yards further out. Can you see it? Jeez, look at the size of that fin!"*

"Yeah Kev, I can see it mate," I replied calmly. "You can hardly bloody miss a fin *that* tall."

Maybe a hundred and twenty meters further out to sea from where we were sat adrift, a sharp, narrow, black pointed fin rose some three feet above the surface of the water. It wasn't moving anywhere, it was virtually stationary, as if simply drifting along with the current whilst using it's tall black fin as a sail. Nik *and* Kev clearly wanted to see if we could get any closer to it, but I told them both we'd not got a chance in hell of doing so. I did, however, ask the pair of them if they weren't just the tiniest bit scared, what with being *that* close to a fish *that* size in a tiny little inflatable boat. Both of them just stared at me, then asked me what being scared was all about exactly. I told them both that I'd experienced that dreadful, nauseating feeling on several previous occasions, but without going into any kind of detail I simply hoped they'd never get the chance to find out for themselves. And then I came clean with the truth.

"Sorry to have to disappoint you Mister Staines, but that ain't no shark, it's a sunfish," I said, wiping the enthusiastic grin off his face. "They don't normally frequent these waters, but due to a certain amount of global warming over recent years, the change in climate has hugely affected some of the Atlantic currents, and we seem to be getting all kinds of unusual visitors popping up everywhere nowadays. It's a bit like the El Niño effect in the Pacific I guess; even the Sargasso Sea has relocated itself some thousand miles or so further to the east. Still, I suppose that means the common European eels haven't got quite so far to swim anymore, so it's not all bad. Anyway, like I said, all sorts of odd creatures have been drifting our way lately, and the sunfish is probably one of the oddest of the lot. It's almost completely spherical, and it's dorsal and pectoral fins are each about half the diameter of it's body. Which means that our slow moving little monster over there is about six feet tall across it's body, or twelve feet tall from fin-tip to fin-tip. They have an anal fin as well, so they can actually swim, although generally they just tend to drift around on the ocean currents, gulping mouthfuls of crustacea in much the same way as the basking shark does."

Suddenly, whilst we were staring at it from a distance, it slowly slapped it's dorsal fin flat down on the surface of the water twice in succession, raising it back up vertically again after each gentle slap.

"There ya go guys," I continued, "I have absolutely no idea why they regularly do that, but from a distance that's by far the easiest way to tell the difference between a sunfish and a shark. That, plus the fact that they don't move very fast, although, despite what some experts used to think, many sharks are also perfectly capable of lying still on the surface without the need for water flowing through their gills for considerably long periods of time too. Anyway, a fully grown adult sunfish can weigh anything up to two and a half tons, although despite the fact that they don't actually possess swim bladders, if we tried to get close up to it right now it would simply turn on it's head and swim straight downwards, disappearing from view, but only to resurface again at a different location shortly after we'd left the area. Throughout most of the world they're essentially known as the *'useless'* fish, mainly because they're too bony and not particularly nice to eat. The Japanese, Taiwanese and Koreans eat them though, they consider Mola Mola to be a true delicacy, but firstly, relative to the size of the fish, there's really only one tiny little fillet worthy of considering edible, hence the remainder being simply a huge waste; and secondly, because they're now officially classified as endangered, the EU has them listed as a protected species, so therefore you're not even allowed to catch them in European waters. Some people still do though, simply because they're such slow swimmers, and therefore easy to spear when diving for them, but it's not only illegal, it's also both wasteful and cruel. So there ya go lads, that there's a sunfish, and here endeth your first and only lesson on the common mola, the largest and heaviest of all the bony species of fish in the whole wide world."

"Thank God for that!" said Kevin rudely. "Anyway, there was me thinking we was being hunted down by a great white shark, and we was probably gonna need a bigger boat to catch the bugger with. No such luck eh Skip? Hey ho."

"Yeah, plus all that talk about eating fish and stuff, I'm bloody starving now, I am," announced Nik hungrily. "Can we go get something to eat now please Skip?"

"Whatever you want Roger," I replied, pacifying his one and only thought process for the time being, "whatever you want."

I reconnected the kill-cord, Nik fired up the outboard, and more or less right on the top of the tide we headed back off up the Camel against the oncoming onslaught of sailing ships and motor yachts that all appeared to be in some kind of race with one another as they fought their way hastily back from whence they originally came.

Christopher John Reason

SNORKELLING WITH AN ATLANTIC SUNFISH, OR
COMMON MOLA

CHAPTER TWENTY~FOUR

There was even more mayhem going on as we approached the entrance to the inner harbour at around a quarter to nine. Most of the larger yachts, including a sixty-foot catamaran that had taken up a *ridiculous* amount of space, had set sail well before the JQ had slowly drifted back in to load her early morning contingent of pre-booked paying passengers in her usual manner. However, now that she'd departed and the tide had turned, there were countless smaller yachts and motor cruisers all jostling for position whilst attempting to escape through the narrow harbour exit without colliding into each other and causing significant amounts of damage. By the looks of the assorted fenders bouncing around all over the place, accompanied by the intermittent screams, shouts and angry Welsh swear words, it wasn't going altogether too well, so I decided to stay well out of harm's way and secured the RIB to the far end of the southern outer floating pontoon, in between another couple of small inflatable tenders. I clipped the kill-cord around my waist and climbed the ladder up onto the harbour wall, closely followed by Nik and Kev, and as we walked slowly together around the end of the long line of fairground rides, then stepped back onto the paved inner quayside, we couldn't help but hear a long, loud, single blast from a very powerful air horn. I peered through the sea of swaying masts and spotted the Jaws fast trip boat, fully loaded with paying passengers, her skipper doing his level best to battle his way through the melee of departures and head off down the Camel at a high rate of knots, but succeeding in achieving absolutely nothing other than adding to the clearly unorganised chaos that surrounded him. *'Hey ho, time for breakfast,'* I thought cheerfully to myself. As we ambled over towards the Marovonne, we just happened to pass Steve, stood on the quayside staring vacantly into the midst of the mayhem, jaw dropped, cap in hand, scratching his head in sheer disbelief.

We left him to his bewilderment and skipped merrily back aboard ship, hopping down into the wheelhouse to that delicious early morning smell of freshly cooked bacon. Helen had been running the galley, bless her, and was now sat down in the saloon alongside Sarah and Benny, with Rue and Alan sat on the aft end of the L-shaped sofa-bench, all five of them tucking in to a delicious-looking full English with tea and buttered toast.

"The grill's still hot," said Helen, squirting ketchup all over the table through a misshapen bottle top. "There's just about enough of everything left for all three of you, but I reckon we're pretty much done after that. Other than milk and cider the fridge is beginning to look rather bare."

"Would you mind doing the honours please Nik?" I asked lazily.

"No problem Skipper," replied Nik eagerly, "you go put yer feet up, I've got this one covered."

"Cheers buddy," I said, patting him on the shoulder. "So, tell me young Benny, how's ya head feeling this morning? Pounding away like a jack-hammer in a quarry by any chance?"

"Hahaha," laughed Benny jovially, "it certainly was when I first opened my eyes. And then Alan trod on me on his way to the showers, so that didn't help. But then Rue came along and scraped me up off the floor, then dragged me along there with him, so that certainly *did* help. And now that your dearly beloved has cooked me this wonderful breakfast I feel absolutely fine once again. So, anyone know what time the pubs open up today?"

"Er, actually mate, like *no!*" I answered him, in a fairly weak attempt at being authoritative. "I think they're probably best left alone for a while, at least until later on this evening, don't you? Anyway, I need to go get the girls all packed up and back off on their way home before I consider anything else, so it's organisation and effort first mate, then fun and games after, just like the good little boy-scout that I am Benny-boy."

Nik and Kev both stepped back down into the saloon, Nik carefully placing three more full English's down on the table, whilst Kev briefly screamed in agony, having just scalded himself by tripping down the step with an over-filled pot of freshly brewed tea. Fortunately he didn't spill too much of it. The three of us sat next to each other and got stuck in, Nik's cooking abilities coming a very close second to Helen's. Whilst Sarah kindly poured more tea for everyone, Rue was the first amongst us to come up with a practical suggestion.

"I think we should go on a sensible food shopping mission," he announced. "Neither Alan nor I can afford to continue eating out in pubs, cafés and restaurants like you wealthy buggers can, so I think we should go find a supermarket and restock the fridge so we can continue to cook our own meals aboard."

"Okay, well firstly Rue," I immediately replied to him, "none of us here come even remotely close to being wealthy. I know I might be able to afford cheap pub grub most nights, plus the occasional special treat if I'm lucky enough, but Kev's pretty much in the same boat as you are, if you'll excuse the pun, and Nik's generally worse than skint; he resorts to beg, steal or borrow on a daily basis. And secondly, well, what a damned fine suggestion my good man. The only problem being, there ain't a decent supermarket in Padstow. However, there is one in Wadebridge, there's a giant Co-op store right on the river. So, now you come to mention it, *ooooh*, I do believe I feel another cunning little *Chrissy-plan* coming together. Why don't you and Al scribble down a full shopping list down on that there notepad whilst I go sort the girls out, then when I've got them going on their way we'll see what we can do about it. Sound like a plan?"

"It only sounds like half a plan to me," replied Rue suspiciously, "still, at least it's a start I suppose."

Once we'd all finished I helped Helen and Sarah cart the dirty dishes back up into the galley, and whilst they headed back off down below to pack their bags, I left Nik and Kev to tackle the washing up and went to check on Helen's car for her. I stepped ashore and checked the electric meter first; *still full, how odd!* The fairground guys were gradually beginning to set up in preparation for what, for them, was hopefully going to be an exceptionally busy bank holiday Monday. At least the weather certainly looked set for it; not a cloud in the sky yet again. Having said that, clouds were the least of my concerns right then, in fact they might just as well have been welcomed. I walked along the quay to the end of the fairground, to where their generators were located, immediately adjacent to which were the first three parking spaces. Two Ford Transit vans, one white, one blue, with a metallic lilac Vauxhall Astra parked between the two. The front half of all three vehicles were plastered in a thick layer of white, crusty guano, and I mean plastered! *Covered in seagull shit, hey ho, what a bloody mess!* Still, never mind, that was easily rectified. What wouldn't be quite so easy to rectify wasn't actually my problem, and brought a wicked little smile to my face anyway. Both Transit vans had been fitted with the local authority's bright yellow impenetrable wheel clamps, whereas Helen's Astra had miraculously been left entirely untouched. *Oops, I wonder who's fault that might've been then?!!?* I wandered back aboard ship and hopped down into the aft store-room, passing Rue and Alan along the way, who were both busy arguing over what type of cheese went best on toasted white bread. *'Mmmm, Roquefort!'* I thought briefly to myself, as I climbed back ashore with a neatly coiled up fifty-meter hosepipe.

Halfway between each Lucy box was a water standpipe with a fast-fit hose connection, and I clipped the pipe on to one then turned the lever to the *'ON'* position. The hosepipe itself proved only just long enough to reach the front of the Astra's bonnet, however the adjustable nozzle that was attached to the end of it provided a more than adequate jet of water to gradually remove the sun-baked layer of encrusted bird turd, and within ten minutes or so I had Helen's pride and joy looking all sparkly and brand new once again. Now that I could see clearly through the windscreen once again I noted that the parking ticket had not long since expired, but at least the Astra didn't have a ticket, let alone been clamped, unlike the pair of tatty old Transits, more fool them. I disconnected the hosepipe, drained it, and returned it to it's rightful location down in the ship's storeroom. As I stepped back up into the saloon, Rick stuck his head around the door and politely said good morning to all six of us, the girls still packing up downstairs.

"Looks like some of us around here have found fame once again," he proclaimed smugly with a broad grin across his face. "Seems it's your turn to make the front page of the local papers Chris. Honestly, you and Benny, the pair of you together, what are you like?"

Rick laughed as he handed me the Monday morning issue of the Cornish Daily Independent, which he said he'd just *borrowed* from the Quayside Café a little earlier. I unfolded it and laid it flat, face up in the centre of the saloon table for everyone to see. The bold headline splashed across the front page was once again typically over-dramatic, and not entirely accurate, honest or true either!

IDIOTIC TOURISTS ATTEMPT TO SET UP CAMP ON SANDBANK IN THE CAMEL ESTUARY AT LOW TIDE, SPARKING OFF A MAJOR ALERT!

Following Saturday's highly successful annual May Day celebrations in Padstow, a young and irresponsible pair of travellers succeeded in pitching their tent the following day in the middle of the Town Bar sandbank whilst the tide was out. Clearly unaware of the fact that the waters around the United Kingdom's coasts are tidal, and more specifically the potentially treacherous waters of the northern Cornish coast, they failed to obtain any local knowledge whatsoever and put their own lives significantly at risk. Whilst it remains unclear as to precisely how they gained access to the sandbank in the first instance, it is assumed that they simply considered the peace and tranquility of such a beautiful part of our wonderful county to be the perfect place to set up camp for the night. Both the stupidity and futility of their careless misadventure caused considerable consternation amongst many of the locals, those who understand the nature of our coastal tides far better than outsiders ever will, and consequently a considerable number of 999 calls were made to the emergency services.

As the incoming tide began to rise, clearly unnoticed by the idiotic travellers who were seemingly oblivious to their surroundings whilst sleeping in their tent, the local lifeboat crew were alerted to their impending peril and put on standby, and a Coastguard helicopter based at RNAS Culdrose was also scrambled in readiness. The emergency services were subsequently stood down once Padstow's own Harbourmaster was able to take control of the situation, and after presumably alerting said idiots to the foolishness of their exploits, was able to dispatch a harbour launch in order to effect their rescue. Whilst it's understood that both would-be campers were severely reprimanded by the appropriate authorities following the potentially tragic event, it still remains a sad indictment of the many foreign visitors to these shores who regularly fail to prepare themselves with the basic but essential local knowledge required to keep themselves safe!

In other matters around the region ...

"HOORAH!" shouted Benny, "FAME AT LAST!"

"It wasn't meant to go quite that far," I commented to Rick in my own defence. "It was only meant as a lighthearted joke, and would've remained so had the Tor picked us back up again when I flagged them down. But hey ho, all's well that ends well, and at least we managed to hit the headlines once again, so happy days."

Benny and I chinked tea mugs together and called *'cheers',* whilst Nik, Kev, Rue and Alan all stood up and gave us a brief round of applause, to which we both bowed graciously. Rick then asked what time Helen was thinking of leaving, and I replied that the plan had always been to aim for around one o'clock-ish, however, providing all four girls were packed and ready, then there was no reason why they shouldn't leave whenever they felt like it. Rick said that Jo was all packed and raring to go, seeing as how she wanted to get back down to Falmouth as early as possible, but that Ben and Karen had taken a wander into town to grab a few bits from the Spar shop, and he wasn't entirely sure just how long they were likely to be. I told him that Helen and Sarah would more than likely be ready to leave within the next twenty minutes or so, but that equally they'd be happy to wait until Karen got back as they weren't in any kind of rush themselves. Rick pulled his phone out of his pocket and dialled Ben's number, then, after a brief conversation which I wasn't privy to, he hung up and said; *'They'll be back in ten minutes.'* I told him I'd go see how Helen and Sarah were getting on, and to tell Jo not to stress about anything, they'd all be on their way very soon.

Some thirty minutes later, bags all piled into the boot, Helen reversed her Astra out of it's tight little *'reserved'* parking space, then stepped back out onto the quayside. Everyone had come along to wish the four girls a safe journey, and before they all climbed into the car there was much hugging and kissing going on. In actual fact, realistically, probably far too much! Jo gave Rick and Kim, Will, Shabby, Mel and Little Karen a quick hug, then jumped hurriedly into the front passenger seat. Karen gave Lloyd and Cathy, Derek, Giles and Nikki an even quicker hug, then threw her arms tightly around Ben's neck as if she never wanted to let go. Sarah gave Nik and myself a quick peck on the cheek, after which Kevin picked her up and told her he was never going to put her back down again; and after Helen had given Alan and Rue a quick hug, kissed Benny on both cheeks, she threw her arms around me and asked me, in a pleasant but semi-demanding kind of way, to please try my best not to stay down in Padstow for too much longer. I comforted her with the promise that I'd be back in Bristol before the following weekend, which put a smile back on her face and cheered her up no end. Then, all too suddenly, they were gone. Karen and Sarah climbed into the back, Helen slammed the front door behind her, revved the engine, stuck it in gear, and off they all toddled. Helen tooted the horn three times on the way out of the car park; once at Tom and Catriona, stood on the roof of the *Kathleen B* waving goodbye, once at Rob and Little Kim, stood up on the bow of the *Clair de Lune* doing much the same thing, and finally to all eighteen of us that were still stood in a huddle together on the corner of *Car Park Quay*, watching as four skinny, bare arms waved frantically out of each of the car's windows as it disappeared off up the hill towards the Metropole and beyond.

"Okay, that's got shot of the birds, let's go have some *real* fun!" said Nik cheekily.

"Shall I, or will you do the honours?" I asked Rick.

"Will I do what honours?" he replied quizzically.

"Chuck Nik in the harbour?" I qualified my question with a smirk.

"WE WILL!" shouted Derek, Will, Ben, Giles and Benny in unison.

All five of them tried to make a grab for Nik at the same time, and I don't think I'd ever seen the poor lad run quite so fast in all my life. In ones and twos we then gradually dispersed, each heading off with their own personal agendas in mind. Mine was shopping. It was just approaching midday, so at least the girls had got away a little earlier than expected. Plus I knew that the Co-op in Wadebridge stayed open until 4pm on a bank holiday, the same as it did on a Sunday. Low water would be around 1.30pm, which would make it a little bit of a struggle to reach Wadebridge through the narrow, shallow, reeded channels of the upper Camel as the calendar ticked ever-closer towards spring tides, but with a shallow draft such as the little RIB had, especially when planing, then I figured we'd make it okay. So we still had plenty of time, not only to make it up to Wadebridge and enjoy ourselves along the way, but also to get the shopping done and still make it back in time for dinner. Fortunately for all concerned I'd left the RIB outside the inner harbour, which was now shut until 17.40hrs, two hours before high water. That said, I still wasn't about to allow any of my own crew to go legging it off to the pub whilst we still had a list of responsibilities to take care of, albeit a short list. Talking of lists, I asked Rue and Alan how their shopping list was coming along.

"All done," replied Alan positively, "and sat there on the side waiting. It's not a massive amount, so it should all fit in the fridge-freezer okay, but I reckon it should be enough to see the five of us through to the end of the week, so hopefully you won't need to go again. That's providing Benny's not staying aboard any longer of course. Anyway, we've guesstimated it to around a hundred quid in total, that's including the booze, so there's forty quid folded inside the list, twenty from me, and twenty from Rue. That should cover it for the five of us okay."

I looked questioningly at Benny, who immediately retorted with a seemingly innocent but notably defensive reply.

"No man, I can't afford to stay," he said, "I have some important business to take care of back in Tintagel where I told you I don't actually live. Or do I? Who knows? Anyways, I gotta get back there man, so after you's guys have left, I guess I'd best start making me way back up yonder hill and catch up with me crazy old mates in their busted up old camper vans. They'll give me a lift back home I'm sure, wherever or if ever I should happen to find out where home actually is."

"No change there then my dear friend," I said to him somewhat unsympathetically, as I threw my arms around him, squeezed as tight as I could, and gave him back some of his own medicine.

I told Nik to go grab the waterskis and a pull-rope from the ship's storeroom, as I fancied a bit of fun on our way up to Wadebridge. I then wished Benny all the very best in his hunt for a new abode in the magical, mystical land of King Arthur and his long-lost knights of the round table, and knowing Benny as well as I did, I was pretty sure it wouldn't take him much more than an hour or two to do so! Nevertheless, I wished him the fondest of farewells, and told him that if he couldn't manage to find his unreliable group of mates anywhere, then he should feel free to make his way back aboard the Marovonne for the night. As things happened to pan out, he had no need to take me up on that offer, although I will add that more than a year went by before I had the pleasure of bumping into him once again, this time in a surprisingly different location altogether. *(Yet another misadventure book? We'll see!)* Nik called up from down below asking me if I wanted the wetsuit too, but I just shouted back down; *'Wetsuits are for wusses!'* I fetched my all-important grab-bag from my cabin, stuffed a clean pair of shorts and a tee shirt inside, and stepped back up into the wheelhouse. *'Ready guys?'* I asked enthusiastically. Nik and Kev both nodded in agreement, and after shoving my phone, my wallet, the list and the cash into the side pocket of my grab-bag, having managed to extract twenty quid out of Kevin but absolutely zilch out of Nik, the three of us said *'chow for now'* to Al and Rue, then headed off towards the ladder that led down the outer side of the harbour wall onto the southern floating pontoon. Once I'd reached it's wooden-planked surface, Nik passed me down the skis, and Kevin, most responsibly of him I might add, passed me down a spare can of fuel. We hopped into the RIB, Nik behind the wheel with the killcord connected, Kev facing backwards on skier lookout, and after I'd safely stowed our assorted clutter, fired up the engine and untied the painter, me stood straddling the other two unoccupied seats.

Nik clunked her into gear, and at one o'clock, half an hour before low water, we chugged out of the outer harbour and headed slowly towards the JQ, which was once again laid to anchor in The Pool just north of the dry and expansively pristine Town Bar. As we rounded the JQ's stern I told Nik to open the throttle to around twenty knots, and whilst I carefully kept my balance whilst still standing, my knees braced firmly against the seat's back rests, we cruised past Rock pontoon moorings at fifteen knots above the speed limit and headed towards the designated waterski area just downstream from the Gentle Jane Moorings, and just upstream from the mussel beds and floating oyster cages on the east side of the estuary. Although we were only gradually approaching spring tides, the Town Bar appeared considerably higher and drier than it had the previous day, but even at low tide the designated waterski area is still some two miles long by one mile wide, with adequate depth throughout, and the minute we reached it, as Nik slowed the RIB to a halt, I kicked off my trainers and threw myself headlong over the side. *'Brrrrr! Hey ho, wetsuits are for wusses, right? Hmmm . . . !'* Kev clipped the pull-rope to the steel ring bolted through the transom, passed me the skis one at a time, and I clumsily pulled them onto my feet as I bobbed around under the water, whilst Nik engaged gear and slowly fed the pull-rope through my looped arm until the handle bopped me on the shoulder. I pointed the tips of the skis skywards, yelled *'GO'* at the pair of them, Nik thrust the throttle fully forwards, and after a moment's hesitation I straightened my legs and rose gracefully up out of the water onto the skis. Not being the greatest skier in the world, I was grateful for the fact that the water was flat calm, and as I held the rope handle tight with one hand I signalled to Kev with the other to tell Nik to reduce speed a little. Twenty-five knots was what I felt most comfortable with, but then Nik already knew that; he just needed reminding occasionally! I signalled Kev again to instruct Nik to circle the clearly-marked designated area in an anti-clockwise direction, such is the generally accepted code of conduct with skiers, although as there were no other boats using the river for skiing at the time I didn't consider it overly important. However, not more than ten minutes later, pretty much spot on low water, a matching pair of rather expensive-looking Sea-Doo jet skis suddenly appeared out of nowhere and began churning the water up, circling the area in a similar fashion to the way we were. Mindful of the fact that we still had a shopping mission to fulfil, and taking into account the fact that I was entirely likely to fall off if the water became much choppier, I signalled to Kev once again, this time giving him the clear one-handed instruction to tell Nik to continue further on up the river.

It's only five miles by river from Padstow to Wadebridge, and we were already halfway there anyway, but after the waterski area finishes just before the mouth of the River Amble, from there on the river becomes significantly narrower. Although there's a good forty knot speed limit all the way up to the town bridge, waterskiing is forbidden anywhere outside the designated area that we'd just left. However, on the misguided basis that *'rules are for fools'*, I carried on regardless. Not only does the River Camel narrow significantly from here on up, but it also shallows remarkably quickly, especially at low tide. I signalled the lads to slow to around twenty knots as we passed underneath the tall A39 main-road viaduct, waving politely from my skis at a couple of canoeists who were passing in the opposite direction, loudly shouting some incomprehensible form of obscenities at me. We continued upstream at as slow a rate as the skis would continue to support my weight on the surface of the water, and just as we were about to pass underneath the town bridge's third arch from the right, one of only four of the remaining thirteen visible arches that actually had water flowing through it, I couldn't help but notice a uniformed police officer standing directly above us, staring wide-eyed in our general direction, and frantically waving his arms above his head. I had absolutely no idea what his problem was, and signalled the lads to continue on through the bridge and then slow to a halt immediately the other side of it. This Nik expertly managed to achieve with all the skill of a seasoned powerboat driver, and as I settled back down into the water I found myself standing on the rocky bottom, both of my skis still underfoot, only waist deep in water and directly underneath the centre of the town bridge's twin-laned main street directly overhead. *'Ha, spot-on perfect! There's no way that copper's gonna find me now!'* I thought to myself. *WRONG!* I threw the rope handle ahead of me and remained where I stood, in the centre of the river underneath the bridge, whilst Kev coiled it up and stowed it back aboard. Nik had already raised the outboard somewhat, due to the obvious shallowness of the river, and after Kevin sat back down Nik spun the boat around and pulled it alongside me. The tide was gradually creeping back in now, which virtually neutralised the flow of the river heading outwards at this point, so precisely where I was stood there was almost no current whatsoever, which was extremely handy. I pulled my skis off one at a time and handed them up to Kev, then pulled my whole body rather awkwardly over the side of the boat and into the back seat. Nik reversed the RIB back upstream, and as he span it back around, once we'd popped out from under the bridge on the upstream side, I smiled and waved politely again at PC Plod, who was peering down at us with a rather angry expression on his bright red face.

"Just ignore him," said Kev nonchalantly, "he'll go away in a minute."

He didn't though! I told Nik to pull the RIB into the slipway mooring bay at the mouth of the little Polmarla River, cut the engine, and I'd hop out and tie her up to one of the quayside mooring rings. Nik did precisely what I asked, raising the outboard still further as he did so, and I stepped nimbly ashore, grabbed the painter, and tied it securely to one of the large iron rings set fast into the concrete wall. As I stood up and turned around, I was confronted face to face by PC Plod.

"You do realise, do you not, that you've just broken the law by waterskiing outside of the designated ski area?" he questioned me, his voice raised ever so slightly in mild anger.

"Indeed I do occifer," I replied cheekily. "Why, do you have some kind of problem with that by any chance?"

"By rights I should confiscate your vessel right now," he said sternly, trying his damnedest to look, sound and act as if he was in charge of the situation.

"What, you alone, versus the three of us?" I answered him back, sounding somewhat surprised. "I think probably not occifer."

"Okay, let me put it another way then," he said, a wry smile creeping over his face. "I don't suppose your name happens to be Chris Reason by any chance, now does it?"

"Bollocks!" I uttered in dismay. *"Rumbled again!* Okay occifer, it's a fair cop, you've got me bang to rights, take me to your leader."

I pushed my arms out in front of me, wrists crossed over, as if offering myself up for being cuffed.

"Your reputation precedes you around these parts Mister Reason, and has done for many a year," he politely informed me, imparting information of which I was already fully aware.

"Has anyone ever come to any harm on my behalf your honour?" I asked him sarcastically. "And when I say ever, I do mean *EVER!*"

"Er, well, er, now that you come to mention it," he stuttered, "given what we've reliably been informed by Malcolm, Padstow's Harbourmaster, the one person that's asked us to keep a close eye on you, simply because they don't actually have any policemen down there in Padstow, then I guess the answer to that must be no."

"You guess?" I questioned him, raising my voice ever so slightly. "Well let me assure you young man, it's very much a *clear and resounding NO!* Now, if you wouldn't mind doing me a big favour please, we're on a mission from God."

"And what big favour would that be exactly?" he asked sceptically, clearly having now climbed right back down off his high horse.

"Keep an eye on our little boat for us for a short while please, we have to go do our weekly shopping in the Co-op."

"On yer bike, will I 'eck, ya cheeky little shits!" he blurted out. "Go on, off with ya's!"

"We ain't got ourselves a bike occifer, we's just got this itty bitty little boat," I blurted back at him, "and if it ain't still here when we gets back from doin' our shopping, you's either gonna be deep in da shit, or deep in da river, one or t'other!"

"It'll be here, don't you worry," he muttered with disdain, then turned on his heels and stropped off back towards the town bridge.

Fortunately, what I thought had begun as something quite serious, against which I had defended myself to the best of my ability, had actually ended up turning into nothing but a touch of lighthearted banter between the two of us. Clearly, and quite possibly fortunately, my reputation had preceded me on this occasion. *Hooray for the friendliness of the people of Padstow and it's surrounding areas!*

"Bit of a close shave there Skipper," said Kev, breathing a sigh of relief.

"No shit Sherlock," I replied with a smirk.

Nik threw me my grab-bag from the front floor of the RIB, having kept his head well down throughout the entire brief encounter with PC Plod, and as subtly as I could manage I quickly changed into my clean set of clothes, threw the wet ones into the back of the boat, and pulled my trainers back on. I then slung my grab-bag over my shoulder, and we marched purposefully together in through the front door of the Co-op, one shopping trolley between the three of us, which, for some unknown reason, Nik insisted on pushing. Rue and Al's list was by no means extensive, but we were in no hurry whatsoever, so we dawdled. About a hundred quid later, which amounted to roughly two large bags full of food and four large bags full of drink, mostly of the alcoholic variety, we exited the store together and pushed the shopping trolley all the way around to the boat. Between Nik and myself, we carefully stashed all the shopping up in the undercover section of the RIB's bow, well out of sight of prying eyes, whilst Kevin returned the trolley to the store and retrieved his one-pound coin. The tide was on it's way in at a considerable rate of knots now, the flow of the Camel having reversed it's direction as the saltwater forced it's way ever-further upstream. *My, how time flies when you're enjoying yourself!* Kev was one of the very last shoppers to return our trolley, just as the Co-op closed it's front doors to the public at precisely 4pm. And *still* we were in no hurry. In actual fact, the gates to the inner harbour wouldn't be closing until nine-forty later that evening, so that was the very latest we could afford to get back and safely offload the shopping back aboard the Marovonne. Although clearly Rue and Alan would be wanting to eat way before then, so probably best we aim for somewhere a little closer to high water. Still, we had another hour and forty minutes to wait before the harbour gates even opened, and we weren't about to carry six heavy bags of shopping up the ladder from the outer pontoons, so we took a quick vote between the three of us as to what to do for the next hour. After all, even with the amount of weight we'd be carrying aboard, added to the relatively fast flow of the incoming tide, it still shouldn't take more than twenty minutes to cruise back down to Padstow. So we voted;

Nik – Pub!

Kev – Pub!

Me, being the skipper, and therefore casting the deciding vote – Pub!

"Okay guys, looks like we're off to the pub for a bit then," I said, feeling thoroughly defeated *(not!)*

"I vote the Ship then," said Nik determinedly, knowing full well that he'd been thrown out of the place on at least one previous occasion. *(Too long a story for this particular book!)*

So the Ship it was, and a beautiful olde worlde staging inn it is too, even to this day. We left the RIB in the secure and capable hands of PC Plod, who'd clearly vacated the area some considerable time ago, and walked across the town bridge, around the corner, and in through the front door of the Ship Inn. I ordered a round of ales, took my wallet from my all-important grab-bag, which I never lost sight of for one single second, handed the barman a twenty pound note and asked for the change in fifty pence pieces. That had partially become a bit of a habit with me due to the never ending requirement to feed electricity meters, although for some odd reason I seemed to have escaped that financial responsibility during this particular visit to Padstow. However, within less than a minute Kevin had managed to prise most of them from my clutches and placed at least six on the edge of the pool table. There appeared to be a bit of a tournament going on amongst the locals, and both Kevin and Nik fancied their chances against them. Not that there was very much happening in the way of prizes; loser buys the winner a drink. But it looked like it might turn into a bit of fun for a while anyway, so I went along with it. Not only that, but when it came to my turn, I seven balled the poor young local lad that I was put up against, and the rules dictated that he buy me two drinks for the privilege of, or possibly the embarrassment of. Either way, needless to say I lost the next game, which thankfully gave me more time to sit down and gnaw my way through the three pints that I'd managed to accumulate.

Five o'clock came and went, and I suggested to Nik and Kev that we ought to get gone fairly soon, but not only were they both enjoying themselves to the max, winning virtually every game they played, they were also both getting more and more drunk by the minute because of it. At six o'clock I decided to put my foot down and call a halt to it, siting the fact that Alan and Rue would undoubtedly be waiting patiently for at least some kind of shopping to be returned from the supermarket, especially given that they'd paid upfront for it.

"Just one more game please Skip?" Kevin asked with a slight slur to his voice. "I've got a tenner riding on this one."

"Go ahead then Mister Staines," I conceded, "just make sure you win it please buddy, then you can buy me breakfast tomorrow morning, instead of making yet another godawful mess up in the galley."

Sadly, he didn't. In fact, he was thrashed by a youngster half his age, who took Kev's tenner and shoved it deep in the front pocket of his jeans with one of the biggest smiles of satisfaction that I've ever seen.

"Come along guys, let's drink up and get our asses back home," I demanded with my usual lighthearted air of authority.

It worked though, and by 6.40pm, one hour before high tide, the three of us left the Ship and headed back towards the town bridge. Upon reaching the east side of the 320-feet-long, fifteenth-century bridge, originally constructed using seventeen arches, latterly reduced to fifteen, nowadays only thirteen remaining visible, of which only twelve actively span the water, we immediately spotted a problem that none of us, *myself in particular,* had anticipated. Apparently, unbeknown to us folks down by the coast, there had been a significant downpour of rain up on Bodmin Moor during the previous night, and some considerable hours later the River Camel was now beginning to swell. Once that brief but excessive down-flow was added to the height of the rapidly incoming tide, which was still steadily approaching a high spring, what we were now apparently faced with was a bridge who's arches we could no longer fit the RIB underneath. *Oh, how time flies when you're enjoying yourself!* '*Shit-fuck-bugger-bollocks!*' I quickly thought to myself.

"Hang fire here a moment lads," I said, stunned at my own lack of forethought, "I think I'm gonna have to make a few emergency mathematical calculations before we proceed any further."

"Can't we squeeze ourselves through that little gap underneath the centre arch over there Skip?" asked Kev irresponsibly.

"No, we most certainly can't Mister Staines," I replied with certainty. "The river's in spate, albeit most likely only very briefly, and the tide's still coming in, and will be for another hour. If you want to risk it, you carry on buddy, but you ain't taking my boat with you, and that's a fact. *No siree!* So, you know exactly what that means, don't you guys?"

"Yep!" replied Nik with a wicked grin on his face. "At least another two hours in the Ship!"

"Best you go play your ass off on that pool table then young Roger," I said, effectively agreeing with his conclusion, "because we're gonna need the winnings to feed ourselves, and somehow I'm gonna have to try and pacify Rue and Al when I tell them they'll have to go eat out yet again, 'cos their shopping's gonna be late on account of my own lack of planning. Which, I might add, is generally pretty unusual for me, although at least there's one thing you guys needn't have to worry about."

"What's that exactly?" asked Kev inquisitively.

"Well in case you hadn't thought about it," I replied, "it's now gonna be dark when we leave here to head back to Padstow by sea. Fortunately however, being the good boy-scout that I am, my trusty old grab-bag just happens to contain an emergency flashlight. Not for us to find our way of course, the river and it's beacons will do that for us all on it's own, but purely as a navigation light, so as to prevent us getting mown down by some nautical juggernaut during our arduous return voyage."

"Do they actually have such things this far up the Camel that late at night?" asked Kev in all seriousness.

"No mate," I replied. "Come on, let's go get back on that pool table and trash the locals."

As Nik and Kev stepped back into the Ship Inn, I pulled my phone out of my bag and called Rue. I explained our current dilemma to him as best I could, emphasising the fact that it would appear to have been entirely unavoidable, and apologising profusely for the obvious absence of shopping. Fortunately he appeared adequately sympathetic towards our beleaguered plight, agreed that the shopping could wait until the following morning, wished us all the very best for a safe and secure return back to harbour, and said that him and Alan would be more than happy to eat battered cod and chips from the local chippy yet again. I thanked him for his understanding, breathed a huge sigh of relief as I hung up on the phone, then stepped back into the pub and ordered myself yet another pint of ale. *There comes a point on certain occasions during my life when I feel glad to get back to work!* However, that night wasn't one of them, and I threw another couple of fifty pence pieces down on the side of the pool table.

Some two hours later, having taken sufficient cash winnings off the locals to be able to afford three portions of locally-made steak and ale pie & mash, along with several more pints of real ale, the three of us staggered out of the front door and made our way back across the bridge towards the small concrete dock that the RIB was still tied up to. The tide was on it's way back out again at quite a rate of knots, and the Camel's brief floodwaters had also receded considerably, so not only was there now adequate headroom underneath the western arches of the bridge, but equally I considered it safe to continue, despite the fact that it was now rather dark. Nik and Kev jumped down into the two back seats of the RIB, narrowly avoiding catapulting the skis overboard, whilst I untied the painter then stepped into the driving seat. Before connecting the kill-cord and asking Nik to start the engine I pulled the torch from my bag, along with a roll of gaffer tape, then stuck it securely to the top of the windscreen and switched it on. And then we were off. I spun the boat around, gunned it directly towards the third archway, the one through which the outgoing tide was rushing at it's fullest, and the three of us neatly ducked our heads as we shot underneath the low bridge then out the other side into clear open water. I thrust the throttle fully forwards, and at a slightly sluggish twenty-five knots, due to the excessive weight that we were now carrying, both in the bags *and* in the blokes, we safely navigated our way back down the Camel and into the brightly-lit entrance to Padstow inner harbour. Drinking whilst sailing at sea is a policy that I flatly refuse to tolerate. Driving a speedboat back down the Camel in the dark whilst almost three sheets to the wind is most likely nothing more than an accident waiting to happen. *We never even came close!*

Christopher John Reason

BRIDGE OVER THE FLOODED RIVER CAMEL AT
WADEBRIDGE

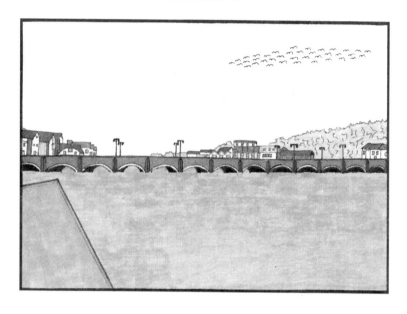

CHAPTER
TWENTY-FIVE

Alan and Rue were sat out on the Marovonne's aft deck, polishing off the last of the cans of Thatchers from the fridge, when I nudged the bow of the RIB into the space between them and the stern of the Joseph at around nine-thirty, just ten minutes before the harbour gates were due to shut. Thankfully they didn't appear to be overly perturbed about having to eat from the chippy yet again, although by their own sad admission they hadn't been able to afford to join Rick and his crew at their little leaving do up in the London Inn that particular evening. By way of consolation, once I'd secured the RIB and switched the engine off, the first shopping bag that Kevin passed up to them was the one that contained another twenty-four cans of Thatchers. At least that put a bit more of a smile back on their faces. That was immediately followed by a second, containing a further twenty-four cans of Tribute, bringing a smidge of a smile to my own face, and then a third, containing bottles of drink which included rum, ginger ale, coke, lemonade, squash, milk, and several bottles of wine. And then a forth, containing much the same kind of thing, followed by two more which were stuffed to overflowing with fresh food. Altogether not too shabby a requisition for a hundred bucks, and definitely more than adequate for the five of us to continue to eat aboard for the next couple of days. Plus, at least we'd made it back in time for Alan and Rue to relax the following morning over a nice home-cooked breakfast, instead of having to spend yet another tenner each in the Quayside

Café. I climbed back aboard myself, as did Nik, and whilst Nik began stashing everything away up in the galley, Kevin removed the torch from the windscreen then passed me up my grab-bag, along with the skis, the rope, and my wet clothing, which I hung over the ship's handrail to hopefully dry out overnight.

As Kev climbed back aboard I asked Rue if he'd seen any further sign of Benny, but on replying negatively I presumed he must've made it safely back to wherever his home for the night may eventually turn out to be, along with his reportedly unreliable bunch of camper-van buddies. I kept my fingers crossed for him. Whilst Kev stashed the skis back down below, I stepped up into the wheelhouse and pulled my phone out of my grab-bag. Oh dear, three missed calls from Helen, best I call her back and make sure her trip back home went according to plan then. Fortunately it had. In actual fact it had gone entirely without a hitch, and I listened patiently whilst she elaborated further over both Jo and Karen's plans for the future. I'm not altogether sure whether Sarah actually had any plans for the future, but Helen and I sure as hell did! *(Yes, I know, book number four!)* We chatted together for a little longer, although I didn't go into too much detail about our ill-conceived little shopping mission, then I wished her a pleasant night's sleep in her newly-decorated little three-bed terraced home back in St George, Bristol, and we lovingly blew goodnight kisses down the phone to one another. I felt happy that she was home safe and sound, even if she did have to get up early to go to work the following morning. Personally, I didn't, although I'd still have to get up early in order to see the Joseph off. I knew Rick was going to aim to make it straight back to Bristol non-stop, which meant he'd have to leave pretty soon after the gates first opened, which meant that I'd need to be up and about come six o'clock in the morning. In which case an early night was called for, which I wasn't overly bothered about, and I certainly didn't fancy anything else to drink; I felt like I'd had way too much already. What I did fancy though was a nice hot shower, partly so that I could wash off all the sea salt that my weary body was still caked in, and partly to sober myself back up just a little before hitting the sack.

I grabbed my wash-bag and stepped ashore with the intention of heading for the shower block, and as I did so both Nik and Kev stepped ashore alongside me.

"Oh yeah, so where are you two young rascals off to exactly?" I asked, as if I couldn't guess already!

"We thought we'd go join Rick and his crew up at the London so we could all partake in a couple of farewell drinks together," said Kev innocently.

"Really?" I replied in mock surprise. "D'you not think you've quite possibly had enough already?"

"Nope!" answered Nik firmly.

"Hey ho, go enjoy yaselves lads," I said with a laugh. "Say '*Hi*' to everyone for me please, and let Rick know that I'll be around to give him a hand first thing in the morning should he happen to need it. Which I'm sure he probably won't, but I shall be around anyway, just in case. In the meantime, I'm gonna go get my head down early."

Nik and Kev headed off into town, and as the harbour gates had now shut I walked across the footbridge and on towards the shower block. As I ambled along in the cool evening darkness, I couldn't help but notice that the moon had disappeared. There was very little in the way of breeze, but as I looked up to the skies all I could see was cloud. I peered over the harbour wall, and the lights of Rock that ordinarily twinkled away brightly across the other side of the estuary had all but disappeared from view. I felt the first spot of rain land on top of my head with a heavy splat, and quickly keyed the code into the door. I exited the shower block some fifteen minutes later, suitably refreshed, and the rain itself hadn't materialised as yet, but the clouds had definitely thickened. I peered over the harbour wall once again, this time not even able to see the Jubilee Queen's masthead light as she lay at anchor down in The Pool. I stepped back aboard ship, and as I wished Rue and Alan a pleasant remainder of their evening, before I headed off down below the three of us acknowledged the obvious potential for a thick sea fog first thing the following morning. For Rick's sake I seriously prayed for that not to be the case, otherwise he'd be forced to rely entirely upon Lloyd's Master Mariner skills all the way down the Camel and back out into clear ocean, and subsequently their somewhat ancient radar from then on, and I climbed into bed and tucked myself in with my fingers firmly crossed for him.

At 06.00hrs the following morning Rick's eight-cylinder Gardner engine woke me up fractionally before my alarm clock went off, as it cranked over and gently purred itself back into life, and I dressed myself in suitable scruffy attire, pulled my trainers on and legged it across to the shower block and back again before the gates were due to open. Clearly my own crew were all still entirely away with the fairies when I got back, but Rick and Lloyd, the Master Mariner, were both standing up in the Joseph's wheelhouse. They were poring over their chart-work together, and making various adjustments to the GPS following their updated tidal calculations, whilst Will and Derek were out on deck tidying things up and sorting out the ship's warps, fenders and electric cables. The wonderful smell of fried bacon was also wafting up from somewhere down below. Whilst we'd all been faffing around with some unexpectedly high floodwaters the previous evening, and also getting just a little drunk into the bargain, Rick had very sensibly taken a stroll along to the Harbourmaster's office in order to obtain the latest inshore marine weather forecast. I already knew that a south-westerly force 2 to 3 had been forecast in the way of wind speed and direction, thus giving a good indication of the likely sea state, which was predicted as calm or slight, potentially becoming moderate with wind over tide at around midday. What I had no idea about was the all-important visibility factor. The fog that had looked like it might be coming down the previous evening thankfully hadn't materialised, and although the sun hadn't quite risen above the hilly horizon behind Rock just yet, it was perfectly light enough to see right across the estuary and far beyond. Unfortunately it was also perfectly light enough to notice that we most likely wouldn't be seeing any sun that day anyway, as the rain showers that had saturated Bodmin Moor two nights previously now appeared to be saturating Padstow itself, and Rock, and the whole of the Camel estuary. Dark clouds lingered overhead as the rain drizzled steadily and rather miserably all around, although thankfully they appeared high enough so as not to affect visibility at sea too drastically. Rick and Lloyd both acknowledged my presence as I called across from the Marovonne's starboard-side walkway and asked them specifically about the visibility detailed in their forecast.

"Poor at first, becoming moderate later is what it says," replied Rick nonchalantly. "If this is poor mind you, then I'm happy for it to stay like this, because it's obviously plenty good enough for us not to need to use the radar, and by the sound of it it's only going to improve. Let's hope this rain eases up when it does improve, we could've done without this right now."

"The barometer fell overnight," I replied, being the most likely explanation I could come up with for the rain, "but at least it's not gone cold, and it's back up on the rise again now anyway, so hopefully it'll improve during the course of your voyage. I certainly hope so."

"Ah, 'twill be just fine me babber," said Lloyd with a confident smile. "This'll ease up pretty shortly, you'm just mark my words, then 'twill be plain sailin' all the way back t' Brizzle, no doubt 'bout it."

"I respect your confidence sir," I said, acknowledging his wise and experienced words of wisdom. "Let's just hope you're right, I don't really fancy this rain much meself either, even though we're not actually sailing just yet. Anyways-up, I know you've gotta go take some fuel onboard before you guys set off, so I'll shadow you in the RIB whilst you run out to the fuel quay down at the bottom end of the outer harbour if you like."

"That'd be much appreciated Chris," said Rick. "I'll run the Joseph down there forwards in that case, then you can give us a shove when we have to turn around and chug back out again."

"No problem my friend," I replied cheerfully, "always willing to help. I'm sure I'd need the same kind of assistance myself if I were to run the Marovonne down into a tight little dead end such as that, but fortunately I won't need to when we leave, our tanks are still roughly half full."

Ben stepped up into the Joseph's wheelhouse and handed Rick and Lloyd a sausage and bacon sandwich each, just as the harbour gates began to power themselves open. I hopped down into the RIB and poured the spare gallon of petrol that we'd left aboard into the RIB's main fuel tank, then threw the empty plastic can back aboard the Marovonne. I connected the kill-cord, fired up the engine, untied the painter, then sat there awaiting Rick's instructions. Kim and Shabby came up from down below, both with bacon sarnies in hand, and stood by clear of the ropes so that they could observe the proceedings. Giles was next up on deck, his whole bacon sandwich clearly shoved into his mouth all in one go, and he stepped aboard the Marovonne and also awaited Rick's instructions.

"Let go aft," Rick shouted through the port-side door, and with immaculately audible timing, Lloyd's extra-loud fart reverberated around the interior of the Joseph's wheelhouse. At the same time Will and Giles untied the ropes that secured the two ship's sterns together, then Giles quickly hopped back aboard the Joseph as her stern gradually drifted away from the Marovonne's.

"Jeez, I sure am glad I ain't taking the same watch as you today buddy," I heard Derek call up to Lloyd, as he stood waiting for further instructions up on the Joseph's foredeck

"You ain't jokin' neither!" confirmed Rick, sticking his head back out of the door and gulping in a deep lungful of fresh air. "Give us a little shove please Chris, there seems to be wind coming from all sorts of directions this morning!"

I laughed as I gently pushed the Joseph's stern a little further away from the Marovonne's, then, just as she was adequately aligned for Rick to power her astern away from the Marovonne, he shouted out of the door; *'Let go for'ard.'* The for'ard warp was easily slipped by Derek alone whilst he stood on the bow of the Joseph, as it had only been taken around the Marovonne's starboard bow cleat just the once, and as soon as the two ships were free of each other Rick reversed the Joseph back into clear water. Moments later he spun the wheel and powered her ahead, and once clear of the inner harbour he spun the wheel again, this time hard over to starboard, and glided gently down the inside of the southern outer harbour towards the fuel quay. He pulled her to a perfect halt alongside the series of fuel pumps at the bottom end of the outer harbour, and with her starboard-side fenders still lowered, Giles and Derek both jumped ashore, then Will threw one of them a bow line and the other a stern line. They made the ropes fast, then Rick switched the engine off whilst he spent the next twenty minutes pumping some three-hundred gallons of red diesel into the Joseph's main tanks. During this somewhat costly exercise I chugged back into the inner harbour to see how Rob and Tom were coming along, as I knew they were both leaving at the same time as the Joseph. Catriona sat under an umbrella on the roof of the Kathleen B when I pulled alongside, and she smiled down at me with one of those beautiful *good morning* smiles of hers. Long Tom had the boat's engine purring away on tick-over, and was in the process of disconnecting his shore-power lead from the Lucy box when I said good morning back, and told her to give me a shout should they need any help at any point, which I was pretty confident, and rightfully so too, that they wouldn't.

I chugged across to the Clair de Lune, still moored on the outside of a group of other small yachts that also hadn't left as yet, and said good morning to Little Kim, who was sat up on the foredeck all on her lonesome, her hair looking awfully damp and ragged. I asked her where Rob was, and she told me he was still fast asleep, so I suggested she come for a little jaunt down the estuary aboard the RIB with me whilst we go see the Joseph off. She said she'd be delighted to, pulled her Doc Marten's off, and skipped down into the passenger seat alongside me. I clunked the engine into gear and chugged back towards the harbour gates. There was still no sign of life aboard the Marovonne, so I continued on around to the Joseph where Rick and the lads were wrapping everything up. Rick paid for the fuel in cash, then stepped back aboard and shouted down at me, asking if I was ready to play tugboats. Little Kim exchanged good mornings with everyone aboard, which now included Rick's Kim too, who was stood just outside the entrance to the wheelhouse wildly waving a tea towel around, doing her very best to waft Lloyd's ongoing poisonous gaseous exhalations well away from the all-important navigational area, and judging by the look on her face she was failing miserably. I ran the RIB underneath the Joseph's bow and wedged it firmly between her starboard for'ard planks and the quay wall. Rick fired up the engine, and just as he shouted; *'Let go for'ard, let go aft,'* even before Giles and Derek coiled up their ropes and jumped back aboard, I heard another loud guffaw of laughter come out of Lloyd's mouth as he stood at the chart table up in the wheelhouse. *'Oh dear, poor Rick,'* I thought to myself, *'I don't envy him his first twenty nautical miles or so!'* I clunked the RIB into gear and gave the Joseph's bow a firm shove, spinning her all the way around until she was facing back north again, which, with a little help from Rick powering her forward and astern every now and again, actually proved remarkably easy. Clearly such manoeuvres would've proved remarkably easier had both our ships been fitted with bow and stern thrusters, however, without going into too much detail, they weren't!

Once they were all set Rick powered the Joseph forwards, then ran her out of the outer harbour and into the narrow deepwater channel that ran down towards the Channel Buoy, and we followed alongside in the RIB. The Kathleen B was a little way ahead of us, and as the rain had ceased some ten minutes previous, despite the fact that there was still heavy cloud high up above, Catriona was still sat out on the roof, her umbrella now folded, taking in the views and enjoying the fresh sea breeze. The rest of Rick's crew had also come up onto the Joseph's decks, and as Rick nudged the throttle forward to increase her speed just a little I ran the RIB from side to side so that both Little Kim and I could not only say good morning to everyone, but more importantly we could wish them all a safe passage back home. Little Karen was stood right up by the aft deck's bulwarks, clutching hold of the fluttering Red Ensign's flagpole as she chatted away to both Mel and Nikki, whilst clearly happy with the fact that it had stopped raining. I nudged the bow of the RIB right up against the centre of the Joseph's canoe stern, and at a steady, quiet, relaxed four knots, Little Kim and I chatted away to the girls for a good few minutes. I then ran us forward and pulled alongside the Joseph's port-side bow, where

Shabby was stood, leaning against the ship's handrails whilst chatting to Kim and Cathy. Little Kim had yet another brief chat with all of them, and after wishing them a safe passage home I spun the RIB around to the Joseph's starboard side so that she could wish the same to Giles, Will, Derek and Ben. By the time the Joseph reached the Greenaway she'd pulled level with the Kathleen B, both of them now pottering along at a steady five knots, and Kim threw a final farewell wave to one and all as I weaved the RIB in and out between the two vessels. As one final parting gesture I pulled the RIB tight up alongside the Kathleen B and persuaded Catriona to go grab me a loo roll from their boat's head, which she obligingly did, and carefully passed it down to me. I then crossed over to the Joseph, pulled level with her wheelhouse door, shouted up at Lloyd to grab his attention, then threw him up the loo roll, which Rick neatly caught one-handed and passed it across to him. In no uncertain terms I suggested to him that he may well be needing it in the very near future. Every single person aboard both vessels, *especially* Lloyd himself, cracked up laughing at my childishly improvised little stunt. I hung around alongside as I listened to Rick transmit a brief message over his VHF's channel twelve.

"Padstow Harbour, Padstow Harbour, this is the Joseph, over."

"Joseph, this is Padstow, go ahead, over."

"Padstow, we'd just like to thank you for your generous hospitality as always, and apologies once again on behalf of the Irish musicians that we had aboard. We'll be back down again at some point during the summer and look forward to another pleasant but peaceful visit, over."

"Joseph, this is Padstow. You're always welcome anytime, as well you know, but if you turn up with amplified live music aboard ever again we won't be accommodating you. You'll be forced to dry out at low tide out in the outer harbour, along with that other crazy Bristolian mob aboard that big old pirate ship named Feasible, if ever they should happen to show their faces down here again, over."

"Roger that Padstow, all received loud and clear and fully understood. Joseph out."

"Have a safe voyage back home Rick, we'll look forward to accommodating you again soon. Padstow Harbour out."

'Ah bless!' I thought to myself. *'They loves him really!'* I sped the RIB forward of the Joseph, quickly span it full circle twice some way ahead of them, then settled it down well out of their way, as we sat there waving whilst leaving both vessels to continue merrily on their way with their own separate passage plans. I slammed the throttle fully open next, and gave Little Kim a fairly decent high-speed joyride on our way back from the leading edge of the fully-submerged Doom Bar towards the sanctity of the inner harbour once again.

At a little after seven-thirty, some forty minutes before high water, I pulled the RIB back alongside the Clair de Lune, and allowed Kim to step daintily back aboard as I kept a tight hold of one of the boat's stanchions. There was still no sign of Rob, so I left Kim to it and gently pulled the RIB alongside the Marovonne's now-clear starboard-side midships. After tying the painter to a stanchion and cutting the engine I climbed aboard and stepped through the door into the saloon, only to find three chaps smiling up at me as they sat at the table eating freshly-cooked breakfasts and drinking mugs of tea. And no, one of them wasn't Nik, and one of them wasn't Kevin either, they were both still fast asleep. However, apparently Rob had noticed Kim and I disappearing off out of the harbour in the RIB together a little earlier, and had wandered around the quay and stepped aboard to enquire as to where we might have disappeared off to. Alan, who'd just returned from a brief visit to the shower block, told him we'd gone to assist the Joseph with a refuelling operation, and then followed them off down the Camel as they'd set off for home, and as he was about to cook a fry-up for himself and Rue, when he also returned from the showers, then Rob might as well stay and join them whilst he waited for Kim and myself to return. Clearly Rob had gratefully accepted their invitation, and the three of them were sat there together enjoying the fresh spoils of our latest shopping expedition. I immediately stepped up into the wheelhouse, grabbed my phone and dialled Little Kim's number. She answered on the third ring, and I told her to get her ass around to the Marovonne *immediately,* and I'd have a cooked breakfast ready for her the minute she arrived. I then stepped into the galley, switched on the gas hob, and within less time than it takes to shake a stick at a chicken, *whatever the hell that might mean,* I'd plated up two more breakfasts identical to the three that Alan had constructed, and with immaculate timing, just as Kim climbed the stairs down from the coachroof, I asked her how many sugars she took in her tea.

"Oh, noon please," she replied politely in her broad northern accent. "Wow, that looks reet triff, yow's a reet gud'un ye knows Chris, ah'm reet grateful fa theece."

"My pleasure sweetheart," I replied sincerely, "it's good to see the pair of you get something hearty down inside you before your long trek home."

"I've no doubt we'll be eating fresh mackerel whilst anchored off Lundy again on the way back," said Rob, casting me a quick glance that was clearly full of enthusiasm.

"Ah, ya can't beat it mate," I said, nodding in agreement. "Ya can't beat Lundy, and ya can't beat freshly cooked mackerel, straight out of the sea, nothing else even comes close."

"I so totally agree," said Rob, wiping his plate clean with the last of his toast. "A life on the ocean waves, now that's the life for me; there's nowt that I love's more, than livin' off the sea."

"Haha," laughed Kim as she cut into her bacon and eggs, "ya's a poet and ya did'ne know it!"

Rue and Al both cackled at her well-used little quip, whilst I winked at the pair of them and continued stuffing my face. Not long after we'd finished, then stashed all the dirty crocks back in the galley knowing full well that Nik and Kev would have to do the washing-up *before* they began their own cooking, Rob and Kim thanked the three of us profusely for their hugely welcomed fry-ups, then hopped up into the wheelhouse and prepared to leave. Kim reached up on tiptoe and threw her arms around my neck, unnecessarily thanking me for the kind of stuff that I'd always considered to be just part of a normal friendship, and Rob shook my hand and told me that they really ought to get going. High water had been and gone, so they'd now be punching a fairly hefty ebb tide for the first few hours of their voyage, and according to Rob making very little headway, at least until an hour before slack water when the rate of flow diminished. After which the beginnings of the next flow tide would sweep them comfortably up into the lee of Lundy Island, where they'd stop over before the commencement of their two-part voyage back home. I wished them both the safest of sails, and as the three of us climbed back up onto the coachroof and stepped ashore together I was pleased to note that the rain had stopped entirely, the cloud had thinned and lightened, and little patches of blue were peeking through here and there. Once again I wished them a fair passage, and as they marched off together back around the quay towards their mooring both Rue and Alan called out fond farewells after them from the Marovonne's prow. As I hopped back down into the wheelhouse I suddenly heard the clatter of pans as Nik began clearing the galley, and I left him to it and joined Rue and Al up on the ship's foredeck.

There soon followed much hustle and bustle from the area around the South Quay where the Clair de Lune was moored, as the remainder of the flotilla of small yachts that had all effectively been hemmed in up until now prepared to leave on the same tide. No doubt one or two would head south towards Newquay, helped along their way by the increasing flow of the ebb tide, whereas others, including the three yachts that had initially followed us in from Bideford Bay, and were also preparing to depart, would be heading north-east and fighting the tide in much the same way that Rob and Kim would be. Reaching their home moorings on the subsequent rising tide however would prove eminently sensible, particularly for those yachts that possessed a single, central, deep fin keel. The sound of small diesel engines firing up filled the air, and as Kim cast off the Clair de Lune's mooring lines from the slightly larger yacht that she'd been attached to, the scurrying of skippers and their crew across teak and fibreglass decks, the clattering together of masts, rigging and fenders, and the loud calls and shouts, occasionally interspersed with the odd swear word every now and again, echoed briefly around the solid inner harbour walls and it's surrounding buildings. The Clair de Lune was the first boat free of the apparent nautical entanglement, and the three of us waved goodbye to Rob and Little Kim as they pottered off out through the open harbour gates and on down the Camel towards the open Atlantic Ocean. It took getting on for a full hour before all the remaining dozen or so yachts had finally sorted out their rigging, prepared their rags and sticks for their various tasks ahead, calmed themselves back down again, then departed one by one, line astern of each other. Once the very last of the visiting yachts had finally left, and both the Jaws and the Sea Fury high speed launches had chugged lazily out through the gates to go anchor back down in The Pool alongside the JQ, and once Nik and Kev between them had cleared up a similar amount of mess that they'd made in the galley by cooking for two as Alan and myself had done by cooking for five, then thankfully sat down peacefully together in the saloon to read through the previous day's copy of the Cornish Independent yet again, Padstow *finally* returned to the tranquil, peaceful little fishing port that most people generally recognised it as all those twenty-odd years ago.

Alan and Rue had wandered off into town together to look around the quaint little gift shops once again, and after the harbour gates had powered themselves firmly shut some ten minutes later, at precisely two hours after high water, the inner harbour, along with the heart of the town that surrounded it, transformed itself back into the idyllic picture of perfection that we'd all come to know and love. The Obby Oss Festival was over and done with for yet another year, the locals had all returned to their normal daytime jobs, the hoards of emmets had long since vanished back to whence-ever they hailed from, no doubt to return once again during the following school's summer holidays, and the May Day bank holiday weekend had finally given up it's very last breath of mayhem, returning the picturesque little Cornish fishing town back to normality. Well, apart from the Marovonne still being present of course, but from where I was stood at the time that really didn't matter. We were the very last of the visiting ships to stay over, and stay over we definitely would for some time still to come. In the meantime I grabbed my camera from my cabin, climbed back up onto the ship's coachroof, and snapped off a couple of shots of the chocolate-box image that now lay before me.

PADSTOW HARBOUR RETURNED TO NORMALITY

CHAPTER
TWENTY~SIX

The noisy clatter began some thirty minutes later. *I just knew the peace and quiet was far too good to be true!* It started with the fairground guys dismantling their thrill-rides. After a good solid hour of clanging and banging with hammers and spanners, half a dozen articulated tractor units pulled into the top end of the car park, then one by one they slowly reversed down onto the quayside, hitched up one of the rides, which had all neatly and cleverly been folded down and compacted onto their own self-contained trailers, and slowly but noisily chugged back off up the hill and out of both sight and earshot beyond. There was a brief moment of silence afterwards before two council workers dressed in bright yellow overalls turned up with a wheelie bin, loaded to the gunwales with an array of assorted brushes and shovels, and began clearing up the mess that they'd left behind. Moments later the unmistakable sounds of a couple of pikeys shouting angrily at the two poor council workers caught my attention as a noisy argument began to ensue between all four of them. I stepped back up onto the ship's coachroof, mindful of the dangers of intervening, whilst also recognising the fact that the council workers were already on a hiding to nothing simply by attempting to communicate with them, and immediately clocked precisely what all the fuss was about. Fortunately for the two guys in yellow overalls the fact that the pikeys vans had been wheel-clamped had nothing to do with their own specific responsibilities, and after they'd managed to calm them down sufficiently, which took some considerable doing, they'd simply directed them towards the nearby office of the Director of Amenities.

Some ten minutes later the two pikeys returned to their vehicles, this time shouting loud incomprehensible abuse at each other, and a few minutes later a small unmarked white van with a yellow flashing light on it's roof pulled up, and a chap who looked more like a nightclub bouncer than a council worker stepped out with a heavy-duty keychain attached to his belt, knelt down on the flagstones and unclamped both of their vehicles for them. Typically ungrateful, the pikeys then threw more incomprehensible obscenities at the poor chap, who simply climbed back into his van without uttering a single word and drove off. The pikeys climbed into their own vans, and the blue one eventually started, but the white one wouldn't, it's battery clearly as flat as a pancake. They jumped back out, and after much shouting, cussing and swearing between the pair of them, one of them pulled a set of jump leads out of the back of his van and popped the white one's bonnet. The blue van was repositioned so that the jump leads would reach from battery to battery, and *fortunately,* the white van then started. They muttered a few more obscenities at each other before climbing back into their respective vehicles and loudly crunching their gears as they drove off towards the car park's exit. As I watched them disappear off up the hill I breathed a huge sigh of relief, mainly over the fact that they'd undoubtedly been forced to pay a fairly hefty fine for something that I'd actually instigated myself.

"Looks like you got off scot-free with that one then Skipper," sniggered Kevin from somewhere behind me, making me jump a little.

I hadn't realised that both him and Nik had joined me up on the coachroof to eyeball the ongoing entertainment, as I was too busy worrying about the potential consequences of the whole situation going horribly wrong, which it so easily could've done. Fortunately for all concerned it hadn't, so I'd dropped my guard, and now I turned to face the pair of them.

"Who cares?" I began, shrugging my shoulders. "Bloody horrible types, that's all I've got to say about 'em. Anyway, them there thrill rides have been teeming with emmets all sodding weekend. How much tax-free cash money d'you reckon the whole lot of 'em made altogether exactly? I reckon a couple of measly little parking fines pale into insignificance in comparison. Plus I'd bet the pair of you a tenner each that both of those vans were neither taxed nor MoT'd. Good riddance to the horrible, wealthy, tax-dodging little shits, they're a breed apart from the rest of us normal folks."

"Are you actually trying to tell me you're normal Skip?" asked Nik cheekily.

"Pot and kettle young Roger," I replied with a smirk, "pot and kettle. Anyway, how d'you fancy a sudden early morning dip just for your lip young laddie?"

"I don't mind at all Skip, if you can catch me that is," he answered me back as he skipped nimbly ashore.

I gave up without even trying, then stepped back down into the wheelhouse as the council workforce, which now included a manned bin lorry and a noisy mechanical road sweeper, began emptying each of the overfull waste bins positioned at regular intervals around the harbour. I decided that the best way to go find some peace and quite would be to take a nice long walk along the beautiful coast path that runs all the way alongside the Camel estuary right down to Stepper Point. It didn't look like it was going to rain again for the rest of the day, as the majority of the dark grey clouds had cleared off, leaving just a myriad of smaller white fluffy ones, interspersed here and there with little patches of blue. I decided to carry an umbrella with me just in case though. Of course, I could always have gone and hired a bicycle and cycled the infamous Camel Trail, and quite possibly even persuaded Nik and Kev to come along with me. However, although the thought certainly crossed my mind, there were three very specific drawbacks to the idea; firstly, walking has always suited me far more so than cycling, it's more relaxing and therefore more enjoyable. Secondly, I wasn't likely to get a whole lot of peace and quiet if I took Nik and Kev along with me, so I'd be far safer just taking a long walk knowing that they wouldn't want to bother tagging along. And thirdly, I've always found it a complete ball-ache trying to cycle with an umbrella up. So a nice, long, peaceful walk in the picturesque countryside all on my lonesome, that's precisely what I fancied at that particular moment in time. I wandered back down into my cabin to change, and pulled a half-decent pair of walking boots out from the cupboard under the bed.

Nik and Kev were both scavenging around the quayside when I stepped back ashore at around a quarter to midday. They were both collecting the odd coin here and there, leftovers from the busy fairground rides that even the council workmen had missed. I told them that if I wasn't back by sundown, which, purely for information purposes only, was at 8.45pm, just ten minutes before high water, then they had two choices. They could either dial 999, ask for the Coastguard, and have them send out a search party; or they could come find me themselves, and best start by looking in the Shipwright's. They both told me to enjoy my little stroll, and I set off across the footbridge over the closed harbour gates wearing jeans and a tee shirt whilst carrying a blue and white Bristol Rovers golf umbrella in one hand. I stepped through the kissing gate and on up into the field with the memorial bench-seats in, each of which provided a spectacular view across the Camel, then carried on along the South West Coast Path, past St Saviour's Point, past St George's Cove where we'd had our little fish barbecue down on the beach with the girls, and onwards towards Harbour Cove, where the grassy little footpath takes a slight detour inland in order to avoid clambering over the rocky boulders that litter the entire length of the southern inshore side of the Doom Bar, in between it's high and low water marks. By now there was only a little over two hours to go until the tide was at it's lowest ebb, and the majority of the golden-yellow sands of the Doom Bar itself were clearly visible off to my right, with small white crests gently but audibly crashing against it's leading edge some half a mile off in the distance, despite the apparent calmness of the actual sea beyond, way out across Padstow Bay. No little wonder that legend has it that this very place is precisely where the mermaids reside, lying in wait to lure passing sailors into inevitable disaster. Sadly these words will now haunt poor Ronnie from the Courageous 2 until his very dying days, although in all fairness that's a story for him to tell, not me.

The footpath rejoined the edge of the high water mark as I continued to walk along the western side of the Doom Bar all the way up to Hawker's Cove, where Padstow's original RNLI Lifeboat Station and it's slipway was located. It was founded in 1827, modified many times over the years in order to accommodate ever-improving lifeboats, then closed due to silting back in 1962. A temporary estuary-moored lifeboat was used between 1962 and 1967, after which the brand new boathouse, along with it's 240-foot-long slipway that still operates to this very day, was opened at Trevose Head, and was officially inaugurated in 1968. In 2007 the significantly improved Trevose Head RNLI Lifeboat Station won the Structural Award For Community Structures, and today it houses the Tamar-Class Lifeboat, the *Spirit of Padstow.* Back in 1999, when I was treading this particular path alongside the Camel, it housed the Tyne-Class Lifeboat, the *James Burrough.* The Hawker's Cove Lifeboat Station however, both back in 1999 and up until today, was and still is used simply as a privately run guest house, along with the small collection of cottages situated nearby. Sadly the Hawker's Bay Boathouse would've won no such awards at any point during it's active lifespan, regardless of it's regular upgrades, but that said it still makes for spectacular accommodation, as well as an interesting topic of conversation, and for those that enjoy their history, as indeed I do, it's ancient but clear and obvious purpose-built structure is a great pleasure to observe and admire as you walk on by.

Next I climbed the steps up over Lellizzick Cliffs and continued straight on walking without a single thought of stopping at the Rest A While Tea Gardens. I wasn't hungry, I wasn't thirsty, I was simply enjoying the walk too much. The now-roughened footpath ran pretty much straight and true from there on, along the top of the low cliffs that overlook Iron Cove until finally reaching the end of the headland at Stepper Point. At this point the footpath itself veers off sharply to the left, then continues in a south-westerly direction, past Butterhole Beach, past Tregudda Gorge, and onwards towards Trevone Village and Bay. I wasn't going to walk that far, six miles so far was plenty enough for me, and I still had to walk six miles back too. However, it's possible to leave the footpath at this point and easily climb down over the rugged stepped cliffs at Stepper Point, hence it's name, and that's precisely what I did. Up on the top of Stepper Point is located the National Coastwatch Institution's Lookout Station, which has recently won the Queens Award for Voluntary Service, and rightly so given the year-round observation services that they provide for all manner of sailors whilst navigating these often treacherous waters. However, I bypassed the Lookout Station, climbed down the stepped cliffs, which many years ago used to be a quarry, and walked through the muddy grass all the way along to the very end, then sat down on the stony ground right underneath what was back then the temporary rock-face-mounted Stepper Point Light itself. Although that light has now been replaced by a more modern solar-powered one, located right at the very edge of the expansive flat ledge that I was sat on at the time, the highly visible bright white light that I was sat directly underneath still flashed out it's more-than-obvious warning every ten seconds, clearly visible at night from some ten miles offshore, and I felt comforted just seeing, knowing, and getting a first-hand feeling for it's clear and obvious reliability.

Daytime navigation into the mouth of the Camel had for many a year been made possible by the observation of a traditional stone daymark, Stepper Point's 40ft tower, affectionately known as The Pepper Pot, having been constructed during the early nineteenth century and located right on the top of the cliff some 240ft above sea level, making it visible during daylight hours at up to thirty miles offshore. However, during the hours of darkness, given the highly dangerous ruggedness of the north Cornish coast, there was absolutely no substitute whatsoever for the light itself, and I remain grateful to this day for it's upgrade and continued maintenance, along with the extremely invaluable and continuing work carried out on a daily basis by the volunteers who run the NCI. Add to that the all-important volunteer work carried out by the RNLI, as well as the Air Ambulance and Coastguard Services, without who's assistance myself and probably a great many of my friends more than likely wouldn't even still be here to this day. So to every individual one of them, not only do I take my hat off and salute them to the max, but whenever I manage to find the opportunity I both donate willingly to their individual causes, as well as help to raise money for them during properly organised charity fund-raising events. *My deepest respects go out to you one and all folks.* Anyway, enough of the maudlin stuff, although I have to admit that's precisely the kind of thing that flows through your mind when you find yourself sat all alone at somewhere as scarily dangerous as Stepper Point, even if the ocean you're staring out at is pretty much dead-flat-calm. *'Best I stop sitting here then!'* I thought logically to myself, then stood up and retraced my footsteps back up the stepped cliffs towards the welcoming safety of greener pastures.

I keep saying it, but isn't it amazing how time flies when you're enjoying yourself. I'd left town shortly after midday, and it had taken me a little over two hours to lazily walk the six miles to Stepper Point. I looked at my watch and noticed that it was now getting on for four o'clock. Not only that, but I was beginning to feel just a tiny bit peckish too, so I decided to stop on the way back at the Rest A While Tea Gardens, possibly with the intention of having a traditional cream tea with proper, fresh, Cornish clotted cream. *'Mmmm . . .'* I thought greedily to myself, and hastily put my best foot forward. A little over thirty minutes later I was sat at a table out on the front lawns of the picturesque little tea rooms, admiring the stunning views across the Camel towards Daymer Bay directly opposite whilst waiting patiently for my traditional cream tea to arrive. I'd been waited on by a young waitress dressed in a pretty little blue and white checked pinafore the minute I took a seat, essentially because I appeared to be the only customer that they had at the time, and I'd immediately placed my order with her without hesitation. And now I was staring up at the sky beginning to wonder whether I should've chosen a table indoors instead of out. The clouds were beginning to darken considerably, and as I clutched my umbrella reassuringly, which just so happened to match the young waitresses pretty little dress, I wondered absent-mindedly whether she might just happen to be a Bristol Rovers fan too. '*What a mind-numbingly ridiculous thought!*' I immediately thought to myself, just as she set a tray loaded with tea and scones down in front of me. Still, what the hell, I asked her anyway, purely as an ice-breaker.

"Plymouth Argyle actually," she replied with a broad, pretty smile. "I'm only wearing this pinny because I don't happen to own a green and white one. If I did I'd be wearing it for sure, *always!*"

"Oh dear," I replied dolefully. "Still, I suppose we all have our crosses to bear, me included."

She laughed as she carefully placed my order down on the table in front of me and removed the tray. Before she walked back down the path and in through the side door of the little café, I couldn't resist but ask her the one inevitable question that everyone in the whole wide world *still* wants to know the answer to. Firstly, I promised to honour her knowledgeably informed opinion, and then I popped the actual question itself.

"So, my dear, do we put the jam or the cream on first?" I asked, keeping it simple.

"Well," she began thoughtfully, "ultimately I suppose it depends on where you come from. However, as you're in Cornwall right now, then it's definitely cream followed by jam."

"Well at least that matches with my own considered opinion," I replied positively. "However, as I personally grew up in the beautiful Devonshire countryside not a million miles away from here, I just happen to know a little differently."

"As indeed do I," the waitress replied with a grin. "I'm not from around these parts originally, I'm a Devonshire lass myself too. Born and bred in Plymouth, hence the affinity with Plymouth Argyle. And whilst I much prefer it up here amongst the laid-back tranquility of Padstow, I'll never forget either my roots or my upbringing. So I know exactly where you're coming from; in Devon they use butter. Originally, many many moons ago, the Cornish could never afford such luxuries, so they substituted the absence of butter with cream, hence the cream first, followed by a dollop of jam on top. In Devon however, where the grass is considerably more lush than it is in the much harsher environment of the Cornish peninsular, and hence why cattle farming is considered to be far more viable, their standards of living became a lot more decadent over the years than the people of Cornwall ever managed to achieve, and the slightly more civilised Devonshire folk subsequently learnt to butter their scones first, then add the jam, and then plonk a dollop of Devonshire clotted cream on top. I've worked extensively in tea rooms in both counties, and I can assure you that these principles still apply to this day, and in my considered opinion are never likely to change, and rightly so too."

"My darling, I entirely agree with you," I gladly concurred. "So in summary, when in Devon, it's butter then jam then cream, and when in Cornwall it's cream then jam. Correct?"

"Absolutely spot-on sir," she replied with a wink and a cheeky little smile. "Oh, and just for the record, *it's pronounced scone, not scone!*"

"Blimey, you really do know your onions, don't you!" I said, praising the accurate depth of her knowledge over the two opposing local customs.

"I'm sorry sir," she replied with a giggle, marching back off towards the café carrying the empty tray, and looking back over her shoulder as she did so, "we don't serve onions here anymore, you'll have to take the long drive down to Plymouth if that's what you're looking for."

I laughed out loud as she disappeared, then neatly cut each of my two scones in half and applied the cream first and then the jam. *'Well, that certainly puts that little conundrum to bed then!'* I thought satisfyingly to myself, as I poured piping hot tea from an ornately decorated teapot into a matching bone-china cup and saucer. *Delicious!* I sat there, peacefully alone, entirely at one with the world, and watched carefully as the heavy clouds up above me grew steadily darker by the minute. It was shortly before six o'clock when I decided to stay for more, and as the heavens hadn't opened as yet I ordered a crab sandwich, along with a second pot of tea, and remained sat at the table in the centre of the neatly mowed, fenced-in little lawn. Knowing that Helen would've been home from work by then I pulled my phone out of my jeans pocket and gave her a call. She answered immediately, and I munched away on my delicious crab sandwich whilst listening to her recount her first day back at the office after her slightly extended bank holiday break. All appeared well on the home front back in Bristol, although clearly the Joseph wasn't due back into port until last lock later that night, somewhere around midnight all being well, so consequently Helen hadn't bothered calling into the Shakespeare after work, as it was unlikely that any of our friends would've been in there anyway. We chatted together for a little longer, following which I blew her a farewell kiss then finished the remainder of my delicious home-made brown-bread crab sandwich. I poured myself a forth cup of tea, then asked the young, polite, and clearly well educated waitress if she wouldn't mind fetching me the bill please. Moments later she set it down at the side of the table inside a small, neatly bound leather folder, and I handed her my credit card without even looking at it. It had just turned seven o'clock when I stood up to leave, and I slipped a five-pound note inside the small leather folder as the waitress handed me back my card. I thanked her for her excellent service, as well as for the fabulous food, but more importantly for sharing her well-founded local knowledge with me. She told me that she was more than happy to have done so, and happier still that her understanding of regionalised cream tea etiquette concurred entirely with my own. I promised her that the next time I had occasion to visit Plymouth I'd make a point of buying some local onions, and she laughed out loud as we parted company on the guarantee that one day we'd be bound to bump into each other again, even if it meant me having to retrace my footsteps back to the tiny little hamlet of Lellizzick.

The first drops of rain hit me hard as I set off back down the little cliffs at the top end of Hawker's Cove, and as I plodded on past the old Lifeboat Station, I put my blue and white umbrella up for the first time. High water was due at a few minutes before nine o'clock, which meant that firstly the majority of the Doom Bar will already have been covered as I walked around it's inner perimeter, and secondly the harbour gates will have opened some fifteen minutes previous. All in all, perfect timing for me to arrive at the Shipwright's for my first most welcomed pint of the day at an estimated 8.30pm, some fifteen minutes before sunset, providing I got a move on of course. Once again I put my best foot forward, and despite the lack of wind I braced my umbrella firmly against the steadily growing shower of rain. It wasn't particularly heavy as yet, however I got the distinct impression that it was going to remain persistent. As the footpath took me back inland somewhat, as I rounded the rough hilly area at the top of Harbour Cove, I peered over the top of the bushes and spotted the Thunder, powering her way down the Camel at some forty miles per hour, with half a dozen paying passengers aboard, whilst leaving a good three-foot-high wake behind her. *'Great to see folks still enjoying themselves, despite the rain,'* I thought to myself as I pressed on. The footpath ran back towards the rocky edge of what remained of the Doom Bar's sands before I rounded the corner and pressed on towards the little kink that rounds the top end of St George's Cove, and after passing the cove, before I continued on towards St Saviour's Point, I stopped once again and peered out from underneath my umbrella, back across the Camel towards Rock Beach.

Suddenly, and mightily unexpectedly too I might add, I spotted someone waterskiing behind a small grey speedboat, heading *down* the Camel, aiming directly towards the flashing light atop the Bar Buoy. The skier was wearing a full-body wetsuit *(bloody wuss!)*, and the driver of the boat appeared to be wearing a bright orange storm-jacket with *HARBOUR BASTARD* written in bold black letters across the back, which I could clearly read every time he turned around to ensure that his skier hadn't fallen off yet. *And where was his observer exactly?!!?* From where I was stood I could even recognise the pale blue wooden skis as being my very own, and right there and then I made the irreversible decision to deny both Nik *and* Kevin any soup for their supper later that night. *The little shits! What the hell did they think they were playing at? Why didn't they at least go use the designated waterski area further up the Camel?* Five minutes later, as I stood there aghast, watching from underneath my umbrella as it persistently continued to drizzle, I found out precisely why they'd turned left instead of right after exiting the harbour; *they were chasing the Thunder!* As the Thunder powered it's way back towards Padstow, having spun it's screaming passengers around in a couple of tight, steeply banked turns just off Polzeath Beach, my RIB, complete with a grim-faced Seaman Staines tightly gripping the wheel with knuckles as white as snow, flew off the top of the Thunder's first huge wake and landed soft and firm on it's second but smaller trailing wake. Nik followed immediately afterwards, launching himself and his skis high into the air off the Thunder's leading wake, then unavoidably dipping the tip of a ski before landing, and crashing headlong face-first into the leading edge of the Thunder's second wake, the rope's handle flying a good forty feet skywards before plopping back into the water. I almost wet myself at the sight of this, as a result of which I was forced to put my umbrella down for a minute or two whilst I allowed myself to get rain-sodden elsewhere instead. *'Right, definitely no soup tonight!'* I thought, reinforcing my earlier decision. As I retrieved my umbrella and looked back out across the Camel, Kevin thrust the RIB's throttle fully forward once again, and pulled Nik easily back up onto the skis. *'Oh well,'* I thought, resigning myself to the reality of the situation, *'I guess there's really only one way to learn, and that's from making mistakes. I'll just keep my fingers crossed that they're not the kind of mistakes that later result in regrets!'* I carried on walking towards St Saviour's Point, watching with growing admiration as Nik successfully executed the very same manoeuvre, this time over the slightly larger wake that trailed behind the somewhat heavier but faster Sea Fury. *'Fair play to him,'* I thought once again, *'at least the young lad's learning. Still, they could at least have asked me first before borrowing the RIB and the skis, but then, at the end of the day, I guess that's just Nik for you; act first, deal with the consequences afterwards!'* After a while I gave up watching them and set my sights on the Shipwright's, hoping against hope that they'd have the sense to pack it in before it got dark, and wondering exactly how much more abuse I was now going to have to take from Malcolm, the Harbourmaster.

Christopher John Reason

STEPPER POINT LIGHT AND DAYMARK

CHAPTER
TWENTY~SEVEN

The sun had already disappeared behind the tops of the buildings as I collapsed my umbrella and stepped in through the front door of the Shipwright's, thankful for putting the ever-darkening clouds out of my mind. Rue was sat at the bar chatting to a couple of the locals, and as I stepped up beside him he offered to buy me a pint, which I gratefully accepted. It wasn't long before Rue finished up his conversation with the locals and turned his attention to me, and consequently it wasn't too long before he put those ever-darkening clouds straight back into my mind once again. It turned out he'd been watching the telly aboard ship, and had happened to catch the following day's weather forecast, which apparently wasn't at all good. When he saw Nik climb down into the RIB, closely followed by Kev carrying a pair of skis, he thought it best he come meet up with me, essentially to warn me about both aspects of his latest observations. Nik had apparently cooked dinner for all four of them, utilising a great deal of our newly-acquired provisions, including several bottles of wine, the majority of which had been consumed by Alan, hence why he'd fallen fast asleep on the sofa just as soon as the DVD movie they'd been watching had finished. Rue had then managed to tune in to a very poor BBC TV signal, surprisingly so given that the aerial atop the foremast would've been pointing in the wrong direction. However, whilst Nik and Kev had washed up and cleared away, Rue had at least managed to catch both the national and the regional news, along with their associated weather forecasts, albeit via a rather fuzzy screen.

Apparently the death toll from Oklahoma City's F5 tornado disaster in the US had reached forty-two by then, however there was nothing of consequence happening in the UK itself on Star Wars Day *(May the 4th be with you!)* other than the all-important weather. And the weather, or at least as Rue was about to point out to me, was all-important to four out of the five of us that were residing aboard ship in Cornwall at that particular point in time. Apparently it had started to rain. *No shit Sherlock!* According to BBC South West though, it wasn't going to let up. *"Drying briefly overnight, early morning showers, becoming persistent for the remainder of the day. And the day after. And probably the day after that too!"* Hey ho, I guess that's what you get for choosing to live in England's green and pleasant land. Anyway, Rue had wanted to discuss it with me, and at least he knew where best to start looking for me; not that it would've taken a huge amount of guesswork I might add. He'd also considered that he had an obligation to inform me about Nik and Kevin's latest shenanigans, although as soon as he brought their little misdemeanour up I told him I'd already clocked the pair of them pratting about in the estuary. *'I've no doubt it'll be me that ultimately carries the can for their irresponsible foolhardiness,'* I'd replied to him, shrugging the matter off with my usual cynical degree of acceptance. I'd deal with Nik and Kev and their inappropriate waterskiing activities in due course, however, clearly in Rue's eyes, and I have to say I'd agreed with him on this one, the weather was actually a far more pressing topic of conversation, so I told him I was all ears.

"Is there really any point in us staying down here any longer if it's just gonna piss it down with rain for the foreseeable future?" he asked me logically.

"Nope," I replied sensibly, agreeing with his analysis. "Other than ensuring that Nik is somehow taken firmly under control, and somehow kept that way too, I can see no other reason for any of the rest of us to stay, given that the weather now appears to have turned. What exactly d'you have in mind buddy?"

"Well," Rue continued, "given that you're leaving the Marovonne down here for the summer, and given that you're leaving Nik aboard as some form of security guard, whether that pans out to be a sensible idea or not, I figured the four of us might just as well get a taxi to the train station tomorrow morning, rather than sit around here in the rain all day long."

"I totally agree with you Rue," I said, acknowledging the practicality of his suggestion. "There's little point in all of us staying down here if it's just going to chuck it down for the rest of the week. But not only that, I'm also beginning to miss my kids too, and as it's technically my turn to have them this coming weekend, providing I give Rachel a call and give her adequate notice, it'd be really nice if I could pick both Tori and Alex up from school this coming Friday afternoon. Plus, into the bargain, if we spend tomorrow travelling home, then I can spend all day Thursday at work, catching up on everything I need to know about before being thrown in at the deep end come Friday morning. So yes mate, I'm on your side with this one."

"Well that's cool then Skipper," said Rue with a smile, "because I reckon Alan's on my side with it too. He muttered something earlier about the weather and trains as well."

It was my round, and I returned Rue's generosity by buying both him and myself another pint. Fortunately I'd just managed to pocket my change before Nik and Kevin walked in through the front door. Kev was still wearing his bright orange *HARBOUR BASTARD* jacket as he stepped inside out of the increasingly persistent rain, but he removed it immediately and tussled his wet hair so that it didn't look quite such a mess. Nik, on the other hand, was still wearing a black, dripping-wet, full-body wetsuit as he stepped up to the bar, his long, dark, sodden hair hanging untidily around his neck, and was immediately asked to leave. Before turning for the exit I asked him where he'd left the RIB exactly, and he told me he'd tied it to the northern of the two outer rising pontoons.

"Before you go get yaself changed and cleaned up young Roger," I quietly demanded, "bring it back inside the harbour for me please, then lash it alongside the Marovonne exactly where it was before."

"Aww, but Skip, I was hoping . . ." he began, in that annoyingly innocent little-boy-lost tone of his.

"There's no *'Aww, buts'* about it matey, it's confiscated, end of!" I replied firmly.

"Aww, but Skip, can we not even run it across to Rock for breakfast tomorrow morning? *Pleeeease?"* he continued, even more annoyingly.

"I'll tell you precisely where you can run it for me first thing tomorrow morning Nik," I said, clearly getting his hopes up just a touch.

"Yeah? Where Skip? Tell me, please?" he asked enthusiastically.

"Back up onto it's cradle on the roof of the Marovonne," I replied, knocking the wind out of his sails.

"Why's that Skip?" asked both Nik and Kev more or less together.

"Because we've decided to head off home tomorrow, that's why," I replied, this time with a hint of sympathy in my voice. "So the best thing you can do tomorrow Nik is to spend the day down here looking for a job somewhere, and if it's all the same to you Kev, Rue and I have decided there's no point in us stopping down here if it's gonna rain for the rest of the week, which apparently it is, so we might as well take the last train to Clarksville, so to speak. That okay with you Mister Staines?"

"Well, seeing as you put it like that Skip," said Kevin understandingly, "and seeing as how there ain't another wetsuit aboard that fits me anyway, both Alex and Tori's are just a tiny bit too small for this here gert hulk of a man, then yeah, what the heck. I ain't goin' to no Clarksville mind. If we's gotta go, then we's gotta go to gert Brizzle innit, right?"

"Don't you go worryin' yaself about that Seaman Staines," I said, winking at Rue, "you can be there by four-thirty, 'cause I've made your reservation."

"Oh, okay, that's cool then," replied Kevin innocently, entirely missing the relevance of Rue's subtle little cackles.

"OUT, PLEASE!" the barman shouted once more at Nik, this time not quite so politely, however, unusually obediently for Nik, he immediately did what he was told for once.

Kevin followed Nik out through the door, and about an hour later, after both of them had very obviously used the shower block and tidied themselves up, they stepped back into the Shipwright's, dragging an ever-so-slightly bewildered-looking Alan along behind them, and boldly announced that it was my round. *'You really do need to get yaself a job young lad!'* I thought to myself briefly, as I shoved my hand deep into my trouser pocket once again. After I'd bought yet another round of drinks, all five of us sat at a table together and discussed not only the logistics of getting home, but also the potential logistics of getting back down there once again later on during the summer. Then subsequently, at some point after the total solar eclipse on August the 11th, sailing the Marovonne back to Bristol again. Nik would obviously sail back home with us, providing he hadn't already been thrown out of Padstow on his ear by then of course, and as I'd expected, Kevin also immediately volunteered his services. So Bristol's three most infamous harbour bastards, Captain Pugwash, Seaman Staines and Roger The Cabin Boy, would all be taking to the high seas once again for yet another well-orchestrated misadventure together. *Excellent!* Having laid it out on the table in that very fashion, Alan's immediate reaction was to say; *'Count me in too please Skipper,'* however Rue wasn't entirely too sure about things himself; he said he was generally never able to make decisions about anything in life until the very last moment anyway. But that was fine, I'd be happy with just the three of us, plus Alan joining us too would simply be an added bonus. And so it was decided. Nik had to go search for a job first thing the following morning whilst the rest of us caught the train back to Bristol. Everyone was comfortably in agreement, *especially* Nik, who was quite clearly looking forward to spending a whole summer down in Padstow living aboard the Marovonne, and we spent the remainder of the evening reminiscing together about how extremely enjoyable that particular May Day weekend had turned out to be. *'I'll drink to that!'* I cheered, then stepped up to the bar and paid for one final round just as last orders were called.

Myself and Kevin were the first two up topsides the following morning, followed very closely afterwards by Rue. Whilst Rue wandered into the galley and gradually began to prepare breakfast for everyone, Kev jumped down into the RIB in order to retrieve the skis and stow them away, and I stepped up onto the coachroof to prepare the crane for hoisting the RIB back aboard. I swung the boom out over the side of the ship, then lowered the cable in perfect time for Kevin to catch and then attach the four clip-on lifting strops. Kev climbed back aboard once again, then I hit the *'UP'* button on the crane's remote control, hoisted the RIB high up in the air, swung the boom around, then lowered the heavy little boat neatly back down onto it's cradle. After securely lashing it down into position I removed the drain bung, then detached the almost empty fuel tank from the engine and passed it back down to Kevin for safe storage well out of harm's way. Finally, just as Nik stepped up onto the roof to offer his assistance, which clearly wasn't required, you should've seen the sad look of despondency appear across his face as I chained the RIB to it's cradle and locked it in place with a heavy-duty padlock.

"Sorry buddy, but I know what you're like, so confiscated means confiscated I'm afraid," I told him firmly, then patted him twice on the shoulder before hopping back down into the wheelhouse.

Nik followed me down, still with a glum look on his face, then perked up a little when he smelt the sizzling bacon that Rue was happily pan-frying in the galley. Kev and I had both got ourselves rather damp whilst craning the RIB back aboard, on account of the fact that it was still raining. It wasn't raining all that heavily, it was just *raining*, like it does sometimes! We dried ourselves off, and I changed my shirt, and by the time we came back up topsides again Alan was sat in the saloon, Rue was dishing up five perfectly-cooked breakfasts, and Nik was in the galley making five mugs of tea. *Marvellous! Just what the doctor ordered!* We sat there together and ate in silence, after which I complimented Rue on his culinary skills, then left him and Alan to clear up whilst I grabbed my cagoule and my umbrella from my cabin. I'd decided it best I go have a good old chinwag with Malcolm the Harbourmaster before we all leave, just to put him in the picture with regard to Nik and the ongoing security of the Marovonne whilst I was away, and although I wasn't entirely looking forward to this little meeting, I zipped my cagoule up, stepped ashore with a modicum of trepidation, and opened my umbrella. On my way to Malcolm's office I checked our electricity meter once again; *still full, on just the one fifty pence piece!* Hey ho, best keep schtoom about it I reckon, but at least Nik'll be thrilled that he doesn't have to keep feeding the meter all summer long.

It was approaching ten o'clock, around half an hour after high water, and the makeshift gangway lashed to the Marovonne's roof that led down onto the quayside was becoming steeper by the day as we rapidly approached spring tides. The harbour gates would've opened at about seven-twenty-five that morning, which meant that Malcolm's office would've opened roughly an hour before that, and as I strolled purposefully towards the entrance, umbrella in hand, I kept my fingers crossed that he wouldn't be in too bad a mood when he saw me.

"*WHAT THE HELL D'YOU THINK YOU'RE PLAYING AT, WATERSKIING DOWN THE BLOODY ESTUARY BEHIND THE TRIP BOATS LIKE THAT? SURELY YOU KNOW WHERE THE DESIGNATED SKI AREA IS, DON'T YOU? WELL, DON'T YOU?*" he shouted at me the minute I entered his office.

"Yes sir," I replied humbly.

"Anyway, listen up please Malcolm," I continued with a broad smile. "I've got good news and I've got good news."

"Coming from you Chris, I find that *extremely* unlikely!" he muttered sarcastically.

"Okay, well it's like this you see," I began, trying my best to sound positive. "It wasn't actually me waterskiing down the Camel last night your honour, it was Nik and Kevin, and it's my duty to inform you that they were doing so *without* my express permission. Anyway, as a consequence of their childish little misdemeanour I've confiscated the RIB and padlocked it securely back onto the roof of the Marovonne. Which means that whilst I'm away working, and Nik stays aboard to boat-sit for me, he won't be able to use the RIB anymore, it's *non-modus operandi*, and will remain as such for the entire duration."

"Thank God for small mercies," said Malcolm, clapping his hands together and holding them aloft. "So, you said you had more good news? Enlighten me why don't you?"

"Nik's going to get himself a job whilst he's down here," I replied convincingly, "so, all being well, you shouldn't have to endure too much in the way of light-fingered thievery going on around town."

"And when exactly has *'ALL EVER BEEN WELL'* when you and your entourage of Bristolian pirate buddies turn up down here in our peaceful little backwater, eh? Go on, answer me that one if you'd be so bold?" Malcolm demanded angrily.

"Well, you guys send out open invitations to a public festival and harbour regatta every year," I replied with a huge innocent smile, "so we just show up and party, just like it says on the invite."

"Yes Chris, of course you do. So, don't you worry, we'll keep an eye on the Marovonne for you, and thank you kindly for not bothering to ask," Malcolm said with feigned sincerity, "now get the hell out of my office, can't you see I'm a busy man?"

"Yes sir, I'm gone, I'm outta here," I replied with obvious relief.

"Oh, and one more thing before you leave Chris," he added, stopping me dead in my tracks. "If I hear of any more shenanigans from your young *'boat-sitter',* any goings-on whatsoever, I shall be on the phone to you immediately, kapeesh?"

"Roger that, and fully understood Malcolm," I replied with genuine sincerity. "Don't worry sir, I shall do my level best to ensure that you have no cause for concern, and hopefully no need whatsoever to call me. And thank you for your understanding, and thank you also for allowing all of us to share in your wonderful annual festivities once again. It's been an absolute pleasure, and I'll see you again in around three months from now, if not before."

"You're welcome Chris, safe travels," Malcolm politely concluded our little meeting.

It was still raining when I stepped back out of his office, and I popped my umbrella back up, then wiped my brow with the back of my hand as I breathed a huge, silent *'PHEW'* and marched happily back towards the Marovonne. Now all we had to do was actually find Nik a job for real, although knowing him as I did, the chances were he could probably manage that with his eyes shut. I took him to one side for a quiet word after I stepped back aboard ship. Rue, Alan and Kevin were all down below packing their bags, having left both the galley and the saloon spotless, so Nik and I sat up in the wheelhouse and chatted amicably together. Essentially I ran through a checklist with him, which he'd already noted down for himself in the back of the ship's logbook anyway, which still lay open on the chart table. It was all run-of-the-mill standard on-board etiquette kind of stuff; isolate the gas supply when you're not using the galley; keep a check on the bilges and listen out for the regularity of the automatic bilge pumps; don't worry about feeding the electricity meter, it appears to be feeding itself; make sure you use the shower block every day, as opposed to the ship's heads; don't mess with any of the controls or the settings that I've left things on; keep the wheelhouse doors closed and locked at all times, and here's a spare key to the starboard-side saloon door; stay the fuck out of my own private cabin *(which I'd be locking up anyway!)*; get yaself a job asap, and don't go getting yaself into any trouble whilst you're down here; *AND RING ME IMMEDIATELY IF ANYTHING GOES WRONG;* etc, etc! I was pretty sure Nik knew exactly where I was coming from with everything. He pretty much knew the ship inside out, and we pretty much knew each other inside out too, so we both felt entirely confident in what we were about to embark on for the next three months, although where exactly *trust* fits in to that equation I've still no idea to this day. Hey ho, bless his little cotton socks! Finally, just as the harbour gates squeezed themselves tightly shut at 11.25am, Rue, Alan and Kevin plonked their baggage down on the wheelhouse floor and told me they were ready to go.

I didn't need to pack a bag myself, I was happy just to leave everything in my cabin, but before I locked the door behind me

I was mindful to carefully stash the still-full bottle of rum out of sight, as well as lock my grab-bag, which now contained the RIB's kill-cord amongst other things, safely in the cupboard under my bed. I then locked up, stepped back up into the wheelhouse, and after giving Nik a big hug and demanding once again that he behave himself during my prolonged absence, I boldly announced; *'Come along now guys, let's get ourselves gone then!'* The very last thing I did before stepping back ashore was to remove the Scull & Crossbones from the Marovonne's stern flagpole, neatly roll it up, then tell Nik to stash it safely in the flag locker. And then we were off. Nik waved the four of us farewell as we trudged off along the quayside through the rain, which had eased up very slightly by then, and around to the front of the Padstow Fish & Chip Café where we already had a taxi waiting to take us to Bodmin Parkway train station. Some twenty minutes and twenty quid later the four of us stood together underneath the platform shelter waiting for the next train, and a further fifteen minutes after that, guess which train should blast it's noisy air horn at us as it pulled itself gradually to a halt? Yep, you've guessed it, the 13.00hrs northbound *rattler!* Which, for those of you not in the know, is ironically not only the cheap-seats trip back home, but it's also the one that stops at every single sodding station along the way. *'Hmmm, maybe someone will invent something called a Kindle one of these days!'* I absentmindedly thought to myself. But as no one had as yet, I just stared out of the window at the luscious green countryside whilst we rattled along at up to 50mph for the next four-and-a-half hours, predictably stopping briefly at every single station along the way in order to pick virtually nobody else up. Still, at least the upside was the fact that Helen had just finished work by the time the train was thirty minutes late pulling in to Temple Meads Station back in Bristol, and after fighting her way through the rush hour traffic she was able to pick us up and cram all four of us inside her little Vauxhall Astra.

First she dropped Rue off on the quayside next to his tatty old MFV, the entirely unseaworthy Accordance, and then she dropped Alan off at the Avon Packet Pub on Coronation Road, above which he had his own room. Next we trekked on through the bustling city traffic, then all the way up the slow-going M32, and dropped Kevin off at Sarah's house in Downend. After that it was back through Fishponds, where I couldn't even be bothered to stop off at work, and on towards St George, where all I wanted to do was take a long soak in a nice hot bath in Helen's recently-purchased home, with it's nicely refurbished bathroom. So that, my friends, is precisely what I did, and the remainder of what happened that particular evening, I'm sorry to have to inform you, is not for public knowledge!

WE'LL BE BACK!

CHAPTER TWENTY-EIGHT

Helen drove into work early the following morning, parked her car in Jury's multi-storey as always, and dropped me off at the same time so that I could retrieve my own vehicle. I kissed her goodbye, wished her a peaceful day at work, then drove straight to my own office in Fishponds. The first thing I did when I arrived, after greeting Roland and Tony, who were the only two to arrive before me, was to telephone Rachel to let her know that I'd be picking Tori and Alex up from school the following day. Thankfully she was perfectly happy with that, as she'd made no other arrangements for the forthcoming weekend anyway, so I'd said fine, I'd drop them back to school first thing on the following Monday morning as per usual. I then began the arduous task of catching up on everything I'd missed during the seven working days that I'd been absent for. That actually took virtually the whole day to achieve, however, once I was back up to speed, and ready to dive headlong into yet another crazy Friday, piecing the following week's programme of works together, I called Helen on her office number and told her not to bother going home immediately after work, I felt a badly-needed pint coming on, so I'd meet her in the Shakespeare just as soon as I could manage to fight my way through the traffic back into town. I guessed I'd probably make it by around 6pm, and I doubt very much if I'd been far out with that in all honesty. Helen was waiting for me as I arrived, as were Pirates Willy and Barnabus *(Brian and Guy),* and over our first drinks together we spent a good ten minutes listening to Brian explain precisely how difficult it had been trying to get both Guy and his wheelchair up the five steep stone steps that led from Prince Street up to the pub's little front terrace where the front entrance was. Hardly surprising, given poor Guy's recent failed hip operation, nevertheless, they'd both still found it all extremely funny, as per usual.

Rick and Kim were next in through the door, followed very shortly afterwards by the Master Mariner himself, Lloyd. I immediately asked them how their latest voyage had gone, and after both Nigel and Anna had welcomed the three of them back home, and served them their order, they came and sat down next to us to chat about it. According to Lloyd there was very little to chat about; the rain had eased up well before Hartland, the Joseph was bang on the nail, the overnight passage had gone as smooth as silk, and after fifteen hours they'd comfortably made last lock back into Bristol at just before noon the previous day. Rick, on the other hand, had simply moaned about the fact that the first few hours of the voyage had been way too smelly. Kim cracked up laughing as the pair of them continued to rib each other jokingly over petty little things, such as who's responsibility it should've been to re-connect the shore-power cable once they'd finally settled back on their mooring, etc, etc. Anna's one and only interjection went along the lines of; *'Thank God you left that dreadful wind of yours back down in Cornwall Lloyd,'* to which Lloyd immediately replied; *'Don't you be worryin' 'bout that moi luvver, there's plenty more where that came from!'*

"Talking of wind," I began, putting my serious head back on as I addressed Rick, "has anyone heard anything from Raymondo yet? He knows there's a bit of a storm-front coming in from the Atlantic as we approach the next spring tides this coming weekend, so he said he was probably going to leave St Mary's this morning at the very latest, in order that they could run home ahead of it. Only thing is, on my way into town I couldn't help but notice just how much the wind is getting up outside already, so it's bound to be a lot worse down in the Scillies right now."

"I've spoken to Ray *and* Ronnie," Rick replied, clearly acknowledging how the weather had suddenly turned since he'd arrived back home, along with my obvious concern. "Ronnie's comfortably holed up in Falmouth on the Courageous for the time being, and that's exactly where he's gonna stay until the weather settles again. And once it does he said he's gonna head back to Padstow at some point, and then probably stop over for the eclipse. Ray, on the other hand, tells a different story altogether. Apparently they *were* going to leave this morning, but they've all been having so much fun ashore together that they've decided to stay over for one more night, so they'll be sailing at first light tomorrow. I reckon the Mermaid Inn in Hugh Town's probably got a lot to do with that!"

"Oh well, at least the Scillies won't be fogbound in this wind, so I guess that's a blessing," I noted.

"I still reckon they'll encounter some pretty heavy seas at some point," replied Rick knowingly. "So yeah, it probably would've been better if they'd've left this morning, but Ray knows his onions out there, and the Roehampton's a relatively fast old bird, so I'm sure they'll be fine."

"Let's hope so," I replied, "especially given that they have the two ladies sailing aboard with them. Anyway buddy, d'you have any particular plans for the eclipse as yet?"

"We sure do," replied Rick enthusiastically, "at least, Lloyd and I do. We're gonna hit Padstow again for the actual event, probably sail down sometime the week before, then we're gonna take a run across to St Mary's afterwards and meet up with Raymondo, 'cos that's where he'll be off to with the Roehampton once again. He reckons you'll get a far better view of it from that much further south, and seeing as it's a once-in-a-lifetime event, none of us really want to miss it. So it looks like we're all gonna be meeting up once again during August at some place or another back down in Cornwall."

"Brilliant! That's great to here!" I replied joyfully. "I can't wait! Let's hope the weather's as kind to us for the eclipse as it's just been for May Day."

The Shaky got steadily busier during the course of the evening, with more and more friends and drinking buddies coming in to chat about our various escapades down in Padstow the previous weekend. Most notably, Shabby arrived for work behind the bar, apologising to Nigel and Anna for being a little late as per usual, then a bit later on Big Mike, a very close friend of Ray and Jamer's, strolled in with his little wire-haired Beddlington Terrier, Bogart, closely followed by Market Phil and Sandy, and oddly enough, all three of them lived on their own individual boats in Bristol Harbour too. Then, finally, the exceptionally tall Robnoxious, a very close friend indeed of both myself and Helen, as well as being well-loved by everyone else around the docks, walked in accompanied by his stocky but soft-as-you-like Irish Potato Hound, Mostin. Helen and I had a right good old laugh recounting May Day tales of mayhem and misadventure to anyone and everyone that was prepared to listen, some of which had half the back bar in fits of laughter, especially Brian and Guy. All too quickly however, as always seems to happen when one's enjoying one's self, the evening came to an end, and one by one our friends steadily filtered out and toddled back off to their respective live-aboards. Determined as Rick and I were to prolong the night however, we succeeded in persuading Helen, Kim, Lloyd, Shabby and Robnoxious to join us down at the Raj in King Street for a late night curry *(with no onions for Rick of course!)*. Rob lived on an old auxiliary fleet-tender boat called Triton at the time, and clearly had to drop Mostin back aboard first, however he managed to catch us back up just as we were being seated, and during the remainder of the evening a highly recommended curry, as hot or as mild as you like, was enjoyed by one and all.

The following morning Helen dropped me back to Jury's multi-storey on her way in to work so that I could retrieve my own vehicle, then I drove back to Fishponds and walked into my office at roughly the same time as the rest of my staff. The first thing I did was to call Nik to find out if he'd managed to find himself a job yet, and he finally picked up the cheap little pay-as-you-go phone that I'd bought him and answered it after about twenty rings. I'd obviously just woken him up, however, good news was apparently the order of the day. He'd been offered a job at his first attempt of asking, washing-up in the scullery of Rick Stein's Seafood Restaurant almost next door to the Custom House. The pay was minimum wage, the hours were pretty anti-social, but it wasn't a bad start for the young lad, and who knew, it could well have led on to far greater things, especially with Nik's natural talent for cooking. He didn't have to start until 5pm, and was required to work an eight hour shift right through until 1am the following morning, hence why I'd just woken him up. Still, I wished him well with his new little venture, then tutted knowingly to myself when he mentioned that at least there'd be plenty of rich pickings on offer whenever nobody else was looking. *Hey ho, what can ya do eh?* The next thing I did was to phone my eldest daughter Michelle and ask her if she and her boyfriend Nick had anything planned for the weekend, and if not did they fancy spending it with me, Helen, Tori and Alex? Her answer was a very positive; *'YES PLEASE',* as a result of which I immediately booked a cheap last-minute deal at Longleat Center Parcs, and paid just half price for a 3-bed villa within easy walking distance of the pool complex. Following the usual stressful battles that I'm regularly forced to orchestrate between suppliers and customers every Friday, basically in order to achieve acceptable completion dates for the following week, I finally left my office just in time to greet my two little darlings as they each stepped out of school, and within a couple of hours the six of us, bags all stashed neatly in the back, were heading off down the A36 towards Warminster in my old 7-seater Shogun.

Early Monday morning it was kids back to school, Helen, Michelle and Nick each back to their respective workplaces, and me with my nose back to the grindstone. *Another day, another dollar!* At six o'clock Helen and I waved as we passed each other, her heading back home, me heading down to the Mud Dock beside Prince Street Bridge to check that the Roehampton was safely back in port. I breathed a sigh of relief as soon as I spotted her back on her usual mooring, and after parking my car in The Grove car park

I walked across to her stern-mounted passerelle and asked Ray for permission to step aboard.

"Permission happily granted young man," shouted Ray cheerfully from inside the saloon, and I walked across onto the aft deck.

The strong winds, which had blown the tall pine trees of Longleat Forest around considerably whilst we'd been down there for the weekend, had begun to ease off come Monday morning, however, some ten hours later it was still dull, grey and drizzling, so I wiped my feet and stepped into the saloon. Jean was busy with a vacuum cleaner, and appeared to be still clearing up what I'd guessed may have been just a modicum of onboard devastation. I asked Ray the usual questions; when did they sail; when did they get back; what was the voyage like? Jean just frowned, shrugged her shoulders, and continued vacuuming. Raymondo asked me if I fancied a pint. Naturally I was never going to refuse, and together we wandered across to the Shaky. Halfway there Ray turned to me and said;

"How does that saying of yours go Chris? *A smooth sea never made a skilled sailor?*' That'd be about right d'ya reckon?"

"That's the one," I replied, picturing the poster on the wall of the Marovonne's saloon. "Why, had a bit of a rough ride home did we mate?"

Nigel served the pair of us with a pint of Bass each as we took an early-evening seat together in the Shaky's empty back bar. I told Raymondo I couldn't stop for too long, I had to get back to St George as Helen would be cooking dinner for eight o'clock. I'd got the impression that Jean was probably doing the same, so for both reasons Ray kept the summary of their voyage home relatively brief.

"We've nicknamed it *'Rock 'n' Roll Friday!'* he began with a wry smile. "She's a great old girl is that Roehampton, she'll power herself through pretty much anything that the ocean's prepared to throw at her, but boy oh boy, did it throw some at her! I reckon it must've been blowing a north-westerly force eight as we ran up past Padstow and on towards Hartland. Dangerous as God only knows what, especially if you ain't got the right kind of engines underneath you. Fortunately she's blessed with both power and reliability, so she took it all pretty well, albeit mostly beam-on. Mind you, I've got a horrible feeling that Shiela's probably still throwing up as we speak, and Jean wasn't best pleased about some of her favourite crockery getting smashed. We'd weighed anchor not too far off St Mary's Lifeboat Station shortly after nine o'clock Friday morning, and it was pretty good going up 'til round about ten miles off Zennor, but then it began to catch up with us. And by the time we passed Newquay it had overtaken us and then we *really* had to hang on to our hats. Well, all apart from Jamer that is, I reckon that cap of his must be welded to his head you know. Not that anyone went out on deck at any point, no way José, not a hope in hell! Anyway, it was still bloody horrible all the way up to Bull Point, but it settled a lot once the tide turned, and we had a pretty steady run back through the Holmes and up into the Avon. We took second lock back into Bristol at eleven o'clock Saturday morning, and we've been clearing the mess up ever since."

"Hmm," I began, finishing the last of my pint, "may have been better to have left a day earlier don't ya think mate? I mean, it's not like it wasn't forecast or anything."

"No real harm done laddie," replied Raymondo with a wink, "although maybe I'll just try to keep her down below the force sevens in future, especially in a beam sea, and *especially* when Jean's aboard with us."

"Or maybe just surf the big south-westerlies back home next time," I added. "Or better still, hug the coast during anything from a southerly to an easterly. But I'll tell you this right now my friend; a north-westerly eight off of Hartland Point ain't the place for me, not in a month of Sunday's, and hopefully not even in my wildest dreams either. Sure, a rough sea makes for a skilled sailor, but there's a very fine line indeed between *rough* and *dangerous* my friend, hence why I'm always so very careful with my forecasts."

"Hey ho," muttered Ray a little cynically, "let's hope we get a good'un when we sail back down for the eclipse then."

I wholeheartedly agreed with him, thanked him for the ale, then warmly shook his hand by way of a *'great-to-see-you-back-home-again-my-dear-friend'* kind of thing. The two of us then thanked

Nigel for his custom, walked back across the road to the Mud Dock together, hugged each other farewell, and I headed back off to Helen's for dinner. The following day was just a normal work-day for the two of us, where nothing out of the ordinary happened whatsoever, and essentially that's how the majority of the summer progressed. I only tended to frequent the Shakespeare every other Friday night, the Fridays that I didn't have Tori and Alex with me, because not having the Marovonne moored in the centre of town would've entailed spending far too much money on taxis, so I generally tended not to bother. I happened to receive a phone call from Malcolm down in Padstow about a fortnight later though, moaning like hell at me about some noisy, all night, drunken party that Nik had held aboard ship on the Saturday night. Apparently virtually every young local in town between the ages of seventeen and twenty-seven had turned up to it, both males and females alike, although oddly enough, many more females than males. Excessively loud music had carried on right up until daylight, which apparently was entirely unacceptable. *'What can I say Malcolm? Providing no one got hurt and no damage was done, fair play to the lad? Leave it with me sir, I'll have a word!'* I called Nik a little later in the day and asked him what the party was all about, and why hadn't he gone to work that particular evening.

"It was a lobster party Skip," Nik replied innocently. "Just your average, run of the mill lobster party."

"And why weren't you working at Stein's that particular night?" I continued to question him.

"I got the sack Skip," he replied bluntly.

"And what exactly did you get the sack for young Roger?" I continued patiently.

"Stealing lobsters Skip," he replied matter-of-factly. "But it wasn't how …"

"I don't wanna hear about it Nik," I shouted down the phone at him, *"now go and find yaself another job please, and make sure I don't get one more phone call from the Harbourmaster on your account!"*

"Yes Skip. I will Skip. But it was like …"

"I've gotta go buddy, I've got another incoming call," I said, cutting him off in the midst of his excuses. "Tell me about it when I see you next. In the meantime, *go find yaself another job!*"

I hung up and took the call that my secretary was trying to put through to me; just yet another run of the mill work problem. On a daily basis they just seemed never ending, but somehow, one way or another, they always got resolved. Fortunately for me, the school summer holidays came along next, and Helen and I took Tori and Alex away with us for a fortnight, and we all had a wonderful time exploring the beautiful little Mediterranean island of Menorca together. *(Reference my first book, The Phoenix)* All too soon that absolutely perfect little holiday came to an end, and once again it was back to the grindstone, however at least that meant that I was one step closer to August the 11th. I was really looking forward to the total eclipse, as indeed we all were, as no one in the UK had witnessed one since June the 29th 1927, way before my time, or indeed any of my friends' time too. *(With the exception of Tankman Jamer of course, but then again, Jamer seemed to be the exception to most rules!)* More so than that however, I was looking forward to not only having my true home safely moored back where it belonged, on Prince Street Wharf right outside the Arnolfini Art Gallery, but also very much so to the voyage back home too, which I had every intention of making as fun and as interesting as possible, weather permitting of course.

I took one more phone call from Malcolm the Harbourmaster during the few remaining weeks ahead, complaining once again about Nik's general behaviour around town. *'So pray tell Malcolm, what's he gone and done this time exactly?'* I asked him as politely as I could manage.

"Well, at least he went and got himself another job after getting the sack from Mister Stein's establishment, so he's been rolling dough out in the back kitchen at Granny's Pasties. So that was all well and good, until he got the sack from there too."

"Don't tell me," I said, beginning to lose patience a little, "he got the sack for stealing pastry?"

"Not exactly," Malcolm replied, the impatience also clearly noticeable in his own voice. "The nice young lady that owns the place, he's only gone and got her one and only daughter pregnant. And not only that, but the daughter's given up working there too now because of it, and they're both living aboard your ship together, and her mother's running around the place going hopping mad."

"And I'm supposed to do what about it exactly?" I asked with little in the way of surprise. "I'm not a fucking gynaecologist you know Malcolm! Or a sodding midwife come to think of it! Yes, I'm sure I could find it in me to feel sorry for her mum, but I doubt very much if she'll make a kidnap charge stick. How old is this daughter of hers, d'you happen to know?"

"Twenty-four, the same age as Nik apparently," he replied.

"Well I suggest you let them fight it out between themselves then, and not get yaself involved," I told him firmly. "I'll have a word when I come down there in a couple of weeks from now, but all I can promise you in the meantime, and her mother too for that matter, is that the young girl won't be sailing back to Bristol aboard the Marovonne with us. Other than that I'm afraid the matter will inevitably remain entirely out of my control. That said, thank you for letting me know, and I'll see you in a fortnight. Goodbye."

'Well, well, well,' I thought wickedly to myself, 'the naughty little Pilsbury Doughboy!'

Lunchtime on Friday the 23rd of July, just a few hours before I was due to pick Tori and Alex up for the weekend, I made a series of phone calls. The eclipse would be taking place on Wednesday the 11th of August, however I'd be dropping Tori and Alex back to Rachel's house on the Monday morning immediately prior to that, being as they'd still be on their school summer holidays, and lucky for them too, because I myself was struggling to take very much time off work at all during that particular summer. My recent local TV advertising campaign had appeared to be working far better than I'd expected it to, and the company was exceptionally busy because of it. Anyway, it was my intention to get the train down to Bodmin Parkway as early as possible on the Monday morning, then to sail the Marovonne back to Bristol just as soon as we had a half-decent weather window after the 11th, and I wanted to have as many of my usual crew come along with me, both for the eclipse *and* for the voyage back home. Which clearly meant that they'd have to take at least a week off work themselves too, so with fingers crossed I picked up the phone and dialled.

Kevin was absolutely fine with it, he'd already planned for it anyway and had pre-booked his holidays at Rolls Royce well in advance. Alan said he was definitely up for it, as he was in between jobs at the time anyway so it would be great to get away. And although Nik didn't even bother answering his phone, I already knew he'd be raring to go, I'd got the impression when I'd spoken to him a few days previously that Padstow was beginning to do his head in just a tad, especially after three whole months alone down there, and he couldn't wait to get himself back to some kind of normality. *Not that Nik's life ever came remotely close to resembling normality!* Rue said he daren't leave the Accordance that particular week because Poppy was due to give birth to yet another litter of pups, and if he wasn't around the chances were that Rommel the Rottweiler would most likely eat them all alive. Poor old Alf couldn't manage to take anymore time off work either, he'd been put on South Gloucestershire Hospital Engineering's emergency call-out duty for the whole of August, and sadly even Helen told me she wouldn't be able to make it either, she didn't have any holiday entitlement left to her for the rest of the year. But that was all good, the four of us together would be plenty enough, and to be perfectly honest, female-free sailing generally suited me far better anyway. I'd actually sailed the Marovonne single-handed on quite a few previous occasions, but on longer offshore passages it was simply basic common sense to have a good crew sail with you, especially one that knew what they were doing. So that was it then, all arranged, just the four of us together it would be, and comfortable with that knowledge I wrapped things up at work, picked the kids up from Rachel's, and Helen and I had a fun weekend together with them, taking them up to Clifton Zoo on the Saturday, the cinema Saturday evening, then down to my mum's in Taunton for Sunday lunch.

Wednesday the 4th of August I was a little late getting in to work. Not that it mattered particularly, it's just that I'd still felt rather envious by the time I'd got there. Both the Joseph and the Roehampton had sailed on the early morning tide that day, the Joseph bound for Padstow via Ilfracombe, the Roehampton bound non-stop for St Mary's, and I'd been determined to wave them both off and wish them calm seas, and safe and enjoyable voyages to their respective destinations. The weather was fine that particular morning; patchy cloud, good visibility, no chance of rain and very warm. The wind had been forecast as force three to four, however, unusually, it would be blowing from the south for the following two to three days, thus rendering a coast-hugging passage as far down as Land's End as good as a dead-flat-calm sea. The long range weather forecast, for what it was worth, was much the same, if not better, as the winds veered gradually back to south-westerlies and decreased a little. I left Helen's house at the same time as she did, with her heading into work and me heading down to the Cumberland Basin.

After I drove my old Shogun across Brunel's little old iron swing bridge and pulled it up alongside the Dockmaster's office Bob greeted me with a warm handshake, just as the powerful Plimsoll Swing Bridge clunked itself back closed, thus allowing the busy early morning traffic up above to continue on it's way, and the Joseph pulled gently alongside the muddy left-hand wall of the Cumberland Lock immediately ahead of the Roehampton. Coincidentally I'd arrived at the ideal time to catch the Roehampton's mooring lines just as Jamer and Arthur threw them across to the quayside, and as Ray powered his ship to a perfect halt I passed each of the ropes through the chain rings and individually handed them back across to them both. Bob had secured the Joseph in precisely the same manner, and handed her warps back across to Derek and Will, who were both stood out on deck yawning. I said good morning to everyone aboard the Roehampton; Raymondo, Jamer, Arthur, Dave and Jean; although Shiela had apparently politely declined Ray and Jean's invitation to join them aboard any further long sea voyages. *I couldn't for the life of me imagine why!* Next I wandered along to the Joseph and wished them all a safe passage too; Rick and Kim, Derek and Will, Shabby and Little Karen, plus of course the Master Mariner himself, Lloyd. I think Lloyd's marriage to Cathy had been declared null and void by then, on account of them never actually getting around to consecrating it. *Anyway, I digress!* We were back on neap tides once again, so as soon as Bob closed the top lock gates and opened the sluices, neither vessel had very far to drop. Some ten minutes later Bob opened the bottom gates, both ships slipped their mooring lines tidily back aboard, and after each had given a single short blast on their ship's horns I waved a final goodbye, hoping that Ray and his crew got to clearly see the eclipse down in the Scillies, and telling everyone aboard the Joseph that I'd catch up with them down in Padstow the following Monday, where we'd all most *definitely* get a good sighting two days later.

Helen and I spent another great weekend together, with Tori, Alex, Michelle and Nick all having fun between them on the Saturday and Sunday, and after kissing Helen goodbye as she left for work early on the morning of Monday the 9th, a kiss which involved a long farewell hug during which she quite clearly didn't want to let go of me, I dropped my two little'uns back to their mother's, then picked both Kevin and Alan up on my way to Jury's multi-storey car park, which was where my tatty old Shogun could safely stay for yet another week or so. The three of us then caught a cab to Temple Meads Station and bought tickets for the first available *high-speed* train that would stop for us at Bodmin Parkway. Kevin had his rucksack with him, Alan had packed a hold-all, *and all I had was my wallet!* Some ten minutes later we were settling into significantly more comfy seats than they'd been onboard the slow old rattler, and as we pulled out of the station at precisely 10.30am we settled back to enjoy the two-hour journey to Bodmin. Along the way, after first ensuring that both of my travelling companions had eaten breakfast that morning, which indeed they had, I began to set out our potential forthcoming itinerary. It wasn't complicated. After the spectacular once-in-a-lifetime solar event on Wednesday the most practical day to sail tide-wise would be the following Saturday. Once again we'd be running up towards spring tides, which meant we'd be getting a good old shove up the Bristol channel, but although that would allow us to make it back home in just the one hit, I thought it'd be quite nice to stop off at Lundy Island on the way back, spend an evening in the Marisco Tavern, then complete the voyage the following day, which would mean taking last lock back into Bristol during the hours of daylight, after which we should be back on our mooring outside the Arnolfini for around seven o'clock that evening. The tides were perfect for it, the seven-day weather forecast looked ideal, and all being well we'd arrive in perfect time for yet another Sunday evening in the back bar of the Shakespeare, albeit without Jamer et al. Both Kevin and Alan agreed that it sounded like a perfect plan, and so I elaborated still further.

"It wouldn't have been fair of me to favour one of you over the other on the voyage down Al," I began, choosing my words carefully. "Either *you* would've felt left out, or *Rue* would've felt left out, and so I'd mentioned nothing whatsoever about it. And furthermore, we already have a *Pirate Willy* and a *Pirate Barnabus* in Brian and Guy; they both sailed down to Lundy with us on that fateful day when we only just made it back home again by the skin of our teeth. *(Reference my second book, The Lundy Misadventure)* However, as there's just going to be the four of us sailing on this particular return voyage, it gives me great pleasure to announce that you are hereby promoted."

"Promoted to what exactly?" Alan asked, totally baffled.

"You mean promoted to *who* more like," I replied with a childish little grin.

"Okay, promoted to who then?" he asked quizzically, *still* baffled.

"Master Bates of course!" I announced with an air of authority.

"Hahaha," guffawed Kevin loudly. "So, for the journey back, we've got Captain Pugwash, Master Bates, Seaman Staines, *and* Roger The Cabin Boy; brilliant thinking Skip.

"Captain *Horatio* Pugwash if you don't mind Mister Staines," I replied proudly.

Alan still looked baffled. Hey ho, I felt sure he'd catch on at some point during the week ahead. The train pulled to a halt at Bodmin Parkway shortly after that, and fortunately for the three of us, as we were the only ones to disembark, there was just the one taxi waiting on the off chance. We *were* that off chance, and we hopped in and asked the driver to drop us outside the Custom House on Padstow harbourside. Twenty minutes and twenty quid later we stepped aboard the Marovonne to the overwhelming greetings of young Nik, who I could tell by the way he was holding a plastic flagon of Cripplecock Cider, clearly hadn't bothered trying to find himself yet another job. Oh well, it really didn't matter, he was alive, he was well, and he was happy, if a little drunk, and I gave him a big hug and told him just how proud of him I was, even though, realistically, I actually wasn't. Still, it was genuinely good to see my very closest-ever buddy once again, and as he gave Kevin a hug too, then shook Alan's hand, I immediately snatched the flagon out of his hand and downed the remainder of it myself in three long gulps. *Welcome back to Padstow, the 21 Gang reunited yet again, plus one!*

Christopher John Reason

IN SEARCH OF THE TOTAL SOLAR ECLIPSE: CAPTAIN HORATIO PUGWASH, MASTER BATES, SEAMAN STAINES AND ROGER THE CABIN BOY

CHAPTER
TWENTY~NINE

The harbour gates were firmly closed at one o'clock that particular Monday, the tide having risen as far as it was likely to some couple of hours previously at half way between high water neaps and high water springs. Whilst I left Kevin and Alan to settle themselves back in, and catch up with Nik's recent mischievousness, I took a wander across the harbour-gates walkway bridge towards the Joseph, which was moored against the North Quay in precisely the same position she'd been moored when Wylde Green had played aboard during May Day. That event seemed like an age ago by now, and despite the fact that a reasonably sized flotilla of yachts had also sailed across from Swansea to witness the eclipse, Padstow's inner harbour and it's surrounding streets, with their wide variety of pretty little cottages and shops, all appeared as serene as ever. The flotilla of Welsh yachts, both large and small, were all moored together on the South Quay, their rigging making little in the way of clattering noises in the light breeze that was still blowing from the south, whilst Padstow bathed once again in the warm summer sunshine emanating from yet another cloudless blue sky. As I cheerfully stepped up alongside the Joseph and peered down onto her aft deck, Rick, Kim, Shabby and Little Karen were sat chatting together in a group of matching folding chairs neatly arranged around the ship's mast, whilst Lloyd was laid more or less prone in a comfortable deckchair on the far port side of the deck, snoring lightly underneath a tatty straw boater that was neatly pulled over his face to shade it from the sun. So as not to wake Lloyd I quietly wished Rick and the girls a good afternoon, and then commented on how beautifully ideal the weather was looking for a perfect viewing of Wednesday morning's eclipse. I asked Rick how the trip down had gone, to which he replied; *'Entirely as planned, no dramas whatsoever in Ilfracombe on the way down this time, just plain sailing all the way.'* That was the news that I'd been waiting for, and which I was extremely pleased to hear about.

I then asked him as to the whereabouts of the rest of his crew, as in Derek and Will, and he told me they'd wandered into town to find something to eat along with Ron and Johnnie from the Courageous, which just happened to be moored alongside the Marovonne. She'd appeared totally and securely locked up when I'd first spotted her moored along our starboard side, so I was right to presume that Ron and Johnnie had gone ashore, and I reckoned I could take a reasonable guess as to where I might happen to find them too. I told Rick and the girls that I'd catch up with them later, wandered back around to the Marovonne and told Nik that I needed to have a serious conversation with him at some point in the very near future, but for the time being I was going to head on up to the London Inn for a pint of Walter Hicks' HSD and a fresh crab sandwich. Nik immediately shouted down below to Kev and Al, and as I ambled off along the quayside the three of them stepped ashore and joined me. *'Oh dear, what could possibly go wrong next?'* was actually furthest from my mind at the time. There'd be no misadventurous shenanigans during this particular visit to Padstow, I was there solely for two reasons only; one, to witness a total eclipse of the sun for the first and probably the only time ever. And two, to prepare the Marovonne for her sailing back home. Not that she needed much in the way of preparation, she was already fuelled and ready to go, but I always worked out my passage plan by way of dead-reckoning and wrote it all in the ship's log a day or two in advance as a matter of course anyway. I'd always felt it important to calculate everything the old-fashioned way, rather than rely entirely on modern electronics such as radar and GPS, which, as the RYA constantly have a habit of pointing out, could all potentially fail at any given moment. Either way, there's no substitute for a chart, a compass, a clock, a plotter, a pair of dividers and a pencil, especially when running a big spring tide back up the Bristol Channel *(I've deliberately left out a sextant, however I'm sure all will become clear at some point, ha-ha-bloody-ha!)* That said, I could see no reason why we shouldn't have ourselves a little fun whilst on our way back home, which was another thing that I needed to talk to Nik about, however, initially there was a far more pressing matter that needed clearing up, and the sooner I dealt with it the better.

No little wonder that Johnnie was in the London Inn, and I warmly embraced him the minute I stepped through the door. Derek and Will were in there too, both munching their way through what looked very much like freshly-caught sea bass and chips, and good old Ronnie, as generous as ever, put his hand in his pocket and ordered all four of us a pint of ale. Kev and Al took one look at Derek and Will's food and both ordered themselves exactly the same, whilst Nik told me that he'd already eaten, which was more than likely a blatant lie, but I ignored it anyway and ordered myself a crab sandwich. Whilst we were waiting for our food I took Nik to one side with the intention of giving him a stern little lecture.

"What's all this I hear about you getting Granny's young daughter up the duff then Roger?" I began sternly.

"It's all lies," Nik replied firmly, albeit with a pleading look in his eyes as he stared directly into mine.

"Okay, so who's lying exactly then Nik?" I asked him, a lot more authority now noticeable in my slightly raised voice. "Malcolm the Harbourmaster? Granny whatever-her-name-is? Her poor young daughter Hilary? Or you maybe? Spit it out please sunshine, I *need* to know!"

"Okay Skip, well it's like this," Nik began, his sudden sadness quite obvious. "Firstly, Hilary ain't poor, she's a successful, clever, conniving little scam-monger. Secondly, she ain't even Granny's real daughter, she just told people she was whenever she was working there. Thirdly, I forced her to go to the chemist and get one of those Clear Blue One-Steps, which she did, and she told me it had shown up positive. That's when I let her stay aboard ship, but when she realised that I didn't actually own the Marovonne myself, and I didn't even have two pennies to rub together once we'd both got the sack, which, to be fair, was actually just for snogging when we should've been rolling, then she told me herself that she'd been lying to everyone, including me and Granny, but now she didn't even have anywhere else to go. So lastly, that's when I blew her out. I don't need wind-up merchants like that in my life Skip, she's a proper nasty type is that one, a full-on Cornish bitch. Fortunately she ain't livin' in Padstow no more, I think she buggered off back to Camborne where she'd originally come from."

"So why was Granny hopping mad over it all then?" I continued questioning him. "And where exactly does Malcolm come in to the equation? He was pretty quick to ring me and tell me about it."

"Granny was just pissed off because we were the only two staff she had at the time, but she managed to find replacements for us really quickly," Nik continued, sounding more and more convincing by the minute. "And Malcolm wasn't involved, it's just that everyone knows everybody else's business all the time down here. Honestly Skip, I'm not kidding, this town is loads worse than Bristol Docks. You can't even take a shit without someone asking you if it was solid or runny."

"Okay buddy, I think maybe we'll let it rest at that shall we?" I said, choosing to believe him rather than delve into the whole issue any further, and potentially open an even larger bucket of worms. *Bloody lobster parties, honestly!* Go on, go order yaself a crab sandwich. Oh, and whilst I think of it, for what it's worth my young friend, thank you for boat-sitting for me."

"You're welcome Skipper," Nik replied with a grin as he stepped up to the bar. "For the most part it's been good fun, although I'm not sure I'd want to spend another summer down here, it's way too quiet for my liking."

Derek and Will wandered back to the Joseph after finishing their lunch, but I stopped on in the London for a while after my own, returned Ronnie's generosity, and bought a round for everyone else too. Shortly after that, determined to keep my senses about me for the remainder of the day, I left the five of them to it and took a stroll into town. Something caught my eye whilst passing the little newsagent's shop, and I stepped inside to take a closer look. It was an A5 booklet by Pam Hine entitled The Total Eclipse Of The Sun in Cornwall and South Devon, Wednesday 11th August 1999. After briefly glossing through it I bought a copy and took it back aboard ship with me, then spent the rest of the afternoon and early evening researching detailed information about the eclipse itself. Finally, later that evening, after Nik, Kevin and Alan staggered back aboard ship ever so slightly the worse for wear, I made do with fish and chips from the chippy and ate them whilst sat all by my lonesome down on the harbourside, staring periodically up at the clear, dark, moonless night sky as a billion trillion stars once again twinkled brightly high up above. Ironic though it may sound, as I sit here now writing this particular chapter during the COVID pandemic of 2020, I drifted into a comfortable slumber later on that night and peacefully dreamt about the *Corona*.

After a long, well-earned lie-in the following morning, I awoke to yet more bright sunshine, little white fluffy clouds, the usual squawking of the large resident flock of seagulls, and the delicious smell of the ocean. *'Hmm, the tide must be in,'* I immediately thought to myself, *'which means that the gates must be open. Which in turn means that I'll have to trek all the way around the harbour in order to use the shower block. Hey ho, best I get myself going then!'* I told Shabby I couldn't stop to chat as I hurried on past the Joseph, however, some thirty minutes later her offer of a hot cup of coffee was most welcomed, and I hopped over the Joseph's handrail and plonked myself down in a comfy chair in between Lloyd and Karen. Rick and Kim had apparently wandered off to the car park together, although no one seemed to know precisely why. Derek, Will, Ronnie and Alan had all taken a long coastal walk together, with the possible intention of stopping for lunch at the Rest A While Tea Gardens up near Lellizzick, and by my previous recommendations I can't say I blamed them in the slightest. And *apparently,* Nik, Kevin and Johnnie were all still fast asleep, away with the fairies. I wondered, only very briefly mind you, what time they'd managed to get to bed earlier on that same morning! Shabbs popped her head back up from down below, passed me over a mug of coffee, then climbed up onto the deck and sat herself comfortably back down in the one remaining folding canvas chair. I asked all three of them together if they knew much about the eclipse itself, and when all three of them said *'no, not really,'* I decided to enlighten them all with the knowledge that I'd just gleaned from Pam Hine's little booklet.

"Okay," I began, taking a deep breath, "well it kind of goes along these lines you see. As the Earth rotates around the Sun, and the Moon rotates around the Earth, the Moon blots out bits of the Sun all over the Earth far more regularly than you might think. For the most part these *blottings-out* are just partial eclipses, and even those are rarely seen this far north of the equator, but they're still probably far more common than most people realise. Total eclipses, however, although they still happen over a regular cycle, in comparison to the average human lifespan they're particularly rare, and as far north as the United Kingdom they're exceptionally rare indeed. The reason why they happen at all, albeit infrequently as far as us humanoids are concerned, is because of the way the elliptical orbits of these three celestial bodies tend to *wobble* slightly, and one of those perfectly regular wobbles is just about to peak once again. The last time a total solar eclipse was visible from somewhere in the UK was on June the 29th 1927, and the next time one becomes visible from England's green and pleasant land will be on September the 23rd 2090. I'm planning on watching that particular one from the top deck of my superyacht in Lymington Marina."

"Bloody hell Chris," interjected Lloyd suddenly, "you'll be a hundred and thirty-two years old by then my friend!"

"Hey, well added up Lloyd," I complimented him. "Pretty quick thinking for a mathematics supply teacher, you've got that one spot-on matey! Anyway, we've all gotta have our own set of life's little dreams and ambitions."

"Mine's just to see this one," stated Karen a little more realistically, "I'm really looking forward to it."

"And so you should my dear," I continued, "thankfully it's looking very much like the weather's going to be absolutely perfect for it. Anyways-up, the process itself will gradually begin it's cycle at precisely 09.37.20 BST, which is when the leading edge of the circumference of the moon will first start to cross in front of the sun. The entire process, from start to finish, when the trailing edge of the moon's circumference finally allows full visibility of the sun once again, will last for exactly three hours, sixteen minutes and thirty-one seconds, so you'll have plenty of time to take loads of photos, providing you use an extremely dark-tinted polarising filter fitted over the front of your lens. *(Critically important note—don't EVER look at the sun with the naked eye, not even for one single split second!)* The 100% total eclipse however, which obviously occurs exactly halfway through this three-hour timespan, will last for just sixty-six seconds up here in Padstow, the midway point occurring at precisely 11.10.35 BST. So basically, erring on the side of caution, you'll be able to see the sun's bright luminescent corona shining all around the perimeter of the moon like a perfect halo from ten past eleven until just after eleven minutes past eleven. Are you listening Lloyd? That means no nodding off in the sunshine just before lunchtime tomorrow."

"Oi dussn't need t' be lis'enin' Chrissy me boy," Lloyd said, smiling knowingly at me, "oi already read perzactly the same book as wot you done."

"Okay matey," I replied, smiling back at him, "then you'll know all about Baily's Beads then won't you me old mucker!"

"Baily's Balls?" asked Lloyd jokingly. "Woss them all about then matey? I always thought 'im there Baily never 'ad no balls!"

"Well, you know what thought did, don't you Lloyd! Anyway," I continued, "Baily's Beads are a little bit like solar flares that shine out brightly around the uneven surface of the moon's leading edge, kind of in between the moon's mountains if you like, and you'll see them quite clearly for about half a minute immediately before the corona itself appears for it's 66-second duration. You'll then see them again for another thirty-odd seconds as the moon gradually begins to slide away from fully blotting out the whole of the sun completely. And then that's it. A small sliver of the once-again-visible sun will gradually start to grow as the moon's orbit continues to take it on past the sun, then a little over an hour and a half later the sun will become whole once again. There'll be a partial solar eclipse, varying from 40% to 60% depending on where you are in the UK, on March the 29th 2025, and another one that could quite possibly exceed 90% just before sunset on August the 12th 2026, but you won't be able to see another *total* solar eclipse from anywhere in the UK for another ninety-one years, so let's hope that this one lives up to all the hype that we've been fed about it for the last year or so."

"Here, here," said Karen, "I'm really, really super-excited about it now."

Rick returned from the car park shortly after my little educational speech, and skipped back down onto the Joseph's deck to join us. He was looking a little rosy-cheeked at the time, wearing an expression that was quite difficult to read, although I would've summed it up as being a cross between bewilderment and relief. He was alone, and apparently Kim was no longer going to continue with their voyage across to St Mary's, but I courteously refrained from asking him the reasons behind that decision, and simply suggested that we go join whichever of our friends that would inevitably have arrived at one or another of the town's many pubs by then, hopefully for some kind of alcohol-free lunch. I rang Kevin, who told me that Nik, Johnnie and himself were all in the Custom House together, eating gammon, egg and chips, etcetera, and no, drinking bottles of red wine with their lunch definitely did *NOT* constitute *"alcoholic consumption"* in any way, shape or form *whatsoever!* Rick, Lloyd and myself wandered around the quayside and joined the three of them in the Custom House, leaving Karen and young Shabbatha back aboard the Joseph, whereupon Rick immediately stepped up to the bar and ordered himself a double shot of neat brandy. Oh yeah, and a large cappuccino, which Lloyd and I both followed suit with, although both without the brandy. It wasn't much longer afterwards that Rick, Lloyd and I ordered decent-sized hearty meals for ourselves, and it wasn't much longer after that when Shabby and Karen walked in and joined us with precisely the same purpose in mind. Some considerable time and several phone calls later it wasn't all that much longer before Derek, Will, Ronnie and Alan joined up with us too, and it has to be said I'm afraid, but it wasn't too much longer after we were all sat back together once again that a pack of playing cards came out too, and the remainder of the evening deteriorated rapidly into precisely what we'd all by now come to expect from holidaying in Padstow!

THE TOTAL SOLAR ECLIPSE – 11/08/1999 – PADSTOW, N. CORNWALL

Moderately hungover once again, I awoke the following morning a little after nine o'clock, just thirty minutes before the eclipse was due to commence. I quickly dressed, dashed up into the wheelhouse, excitedly flung all the doors wide open, only to learn that not only Padstow, but virtually the whole of Devon and Cornwall, was covered in a low-lying thick layer of dense cloud. Not only that, but as there wasn't a single breathe of wind, the thick cloud was completely unmoving. It was quite eerie, and actually genuinely unnerving. I jogged around the harbour to use the shower block, politely saying good morning to everyone along the way, and as I jogged back again some fifteen minutes later the cloud cover was as dense as ever. *'Maybe it'll clear come eleven o'clock'* I thought hopefully to myself. *Wishful bloody thinking!* Sadly, 1999's total eclipse of the sun, as viewed from North Cornwall, was about as exciting as a damp squib; we might just as well have been watching paint dry! It wasn't altogether too bad a day though, in fact some of it was really quite spooky. Firstly, despite the thick cloud cover, it didn't rain once all day long in Padstow, although apparently it pissed all over many other people's picnics across many other parts of England *and* Europe. But secondly, it was the behaviour of all the animals in the vicinity, both wild and domesticated, both near and far, that became somewhat alarming.

Almost from the very beginning, as the four of us sat together in our little folding canvas chairs, nursing mugs of coffee out on the Marovonne's foredeck at shortly after nine-thirty, the noises first began with the seagulls, as a huge flock of them took to the air and began screeching loudly as they circled the rooftops. Cormorants flew low back and forth up and down the estuary, as if having lost their sense of direction entirely, squawking ever-louder as they came and went. The air temperature began to drop noticeably, as if autumn had suddenly set in. And then the cows started. From both sides of the estuary they were clearly visible, standing in the fields with their heads pointed towards the clouds, mooing loudly until their throats became hoarse with the effort. And talking of horse, yes, they began too, not only neighing louder and louder, but clearly visible in the fields above Rock Village prancing and bucking as they cantered around in circles, becoming evermore energetic the darker it got. By ten-thirty the sky had darkened sufficiently for all the street lights throughout the town to have automatically switched themselves on, and around the back of several nearby buildings we could clearly here several small gaggles of geese honking loudly over and above the clucking and panicky fluttering of countless chickens. There was no movement of traffic whatsoever, as everyone had stopped to marvel, unfortunately not at the actual sight of the eclipse, but at the eerie sounds of the spectacular phenomenon that was occurring around them. Cockerels began crowing, and not just the once either, but the darker it became, the more continual their crowing became. Never in a million years would I have dreamt their were so many cockerels living in downtown Padstow! And still it became darker, and then, as if upon a dog-trainer's instant command, the barking and howling of countless pet mutts and hounds, both indoors and out, began to drown out the cawing and crowing from the huge flock of rooks that encircled the treetops on the outskirts of town. The whole cacophony of animal noises wasn't exactly deafening, however, listening to it in the darkness in the absence of any other sounds coming from around the harbour was a unique, unusual and entirely spooky experience. Then, all of a sudden, the noise stopped, the sky went pitch black, and I felt a sudden urge to pull a fleece over the top of my tee shirt. A couple of seconds after ten past eleven, it was just as if someone had turned off a light switch, and everything went both deathly silent and just a mite chillier. The dogs suddenly became completely silent *(thankfully!),* and apparently, although we couldn't see because of the pitch darkness, all the birds settled either down on the ground or back in their roosts. The cows lay down in the fields whilst the horses stood still, the chickens, geese and cockerels made not a single peek, and for precisely sixty-six seconds we sat together in the eeriest silence that I've ever witnessed. It was uncannily spooky, and with the exception of the street lights, we were surrounded by complete and utter darkness.

Moments later, the silence was shattered as Nik's poor attempt at singing echoed around the harbour, as he aimed his voice towards the Joseph moored across the other side;

"And if you're head explodes with dark forebodings too, I'll see you on the dark side of the moon!"

"The *lunatic's* the only thing in your head Nik!" I sarcastically whispered back at him.

Seconds after that, at precisely 11.11.08 BST, it gradually began to get light again, and the cacophony of animal noises started up once again. They began much quicker than they'd originally started, but they clearly weren't quite so loud or energetic this time, and as it gradually became lighter, as well as noticeably warmer once again, so each of the animals steadily became less and less terrified, their barks and squawks and neighs and hoots becoming quieter by the minute. Apparently, or so I've gleaned from a very similar effect that occurs when a tsunami is about to hit a coastline somewhere, this phenomenon happens in order of brain size. Consequently the dogs were the last animals to join in with the cacophony as it began, and the chickens were the very last to shut the hell up as things gradually got back to normality. At quarter past twelve the street lights switched themselves back off again, at half past twelve the now silent flock of seagulls settled themselves down in the centre of the still-dry but steadily-shrinking Town Bar, and at precisely 12.43.52 BST the moon's shadow finally parted with the face of the sun, car engines gradually began to fire up one at a time, and the town of Padstow returned to complete normality as if nothing had ever happened. *'Hmmm, talking of Bar!'* I thought to myself briefly, not too long after which all twelve of us were sat around one of the large pine tables at the far end of the Shipwright's, pints in front of us whilst waiting on our food orders, and excitedly discussing amongst ourselves the finer points of the event that we'd just witnessed.

It was such a shame that we hadn't got to witness the actual eclipse itself, although in reality, very few people in the UK had, there was cloud cover virtually everywhere. Apparently the clouds parted just briefly enough for the folks stood on Perranporth beach to witness it in all it's glory for around half of it's duration, whereas the whole population of Alderney, along with a great deal of Northern France, had a spectacularly perfect sighting of the whole event. Apparently several cross-channel ferries stopped mid-channel to allow both amateur and professional photographers to set up their tripods, and three Concordes were specifically chartered in order to get an even more stunning view from way up above the clouds, as they tracked the path of the eclipse and managed to make it last three times longer than it would've appeared to those who were stationary on the ground. I learnt shortly afterwards that the best viewing of all was to be had around Lake Balaton in Hungary, although I wasn't entirely sure we'd've been able to sail the Marovonne across there in time to witness it. Remarkably, the cloud cover cleared above Birmingham up in the midlands for most people to witness a partial eclipse, and even more remarkably, as I subsequently learnt much later on, the skies above the Scilly Isles were as clear as clear can be, so Raymondo and his crew aboard the Roehampton all had a perfect viewing for exactly forty seconds longer than we would've done. *Hey ho, better luck next time! I guess I'll just have to wait now until Lymington 2090!* Still, at least I'd managed to buy myself a souvenir tee shirt in the little gift shop next door to the Quayside Café on the waterfront immediately after I'd finished my lunch, just so as to have myself a permanent reminder of something that I never actually got to see!

1999 TOTAL ECLIPSE SOUVENIR TEE SHIRT

CHAPTER THIRTY

The following day Rick and his crew began to prepare the Joseph for their roughly eight-hour voyage across to the Scilly Isles, and at a cruising speed of eight knots, the Joseph would be using just sixty-four gallons of fuel there and back, so he had no need whatsoever to refuel. The Joseph's twin 500-gallon tanks, similarly to the Marovonne's, were both more than half full. Once they reached St Mary's however, due to the regular comings and goings of the flat-bottomed Scillonian passenger ship in and out of Hugh Town Harbour, ships such as ours, the Roehampton included, were generally requested to lay at anchor out in the shelter of the bay, which meant that one had to run ashore using the ship's tender if ever one needed anything, *such as a pub for example!* This also made buying provisions locally for onboard consumption a bit of a drag, because although Rick always carried a fairly decent inflatable dingy aboard, along with a small but reliable outboard motor, he didn't have access to a high-speed RIB such as the one I carried aboard the Marovonne, and to be perfectly honest the layout of his decks simply wouldn't have accommodated one anyway. What he did have was more than adequate for running back and forth to the shore with, however, although there's a Co-op food store right on the Town Beach seafront at Hugh Town, it made far more sense to take more provisions aboard whilst still moored against the quayside in Padstow, where access on and off the ship was a thousand times easier. Consequently Rick went off to the Spar shop, and the newsagents, and the off licence, and both Shabby and Karen accompanied him to lend a hand with the shopping, no doubt along with a few practical ideas of their own too.

In the meantime, whilst Nik and Kevin continued to sleep, seeing as the majority of our own provisions had already been consumed by then, Alan and myself chose to have breakfast once again in the Quayside Café. Whilst I sipped from my piping hot mug of tea and waited for my bacon and eggs to arrive, I picked up a copy of the previous day's Cornish Daily Independent. Thursday's edition was late being delivered, so there was no news just yet as to the non-spectacular lack of sightings of the long-awaited total eclipse, however, Wednesday's edition, still sat on the little table just inside the front door, had an *extremely* interesting headline splashed across the front of it, and I read it out loud to Alan.

GREAT WHITE SHARK IS SPOTTED OFF CORNWALL

Just when you thought it was safe to have a holiday here in the UK . . . the first sighting in British waters of a great white shark, the species in the film Jaws, was claimed yesterday.

Shark fisherman Phil Britts said he saw the fish, which he estimated was 16ft long and weighed 1,500lbs, a mile off the Cornish coast at the weekend. It surfaced beside his 28ft Padstow-registered boat, the Blue Fox, and was seen by all seven people on board, he said.

Although Mr Britts took no photographs, experts last night did not rule out his sighting of the most feared fish of the sea. Britain's leading authority on the great white, Ian Ferguson, chairman of the Shark Trust, said that from Mr Britts' description, it was possible.

In other matters around the county, the weather forecast so far is looking absolutely ideal for a perfect viewing of today's total eclipse of the sun, which is due to occur at a few minutes after eleven o'clock this morning . . .

'Hmmm,' I thought deviously to myself whilst tucking into my breakfast, *'I feel yet another cunning little Chrissy-plan coming on!'* Oddly enough, when Alan and I stepped back outside the café after finishing up and settling the bill, we stepped out once again into glorious sunshine. The virtually static clouds that had still been hanging around when we'd first arisen had all but disappeared, because whilst we'd been munching away in the café a warm and welcome fresh south-westerly breeze had picked up and blown most of them away, and apart from a few large white cumulus hovering low above the far hillsides, and some little wisps of stratus high up above, the sky was mostly clear and blue once again. *How very odd that the eclipse should cause that one day of chilly cloudiness during its occurrence amongst an otherwise typically warm and sunny August!* Still, once again it felt like the perfect day for yet another coast-path stroll, so I left Alan to sort Nik and Kevin out and headed off across the fields towards St Saviour's Point, with the intention of maybe taking a peaceful wander down to St George's Cove whilst I slowly let my breakfast go down. I couldn't get over how green and so beautifully lush the surrounding hills were as I trod the well worn path past the commemorative bench-seats, and without thinking properly I accidentally took the right fork and ended up down by the ferry slip at St Saviour's Point.

Oh well, in for a penny, in for a pound! It was a little after eleven o'clock in the morning, high water not due until shortly before three that afternoon, and the Black Tor was about to drop it's very few passengers off right in front of me as I skipped down over the last couple of rocky steps. I stood politely to one side as two middle aged couples said good morning to me after alighting from the ferry's lowered bow-ramp, then I stepped aboard myself and paid the skipper, who again, thankfully, I didn't recognise, for a return crossing. As I was his only new passenger we chatted incessantly during the ten-minute trip across to Rock, mostly about the spookiness of the previous day's eclipse, after which I hopped ashore and wandered across the street to the Rock Inn. Once inside I bought myself a large cappuccino, then took it upstairs with me and sat at a table outside on the balcony, in the sunshine, overlooking the estuary, all alone. What a marvellous little bit of peace and quiet I then had for a good hour, although at one point I still wished someone would get around to inventing something called a Kindle. *Hey ho, maybe one day!* My thoughts turned once again to my next cunning little *Chrissy-plan*, and how best to pull it off, even though

I had every confidence that I'd manage to achieve it just perfectly. *Great white shark eh? We'll see about that then, won't we lads. Capn Pugwash and his trusty young crew will soon have you chopped up into little pieces and packed neatly away in the freezer!*

Over my second cappuccino I roughly ran through the various timings of our two separate voyages back home in my newly uncluttered mind. I'd work them both out accurately after Rick had left for St Mary's the following morning, and after picking up a full marine weather forecast from the Harbourmaster's office too, and then I'd write everything down in the ship's log as a definite proposed passage plan. However, basically, it was roughly an eight hour sail from Padstow to Lundy, and we'd be leaving Padstow at around seven o'clock Saturday morning, after which, given a good shove up the Bristol Channel by the rapidly approaching high spring tides, it was another eight hours from Lundy to Avonmouth, so if we weighed our anchor off Lundy at ten o'clock Sunday morning and took last lock back into Bristol, we should comfortably be back on our mooring outside the Arnolfini by somewhere around seven-thirty Sunday evening. Having got all of that straight and clear in my head, with the exception of the finer details that I'd work out later, I hopped back aboard the Black Tor for the little jaunt back across the estuary, and this time, due to the fact that the tide was now rapidly on the rise, the skipper dropped myself and another young couple off on Padstow Harbour's northern outer wall, and as the harbour gates were open by then I walked all around the quayside's perimeter and stepped lazily back aboard the Marovonne.

Later that evening it was time to say farewell to Rick and the crew of the Joseph, as they'd be casting off shortly before the harbour gates closed two hours after the 03.55hrs high water the following morning, bound for the Scillies, and I wasn't entirely sure that either myself or any of my crew would be around to see them off at a quarter to six in the morning. On that basis we all agreed to go for one final meal together, and as Rick was effectively in the driving seat it became incumbent upon him to decide where to go. After some considerable deliberation, Rick finally suggested St Petroc's Bistro, which everyone else was perfectly in agreement with due to their highly varied menu. Despite the fact that there were twelve of us we found there was no need for us to book a table, as we'd eaten as early as they'd allowed us to, almost immediately after they'd opened, basically because the crew of the Joseph needed to get an early start the following morning, and as a result of that we were the only customers in there at the time. The choice of venue turned out to be ideal, as everyone really enjoyed their food, and the reasonable-quality wine wasn't overly expensive either, and by nine o'clock that evening, after a round of assorted floater coffees, we all found ourselves settling the bill for our own meals. With the exception of myself, who obviously had to pay for Nik's as well, on top of my own. Having all supped up and paid, we then trekked back off around Drang Lane together and stood on the South Quay by the inner slipway staring out across the tranquility of the calm but brightly lit harbour. As the somewhat despondent gaggle of Welsh yachts had left earlier that day in order to head back north towards Swansea, the inner harbour was now virtually clear of all other visiting craft, and on that basis Rick agreed that he'd have no trouble whatsoever backing the Joseph away from the North Quay and swinging her around to face the harbour exit without the need for any assistance. After we'd all wished Rick, Lloyd, Derek, Will, Shabby and Karen a safe voyage and a happy holiday in St Mary's, and asked them to pass on our best wishes to Ray and the crew of the Roehampton, we took it in turns to hug and shake hands with one another, then Ron, Johnnie, Kevin, Alan, Nik and myself all stepped into the Custom House for a final nightcap or two together. Personally I only stayed for one, although I'd got the impression that Johnnie and Nik may well have been staying on just a little later than myself.

Somehow I vaguely remembered listening to the Joseph's engine start up in the early hours of the morning, despite the fact that it never actually woke me fully up, and when I finally surfaced and wandered up into the Marovonne's wheelhouse at around a quarter to nine there was no longer any sign of her, and the harbour gates by then were once again firmly shut, the outgoing tide heading rapidly towards low water. As I grabbed my wash-bag and stepped ashore I heard Ronnie fire up the little Lister diesel engine aboard the Courageous 2, and I waved cheerfully at him as he stood at the controls in his own wheelhouse, then I turned and marched promptly off towards the shower block. When I returned some fifteen minutes later, I was surprised to notice the Courageous no longer moored alongside the Marovonne, but instead Ronnie had moved her across to the South Quay and moored her alongside the harbour wall that the Welsh yachts had previously been moored against. This made a huge amount of sense, as firstly he and Johnnie no longer needed to clamber across the Marovonne's decks in order to get ashore, and secondly he knew that we'd be leaving relatively early the following morning, so he'd have to be moving the Courageous in order to let us out anyway. What I hadn't reckoned on was Ron moving his little ship across the harbour all by himself, as there was clearly no sign whatsoever of young Johnnie just yet. Still, Ron was both an extremely skilled and experienced sailor in his own right, and was perfectly capable of manoeuvring and mooring the Courageous single handed.

By this time we needed more provisions aboard our own ship too, as we'd virtually run out entirely. We wouldn't be needing a huge amount, but certainly enough for two breakfasts and two main meals for the four of us, and plenty to drink too, although nothing whatsoever of the alcoholic variety. Alan was next up, and he headed off to the shower block with his kit, followed not long after by Kevin, who did precisely the same thing, passing Alan on the centre of the walkway over the gates on his way there just as Alan was on his way back. There was little point in waiting around for Nik and his inevitable hangover, so I scribbled a comprehensive shopping list in the notepad, tore the page out and shoved it in my pocket. Once again, after Kevin had returned from the showers, the three of us marched around to the Quayside Café for breakfast together, coincidentally arriving at more or less exactly the same time as Ronnie. We grabbed a table for four just inside the front window, and laid bets between ourselves as to precisely what times Johnnie and Nik would finally surface, whilst we scoffed our way once again through the little caff's first-class early-morning cuisine.

By eleven-thirty there was only me still left in the running over the odds, so I handed Kev and Al the shopping list, along with a twenty pound note, and told them I'd see them back aboard ship around lunchtime. I left Ronnie to finish reading the previous day's copy of the Independent, the front page of which had sadly summarised the eclipse in just one brief paragraph, and headed off for yet another argument with Malcolm over in the Harbourmaster's office. Not that I had a hope in hell of winning this particular argument, it was all going to be about money, but whatever was due on my mooring fees to cover the previous fifteen and a bit weeks was definitely worth at least a half-hearted attempt at bartering over.

Sadly, my half-hearted efforts at bartering over my mooring fees proved entirely fruitless, however at least it put a smile on both mine and Malcolm's faces. The true figure, at 50p plus VAT per meter per day, for my 20 meters for it's 109 days duration, came to £1,253.50, roughly four times the cost of a quayside mooring in Bristol City Docks at the time! But hey, at least the electricity had been free for the duration *(Shhhh!)*, and the May Day Regatta itself had been well worth the time, effort and money, so I had no complaints whatsoever, and I handed Malcolm my credit card. Which, to my horror, was declined, so I subsequently handed him a debit card, which I knew would take my current account well into the red, but after shaking his hand, apologising for all manner of inconveniences, and thanking him, along with Padstow Harbour Commissionaires generally, for their kind, generous and tolerant hospitality, I left quietly with my tail at least only halfway between my legs, shutting his office door as gently as possible behind me, and breathing a sigh of relief once I was back outside. At least he hadn't shouted at me again this time. When I stepped back aboard the Marovonne I was pleased to see that Nik was up, although once again his eyes looked like piss holes in the snow. I told him, in no uncertain terms, to go jump in the showers, and don't be too long about it either, I had an important mission to send him on just as soon as he returned. In the meantime I stepped up to the chart table and studied the Met-fax that Malcolm had just handed me, then set about concentrating on the local tide times and heights in conjunction with the tidal diamonds printed on my charts, and began plotting a course for the journey home and noting it all down in the log, despite the fact that I'd already made the same voyage countless times previously.

Kevin and Alan returned with the shopping just as I was starting on the mathematics of the second leg of our voyage, and just as they began stashing stuff away up in the galley Nik returned from the shower block.

"What's this mission you've got in mind for me exactly then Skip?" he asked, looking remarkably better than he had when he'd first surfaced from his pit, finally now wide awake too.

"Right then young Roger," I began positively, "d'you know what chum is by any chance?"

"What, as in Pedigree Chum doggy food?" he asked, a puzzled expression coming over his face.

"No, ya daft sod," I replied with a laugh, "chummy-chum-chum. Shark bait. *Blood and guts!*"

"Oh," replied Nik, the relevance of where I was coming from suddenly clicking in with him, "that kind of chum. Er, like, yes Skip, I do, but I wouldn't know where to start searching for it."

"Duh, like, maybe try the local butcher's?" I replied sarcastically.

"Oh yeah," said Nik, as if a light bulb had just clicked on, "I didn't think of that Skip."

"Clearly not!" I said. "However, I did, and not only that, but if you get going right now you should arrive in perfect time before he starts chucking stuff out in his waste bins. You shouldn't have to pay too much for it mind, all we want are his throw-away scraps, but get as much in the way of blood and guts as you can, and make sure it's all properly wrapped and sealed so that you don't spill any of it along the street on the way back, or across the decks either. The butcher's is just up the way, next door to Supasnaps, and his nickname's Del Boy. All you've gotta do is ask him for a large amount of chummy, then hand him this tenner for his trouble."

I sent Nik off on his way, then continued with plotting my chart-work and programming a couple of new waypoints into the ship's GPS. A few moments later both Alan and Kevin stepped up into the wheelhouse and asked me to show them what I was up to.

"Okay Master Bates," I began, addressing Alan for the first time by his official rank, "we'll be casting off and setting sail for the mouth of the Camel estuary at 7am sharp tomorrow morning. High water is at 05.18hrs, so we'll be leaving on an outgoing tide just eighteen minutes before they close the gates. That'll give us a half-decent flush down the river to start with, although once we run out past Newland Island and hang a right we're gonna be punching an outgoing tide for the next four hours, until we hit slack water shortly after eleven-thirty that is. So what I'd like you to do for me please Master Bates, providing it's okay with you of course, is to sit at the wheel and hold us steady on a compass course of 028 degrees. It'll be eight hours altogether before we reach Lundy, four hours of outgoing tide followed by four hours of incoming tide, so a constant 028 degrees will take us on a slightly S-shaped route and then sweep us directly into the deep backwater eddy in the south-eastern lee of Lundy's Landing Bay at precisely 15.00hrs tomorrow afternoon. The barometer is currently reading 1012, which is actually *very* high, and the forecast is for south-westerly force two's to three's, calm to slight seas, visibility good. So that's our passage plan, but I've got a horrible feeling it's gonna be considerably later than three o'clock by the time we reach Lundy, because the first hour or so is going to be exceptionally slow going."

"Why exactly will that be then Skipper?" asked Kev, even though I presumed he already knew the answer.

"Because, Seaman Staines," I replied, staring directly at Alan instead of Kevin as I did so, "*WE'RE GOING SHARK FISHING!* Once we're clear of The Rumps, I'd like our speed slowed down to just four knots through the water please Master Bates, and then we'll make ready my specially-prepared shark-fishing rig, and then, between Seaman Stains, Roger The Cabin Boy and myself, we're gonna catch that damned great white if it's the very last thing we do!"

"I sincerely hope it's not the very last thing you guys do," said Alan looking a little shocked. "I'm more than happy to steer a compass course all the way to Lundy, for eight or even ten hours, or whatever, but if you guys ain't around I wouldn't have a bloody clue what to do when I got there."

"Ah yes, well that'd be another story altogether Al," I answered him reassuringly. "Anyway, once I've set the anchor in Landing Bay I shall need someone to stay aboard on anchor watch. Not only that, but we can't leave the RIB up on Landing Bay Beach, firstly because it's too steep, and secondly because we're approaching high spring tides. So again, if it's okay with you Master Bates, would you mind running us ashore in the RIB, dropping us off, then stopping back aboard on watch for a few hours whilst the three of us climb up that horrible, nasty, steep, rugged old track once again, then picking us back up from the beach after we've staggered back down again after a bit? I have a bottle of rum stashed aboard that you're more than welcome to partake of whilst we're gone, or there's half a dozen cans of Thatchers Gold locked away in my cabin if you'd prefer."

"I'll see how I feel about the booze side of things when we get there," replied Alan sensibly, "that's not overly important in the scheme of things. However, I'm more than happy to run the three of you ashore then sit aboard on watch, and pick you up from the beach when you get back down. We've all got phones on us, so that's no problem at all, providing you don't all get gobbled up by man-eating sharks along the way of course."

"Master Bates, you're an absolute superstar," I said, praising him whilst patting him on the back at the same time. "So, all shark fishing aside, it's Lundy-bound we'll be come first thing tomorrow morning, sailing back to one of my favourite little islands of all, anywhere on this gorgeous blue planet of ours."

Not long after that Nik returned, and stepped back aboard carrying four heavy double-bagged black bin liners, each of them tightly knotted at their tops. I grabbed an old sheet of canvas and laid it out on the aft deck-riser, just in front of the ship's bare flag-pole, and told Nik to set them down carefully and leave them outside overnight.

"What's got in them there black sacks then lad?" asked Ronnie from up on the quayside, clearly on his way back from the shower block.

"Two pairs of sheep's lungs, one pig's stomach, half a dozen chicken's gizzards and a load of assorted offal," replied Nik in a completely matter-of-fact tone of voice.

"Blimey guys," stated poor Ronnie in utter disbelief, "what the hell are you gonna do with that bloody lot then?"

"Bloody's exactly the right word there Ronnie my man!" I replied with a laugh. "Why don't we go discuss it over a couple of farewell ales a little later on tonight?"

"You're on," said Ron enthusiastically. "Me and Johnnie'll meet you all over in the Custom House around seven o'clock this evening."

The four of us cleaned ourselves up and changed shortly after that, then went and sat on the quayside together and ate Padstow's finest battered fish and chips out of plain paper for one final time. Not long after that, over yet another ale or two, I explained to Ron and Johnnie exactly how we were going to catch that great white shortly after leaving the Camel estuary the following morning. Although, more importantly, and probably far more realistically too, I explained precisely what our passage plan was, and just how much I was looking forward to being back up in the Marisco Tavern atop the dizzy heights of the beautiful little island of Lundy once again.

HEADING BACK OFF TOWARDS LUNDY ISLAND

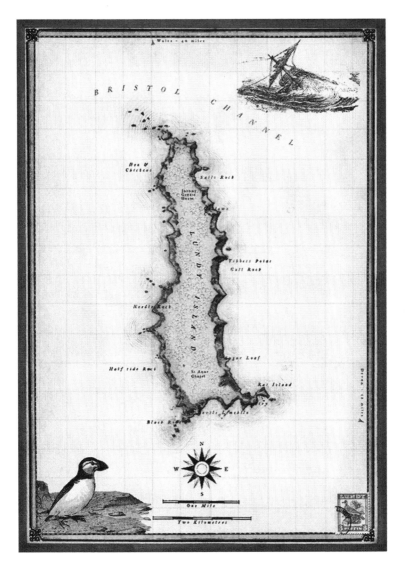

CHAPTER

THIRTY~ONE

Saturday, 14/08/99, 07.15hrs BST, location Brea Hill Spit Buoy, Camel estuary on VHF Channel 12.

"Padstow Harbour, Padstow Harbour, this is Marovonne, over."

"Marovonne, Padstow Harbour, go ahead, over."

"Good morning Malcolm. I'd just like to thank you and your team once again for your excellent hospitality, and to inform you that we'll most likely be visiting again for next year's May Day, over."

"I can't say it's altogether been a pleasure Chris. If you and your associates should happen to visit us again next year, please would you kindly ensure that you have no more would-be pirates and no more amplified music aboard either of your vessels. That said, have a safe voyage home Chris. Padstow Harbour out."

"Roger and understood Padstow. Marovonne out."

I'd awoken to my alarm at 6am, and after using the shower block for the very last time I'd begun my usual routine of engine room checks. I made sure that Nik, Kev and Al had all got up at the same time as me, and whilst they filled the ship's water tank to the brim, then disconnected and stowed our shore-power lead, I'd filled the day tank, topped up the service tank, greased the stern gland, checked all the oil levels and fuel filters, then fired up my wonderful old Gardner 8L3 and left it running for fifteen minutes to warm up. Everything was 100% on the button, and I could just tell that the old girl wanted to get going. It's funny how ships seem to develop a character all of their own, especially old wooden ships with a huge amount of history behind them, and as I'd got to know her over the years, somehow, strangely, I just seemed to be able to sense what kind of mood she was in. That particular morning I'd sensed that she was in an exceptionally good mood, which, coincidentally, put me in an exceptionally good mood too. The last thing I did before asking Nik and Kev to cast off our mooring lines was to run the Red Ensign up the stern flagpole, and after Kevin gave the ship's bow a good old shove away from the quayside with the long wooden boat hook, I spun the wheel hard around to starboard, clunked the gearbox into forward drive, and quietly slipped out through the open harbour gates whilst Johnnie was still fast asleep aboard the Courageous. Ron, however, had woken in time to wave us off, and as he stood atop the harbour wall by the exit I waved back at him, then gave one long blast on the ship's horn, just as we began to creep across the reach of the outer harbour, as if to say *farewell Padstow*. Shortly after passing the Greenaway Buoy I was on the VHF yet again, this time calling on Channel 16.

"Swansea Coastguard, Swansea Coastguard, this is Marovonne, Marovonne, over."

"Marovonne, Swansea Coastguard, go to channel 67 please."

"Roger Swansea, channel 67."

"Swansea Coastguard, this is Marovonne. For information purposes only we are a 65ft single-engined MFV currently leaving Padstow bound for Lundy. In total we are four male adults aboard, our ETA at Lundy estimated at sometime before sundown, over."

"Marovonne, this is Swansea. Thank you for your information sir, all received and understood. Keep a listening watch on Channel 16 please. Swansea Coastguard out."

"Roger Swansea, Marovonne out."

I pushed the throttle forward and took our speed over ground up to six knots, knowing full well that once we'd passed Newland Island, then turned towards the north-east, the outgoing tide would reduce our speed over ground and we'd settle at around four knots through the water. *Perfect! Just what I wanted!* As we passed The

Rumps some two miles offshore I brought our compass heading around to 028 degrees, and then began barking orders at everyone.

"Right folks, this is your captain speaking. Captain *Horatio* Pugwash I'll have you know. Master Bates, take the wheel would you please, and keep that little white needle pointing precisely at 028 for the foreseeable future. Seaman Staines, Roger The Cabin Boy, what the hell are you waiting for, *LET'S GET ON IT!*"

Down in the ship's storeroom I had a large, unused, one-hundred-metre coil of two-millimetre-thick stainless steel cable. It was something that we often used at work for winding up security grilles that we occasionally installed in shopfront windows, and somehow it had found it's way out of one of the company's vans and onboard my ship, probably because it was the safest place to leave such an expensive piece of kit at the time. I also happened to have some small U-bolt clamps for forming loops in the cable, and a couple of years previously I'd managed to get hold of a six-inch stainless steel butcher's hook, with an eye at the top end and a blunt point at the business end. I'd filed the point down until it was needle-sharp, then lashed it to a six-foot pole with some baling twine in order to use it as a fishing gaff. Not that I'd ever got around to using it mind you, I'd never hooked anything big enough off the side of the Marovonne up until now. So I cut the butcher's hook away from it's handle with a Stanley knife, looped the end of the cable through it's eye, then secured the loop with not one but three of the U-bolt clamps. I tightened all six nuts right up tight using a miniature socket set whilst they were clamped in the vice down on the engine room's workbench. So now we were ready to go *serious* fishing.

In the meantime, Seaman Staines and Roger The Cabin Boy were sat out on the aft deck, leaning over the handrails, and having initially slashed a small tear in the bottom of one of the black bin liners, Roger was holding it over the side of the ship slowly dripping a trail of animal blood in our wake. I told Mister Staines to unknot the top of one of the other bags and lob a few entrails over the side, which he quite obviously took great pleasure in doing. I then suggested that young Roger should make the hole in the bottom of his bag just a smidgen larger, and allow a few of the chicken's gizzards to plop over the side along with the increased flow of blood. Again, he appeared to be taking great pleasure in performing this particular little task, and I smiled to myself, comfortable in the knowledge that we had no female passengers aboard at the time. Not that Shabby, my affectionate little Irish bilge-wench, would've had any issues with it I'm sure. Anyway, for the next mile or so we just continued chumming, lobbing small pieces of animal intestines here, there and everywhere, all of which landed with a satisfying splash amongst the trail of bright red froth that followed in the ship's relatively calm wake.

"Okay seamen, let's get some bait on this line and see what Mother Nature's willing to attack us with shall we?" I asked, generating an exceptionally positive response from both of my eager crew mates.

I opened another of the double-bagged sacks, and whilst it was laid firmly down on the sheet of canvas that partially covered the stern deck-riser I carefully pulled out a whole pair of blood-soaked, dripping-wet sheep's lungs. I left them lying on the canvas, then opened the forth sack and partially revealed the raw pig's stomach. Using the serrated knife on my Leatherman I cut the whitish stomach meat into quarters, then pierced the centre of one quarter with the butcher's hook. Next I attached both sheep's lungs, passing the sharp hook twice through the trachea whilst allowing the blood-filled lungs themselves to hang well below the hook itself. Finally I hooked another quarter of the tough old pig's stomach, creating the most delicious-looking offal sandwich that you've ever seen in your entire life.

"Jeezus, that looks sodding *offal!*" laughed young Roger, as I stood up on the deck-riser and carefully lowered the baited hook over the back of the ship.

I slowly began paying out the stainless steel cable from it's twelve-inch wooden drum, but it immediately became apparent that there was a little too much drag on it, and I shouted forward to Master Bates to slow the ship's speed to fractionally under three knots, which he obligingly did with excellent effect. I then steadily continued to pay the remaining ninety metres or so of cable off it's reel, whilst Mr Staines and Roger T.Cabin Boy between them cut the other pair of blood-sodden sheep's lungs into small slivers, and along with more sliced up pieces of pig's stomach and the remainder of the chicken's gizzards, gradually scattered them far and wide throughout the ever-expanding collection of blood and guts that we'd left trailing behind in our gentle wake. Taking great care to ensure that I didn't accidentally lose the very end of the cable, I asked Seaman Staines to stand on it whilst there was still six or seven metres left on the drum, then I unrolled the remainder, threw the empty drum into the saloon, and tied the free end securely around the ship's stern capstan. I then pressed the large red 'START' button on the side of the capstan and wound ten turns of cable onto it, equating to roughly ten metres of cable, and then hit 'STOP'. The three of us pulled as hard as you like on the cable and it didn't slip in the slightest, it was as solid and secure as could be, attached to what was probably the strongest part of the ship. So, we had half a pig's stomach and a pair of sheep's lungs hanging from an extremely sharp butcher's hook at the end of some ninety metres of steel cable, jiggling along at just three knots probably some twenty-odd feet below the surface, and as we continued to launch the remainder of the bits of offal over the side, all we could do now was sit there together and wait.

Just in case we happened to get lucky I decided it best we have a camera close to hand, and I dived down below into my cabin and came back up with my little digital Olympus, which I left safely at the base of the aft crane mast, which ran from the coachroof right the way through the lower deck and all the way down to the keel. And then we sat, and we chatted, and between ourselves we weighed up the odds of hooking something. Still, it was warm, it was sunny, and there was a very light breeze blowing in exactly the same direction that we were travelling in, so it was hardly even noticeable. The sea state was just slight, there were little fluffy white clouds far off on the horizon, and everything was just fine and dandy aboard the good ship Marovonne. So we waited, and we waited, and then we waited some more. And after about an hour, we waited a little more, and then we still continued to wait. And then, *all of a sudden,* we felt a massive jolt that shuddered through the entire ship. It was enough to throw the three of us off balance, and whatever it was appeared to have slowed the ship from three knots to less than one. It felt just as if our sturdy keel had run right across the top of a sandbank, and for a second or two my heart stopped whilst I re-ran my studiously calculated chart-work through my mind. Instantly though I thought to myself; *'What the hell, it's deep water out here, all the bloody way to Lundy Island,'* and as I came to my senses a split second later I reached across the deck with my off-balance left leg and kicked the *'START'* button on the side of the capstan with my foot. The high-powered motor inside the capstan, instead of rotating it almost silently as it normally would've done, despite it's low gear ratio it simply began to groan, and I wondered for one brief moment if the butcher's hook had got snagged in the upper rigging of some kind of shipwreck, so I reached across with my hand and hit the *'STOP'* button. Remarkably, although the capstan ceased to rotate, the whole ship gradually began to move backwards. *'Shit the bed!'* I immediately thought to myself, whilst beginning to worry, and not just a tiny bit either. *'Something's gotten a good old hold of us, and somehow it's managing to drag all seventy tons of us backwards! BACKWARDS? WTF? SEVENTY TONS? REALLY?'* And then, as suddenly as it had begun, the cable went slack, we began moving forwards once again, and within seconds we were back up to our previous three knots. I hit the *'START'* button on the capstan once again, and this time it slowly started reeling in the cable at it's normal, quiet, low-ratio speed. *Then suddenly there was another mighty snatch, this time even more forceful than the last, and the ship stopped dead in the water, with her huge bronze prop still trying desperately to drive her forward!* I let the capstan continue to run this time, despite the fact that it's motor was clearly struggling under the strain, but after a minute or two it eased up again, just a smidgen, and once again the ship began to move forwards, albeit at just one knot.

"What the fuck's going on back there?" hollered Master Bates from up in the wheelhouse.

"Nothing to worry yaself about buddy," I replied nonchalantly, whilst lying through my teeth, "we've got the entire situation completely under control."

"Ever thought about panicking Skipper?" asked Seaman Stains with just the slightest hint of a shake to his voice.

"Don't be bloody ridiculous man," I scolded him. "Now come on, let's reel the bugger in."

"Increase our engine speed to 400RPM please Master Bates," I shouted through into the wheelhouse. "This bitch ain't never gonna stop seventy tons moving at four knots ya know, *it'll take a nuclear sodding submarine to do that!*"

The only trouble was, the more we increased the ship's speed, the more the capstan's motor began to strain, and eventually I shouted further orders to Master Bates to pull her back onto tickover and let her cruise along at just one knot. For the next ten minutes or so we were pulled and snatched from pillar to post, to the point where we almost lost our balance with each and every aggressive movement, although in between each tug we determinedly continued to chug slowly forwards, Master Bates managing to keep us steady on 028 degrees magnetic at just one knot. Clearly we were towing something along behind us that was not only enormously heavy, but by the feel of it's constant thrashing about, also exceptionally angry. Moments later there was another huge tug against the capstan's slow and struggling motor, immediately after which the ship briefly lurched backwards again, her stern being violently tugged downwards with tremendous force. Then suddenly, and most unexpectedly, some fifty metres off our starboard quarter, this gigantic creature launched itself skywards, showing us it's huge white underbelly and baring it's huge rows of nasty, sharp, pointed white teeth, in what appeared to be some kind of wicked, evil snarl.

"Shit Skipper, that's gotta be a twenty-footer at least!" commented a considerably shocked Seaman Staines, as he stared in awe at the almost fully airborne great white.

"Twenty-five!" I replied, having memorised my lines to perfection.

"We're gonna need a bigger boat Skip," said a rather stunned Roger, adding to the atmosphere.

"Yeah, and we've still got sixty-odd metres of cable to go!" I said, reminding them of the reality of our continuing predicament.

Gradually though, over the next twenty minutes that followed, the tugging and thrashing slowly began to ease up as the huge shark began to tire, and bit by bit, in between each thrash, the capstan's motor slowly settled itself back to it's normal pace, and the little puffs of blue smoke that had begun popping out from underneath it's solid base every now and again slowly began to cease. After fifteen minutes the capstan was running normally again, slowly retrieving cable just one metre at a time, and I decided it best to instruct Master Bates to increase the ship's speed back up to her initial three knots once again. After another five or six minutes the poor creature had become almost entirely limp, and as the capstan slowly continued to turn, we appeared to be dragging the massive fish along behind us almost flat on the surface of the water, as it laid fully over on it's side and relaxed it's enormous fins. It appeared to be completely exhausted, and frankly, wouldn't anything be after a forty-five minute battle with one-hundred-and-fifty-two horse power of 70-ton ship. However, *the fish ain't caught 'til the fish is caught*, as I've always said, and I kept the capstan running until the cable pulled the gigantic shark not only right up alongside the hull of the ship's starboard quarter, but began dragging the front half of it up over the stern gunwale. Once again the capstan's motor slowed and strained, but it kept on running, and very slowly, foot by foot, it hoisted the whole front end of the great white right up onto the aft deck-riser and over the empty bait bags that still lay there, leaking what remained of their contents over the canvas sheet. The monster looked as docile as ever now that we'd appeared to have tamed it, but despite the fact that it was no longer thrashing about it stared at the three of us with an evil, nerve-racking look in it's piercing black eyes, it's mouth remaining half open whilst it bared it's razor-sharp teeth, the longest of which must have measured at least four inches from it's fleshy top gum to it's nasty serrated point. I could see right inside it's mouth, and noted precisely where it had been hooked, the bright, shiny, barbless butcher's hook sticking right through the side of it's upper cheek. Not that I was going to put my hand inside it's mouth and attempt to remove it, no siree, not on your sodding nellie. What I did want though was a spectacular photograph of our prize-winning world-record catch, and I briefly hit the '*START*' button on the capstan one last time and dragged the giant fish just a little further aboard ship, just so that Seaman Staines could get the sharks three-foot-high dorsal fin into the picture too. As I did so the great white shuddered and then appeared to growl at me, and I took a step back in shock as one of it's evil, piercing black eyes stared directly back into mine once again. And then it went limp again, but still with it's mouth half open, baring it's teeth, and still with it's horrible black eyes wide open. '*The perfect shot*' I immediately thought, and shouted at Seaman Staines to grab the camera off the side. *Boy, was this going to be one for the record books!*

I stood to one side of the shark's head, my right arm resting casually on top of the ship's starboard handrail, my left arm thrown across the back of it's head. Roger The Cabin Boy stood the other side of it, one knee resting on the aft deck-riser, his left hand holding the old Bowie knife that he'd used to help cut some of the bait up with, and his right arm thrown over the shark's head, with both of our hands almost meeting in the middle, but not quite.

"*Snap it quick, it's a perfect pose,*" I shouted at Seaman Staines, as he stood directly in front of us and prepared the camera.

Then suddenly, the very second the camera went click, something remarkably scary happened. I couldn't figure it out at first. Maybe the shark had recuperated sufficiently after resting for a short period, or maybe it was simply because I'd shouted '*SNAP IT*' just a little too loud, but all of a sudden Roger and myself were both forced to jump to one side as the great white monster thrashed from side to side once again. Thinking that it may possibly have been in it's final throes of death, Seaman Staines failed to take a step backwards like Roger and myself had been forced to do, and having somehow managed to dislodge the barbless butcher's hook from the inside of it's cheek during the course of it's sudden energetic thrashing, the shark then made a terrifying lunge forward, it's razor-sharp teeth snapping down hard and just missing Seaman Staines' right hand by a mere half an inch, but in the process, somehow managing to snatch the little camera neatly from his grasp. As the three of us stood well back from the now clearly enlivened beast, it bucked it's head high above the deck, undoubtedly swallowing the camera, then with three more vicious thrashes from side to side it noisily slid backwards off the side deck of the ship, crashed clumsily back into the water, thrashed it's tail from side to side a few times and disappeared back off down into the depths of the deep blue ocean, sadly with my little camera tucked neatly inside it's fat old belly. For the rest of my life I shall forever regret never being able to show any of my family or friends that amazingly-brilliant, spectacularly-awesome, first-class, top-quality, award-winning photograph that Seaman Staines had perfectly managed to capture. Hey ho, shit happens, as many folks aboard the Marovonne all too often tend to find out whilst fooling around at sea. *Still, we know the truth, don't we fellas!*

I left Nik and Kev to roll the cable back onto it's drum, clear away the mess, and throw a few buckets of seawater over the slightly bloodied decks, as I stepped back up into the wheelhouse and asked Alan to make full steam ahead please. We were only an hour behind schedule anyway, so we'd still make Lundy by around four o'clock that afternoon. I then stepped into the galley, put the kettle on, and made everyone a nice strong mug of fresh coffee. *Ah, a life on the ocean wave eh!* Not that there were anything much in the way of waves. Apart from our own wake that trailed beautifully outwards behind us, the Atlantic was more or less as flat as a pancake all the way up to Lundy Island, and after the four of us took it in turns to swap two-hour shifts at the wheel, we sailed lazily into the lee of Landing Bay, just around the corner from Rat Island off Lundy's most southerly tip, and dropped our anchor into eight fathoms of water. After carefully setting the anchor, before I switched the engine off, I called Swansea Coastguard on the VHF and announced our safe arrival at our destination, following which I fired up the 6.5KVA Deutz two-stroke diesel generator, then carried out yet another full engine room check. Shortly after we'd caught that humongous great white shark earlier on that morning, whilst deeply toying with the exciting depths of our wildest imaginations, Kevin had retrieved the RIB's fuel can from it's safe on-deck storage location, poured the last gallon of petrol into it from the can that was stashed aboard the spare dinghy, connected it to the outboard, then I'd removed the padlock and chain, attached the kill-cord, and slackened off the little boat's tethers. Some thirty minutes later, once I'd double-checked the safety of our anchorage location, and Nik and Kevin had craned the RIB down into the water, Alan was dropping the three of us off on the steeply-shelved pebbly beach at Landing Bay. Alan then ran the RIB back to the ship, secured the painter and climbed back aboard, whilst the three of us began the long, weary trek up the steep rocky pathway that led up into the luscious green fields which covered the flat-topped island some four hundred feet up above.

BATTLING WITH A HUMONGOUS GREAT WHITE SHARK

CHAPTER
THIRTY~TWO

Roughly thirty minutes later the three of us sat together at a wooden bench-seat just outside the entrance to the Marisco Tavern and allowed ourselves a few moments to get our breath back before entering the solid granite-walled establishment. The Marisco Tavern on Lundy had long since been one of my favourite locations of all time, essentially due to it's obvious affinity with the nautical fraternity, and for countless millennia it had always stood out as a beacon in the dark to many a mariner either lost or struggling through heavy weather at sea. I'd visited it on many previous occasions, and strangely enough, as may *possibly* become an integral part of the topic of my next publication, unbeknown to myself at that particular time, I was destined to visit it on yet more occasions after this one. *And not for the reasons that you might be thinking either! (Although that story can wait for the time being!)* Anyway, having got our breath back after thirty minutes of what seemed like a forty-five degree climb up the long rugged track that leads up to the Landmark Trust's jewel in it's crown, we stepped in through the rickety old wooden front door to the tavern and made our way across it's uneven flagstoned floor towards the ancient oak-panelled bar.

The place was busy, in fact far busier than I'd expected it to be, but then judging from the number of tents pitched in the outer field just beyond the walled lawns of the pub garden itself, I'd guessed that the Oldenburg must have sailed across from

Ilfracombe earlier that day and deposited a whole bunch of new tourists, the likelihood being that many of them would be collected again the following day and returned back to Bideford by the very same passenger vessel, from where they'd most likely have to get the bus back to Ilfracombe from whence they came. I knew that was often how the system worked, having done it myself on several previous occasions. So, the pub was full of grockles, *(Emmets in Cornwall, grockles in Devon!)* however, having fought our way through the crowds and reached the bar, finally, there was a face that I recognised. Shaun had been the tenanted landlord of the Marisco Tavern for several years by then, and we'd shared the pleasure of each other's company on many previous occasions during that time. I'd walked up that hill in the summer many a time to find the tavern heaving, just as we had now, as well as trudged up it through the mud and rain in the depths of winter to find the place entirely deserted. One of the things that I've always loved best about the Marisco Tavern is the fact that the front door is never locked. As a time-honoured refuge to potentially marooned sailors, the welcoming warmth of it's cosy interior remains accessible 24/7 to one and all.

I reached across the bar and shook Shaun's hand, then ordered three pints of the island's infamous Lundy Ale, home-brewed in their very own little micro-brewery housed in the big old barn next door. *'Ah, genuine Lundy Ale, it's been far too long,'* I said to Shaun, as the three of us greedily gulped down the first few mouthfuls of Lundy's delicious golden nectar. Having left Alan back aboard with a fridge stocked to overflowing with various assorted delights, and told him in no uncertain terms to help himself to whatever he fancied whilst we disappeared off ashore for a couple of beers and a bite to eat, I felt not in the slightest bit guilty come seven o'clock that evening when I ordered a rare sirloin steak with all the trimmings. Nik and Kev both followed suit, and after a *desperately* long wait, due to the overcrowded bar and the inevitably overstretched staff out in the kitchen, our delicious-looking meals finally arrived. With fresh pints of ale now sat in front of us on the rickety but adequately-solid old pine table, one that we'd managed to baggsy after another family of four had suddenly departed, the three of us tucked in to our gorgeous blood-red steaks, and some thirty minutes later not a single morsel remained between the three of us. As a matter of fact, Kevin had even robbed my very last onion ring in order to mop up the remainder of his pepper sauce, the thieving little shitbag.

Gradually the crowded little pub, with it's warren of nooks and crannies spread out around every corner, along with it's somewhat larger mezzanine dining area up above, which was brightly lit by the high, partially glazed, vaulted ceiling, began to thin out somewhat. Shortly after eight o'clock that evening many people began to trek off across the fields over towards the Old Lighthouse, halfway up Lundy's three-mile-long west coast, in order to witness, as well as probably photograph, what was looking like being yet another spectacular sunset. The sunsets over the Atlantic Ocean as witnessed from the tops of the rugged sheer cliffs along Lundy's western shoreline were very often a wondrous sight to behold, however I'd done enough wondrous sunset beholding whilst recently visiting the picturesque little island of Menorca, so I opted for yet another pint of Lundy Ale instead. I telephoned Alan aboard ship shortly before sunset, partly to ask him if he was okay, and partly to remind him to switch the masthead light on. Through a mouthful of anchovy pizza that he'd not long pulled out of the microwave, which apparently he was washing down with Coca-Cola, having opted to remain teetotal for the remainder of the night, he dutifully informed me that he had precisely zero in the way of incidents to report, and that he was more than happy watching Raiders Of The Lost Ark through the DVD player all on his lonesome. Comfortable with that knowledge I hung up and turned my attention to Shaun behind the bar, along with his two young assistant barmaids, and the tavern's one and only resident chef, who by now was sat at the far end of the bar, mopping his sweaty brow with a tea towel in between taking large gulps from a litre bottle of pure Evian spring water. Several other grockles remained drinking at the bar, but other than that the little old tavern had virtually emptied, leaving the sum total of it's four permanent staff to relax for a while after the mad early-evening clammer for hot meals had finally ceased. There were also around eight or so somewhat more dedicated customers, which happened to include the three of us, continuing to drink together in what had by now become a far more intimate environment. Whilst Shaun briefly had very little to do, his efficient young staff having already cleared up all the empties left behind by the recently-departed gaggle of nature enthusiasts, he asked me the very same question that he always asked me every time we met;

"So, how goes it with the crew of the good ship Marovonne?" he began with genuine interest. "Tell me Chris, have you stopped off this time on your way down to Padstow by any chance? Or are you on your way back from Padstow to Bristol yet again, just like you were that last time you graced our picturesque little establishment with your presence?"

"The latter of the two my friend," I replied quietly.

"Well, at least you have the ideal weather conditions for your voyage back home this time," he continued, clearly remembering the dreadful sea conditions during one of our previous visits. "Given that you must've had a pretty straightforward trip on the way up here, I don't suppose anything of interest would've happened to you along the way by any chance?"

'Haha,' I thought wickedly to myself, *'the perfect opportunity to regale the locals with tales of excitement and horror from the depths of our surrounding oceans, as well as from the obvious depths of my imagination too.'*

"Well, it's funny you should ask that Shaun," I began, addressing my captive audience with a voice filled with excitement and enthusiasm, "because it all began like this you see. Young Roger The Cabin Boy here went off to the local butcher's shop down in Padstow yesterday afternoon and came back shortly afterwards with four large bin liners full of blood, guts, entrails and assorted offal. Then shortly after we'd set sail early this morning, and left the shelter of the beautiful Camel estuary far behind in the distance, we spent a couple of miles or so just laying down a load of chum, then we baited up our shark rig and left it trailing along behind the ship ... "

I'd fully captivated the attention of every single person in the Marisco Tavern whilst I spent the next twenty minutes or so recounting the story of precisely how we'd managed to capture the world's largest-ever great white shark, rendering each of them totally speechless as I left not one single detail to their imagination, whilst at the same time placing full emphasis on the truth and accuracy of my descriptive tale of both danger and excitement, which so very nearly could've ended in tragedy and disaster.

" ... and that, dear listeners, is sadly the reason why I have no photographs available to prove it!"

"I've never heard such a complete and utter load of bullshit in my entire life," laughed Shaun after I'd finished.

"I'll have you know that Captain Pugwash here has a *degree* in bullshit," chirped up Seaman Staines, not just a little miffed at the suggestion by Shaun that I may not have been *entirely* telling the truth.

I began to laugh myself too, following Shaun's lead, then Nik and Kev both began to laugh as well, and as the three of us polished off the last of our final pints of the evening and prepared to leave, the remaining customers and staff together gradually followed suit, their laughter steadily increasing as the ridiculous impossibility of my crazy story finally began to sink in. I settled up the bill behind the bar, shook Shaun's hand once more, and after thanking him and his staff for the pleasure of their company yet again, then promising him faithfully that we'd most definitely be making yet another visit at some point during the following year, the three of us respectfully took our leave and headed off towards the top of the nasty old slope that was about to lead us back down towards the beach, just as dusk began to set in. Moments later Nik stumbled, but Kevin clumsily managed to stop him from falling; then I stumbled, and Nik skilfully managed to catch me; then Kevin stumbled, and I managed to grab the back of his shirt just before he lost his balance altogether; and that's the way we rocked, all the way back down the lumpy old track, until we finally reached the pebbly beach on the shores of Landing Bay in almost total darkness.

I dialled Alan's number on my phone, and when he finally answered I asked him to come pick us up from the beach, telling him that I'd switch my phone torch on and hold it up so that he knew exactly where to find us. Despite the fact that we were rapidly approaching low water, the Marovonne was still anchored in four fathoms some two hundred metres offshore, and somewhere between five and ten minutes later, having secured the RIB's painter back to the ship's handrail, the four of us climbed back aboard and prepared to settle in for the night. Before heading off to my cabin with the intention of having a nice peaceful lie-in the following morning, Alan asked me how we'd got on up in the Marisco Tavern. All I could tell him by way of reply was that I'd eventually succeeded in getting everyone in the bar falling about with laughter, including the three of us.

AND JUST FOR THE RECORD, IT'S PRONOUNCED *SCONE!*

CHAPTER
THIRTY~THREE

Nik knocked on my cabin door shortly after nine o'clock the following morning and told me that I really ought to come up topsides and take a look around. Ten minutes later, not only was I wide awake, fully dressed and stood up on the foredeck, but I was rubbing my eyes in disbelief at what I was staring at. *We were surrounded by sharks!* And I'm not talking about imaginary sharks, and I'm not talking about small sharks either. There were four of them altogether, and each one was getting on for half the length of our ship. They were steadily circling us, their dorsal fins sticking over a metre above the water, their huge snouts almost half that height, their mouths wide open as they sieved and swallowed cloud upon cloud of tiny krill using their massive gill-rakes. Male basking sharks, all of them over thirty feet long, and all of them most likely more than forty years old. It was the most spectacular sight to behold, and if I hadn't already lost my treasured little digital camera to a nasty, vicious, giant great white the previous morning I would've undoubtedly taken a snapshot right there and then. It's funny how you never think to take a photo whenever suddenly and unexpectedly confronted by some of nature's most spectacular sights. Still, I guess capturing that image in my mind and having it remain there forever and a day will more than suffice, simply because it's actually witnessing the experience itself that really counts.

Moments later, as I sat and relaxed in one of the small folding canvas chairs back on the aft deck, Nik served me up with a brace of freshly-caught pan-fried mackerel, perfectly filleted, and accompanied by hash browns and a scattering of wild mushrooms. Kevin then handed me a steaming hot mug of tea, and I began to wonder exactly what it was I might have done to deserve such idyllic perfection. Nik said he'd made virtually no effort whatsoever in catching the mackerel, it was almost as if they'd thrown themselves aboard in a vain attempt at avoiding the gigantic, all-consuming mouths of the four huge basking sharks that were still circling the ship on the surface of the water not fifty feet away from our hull. And what's more, there wasn't a breath of wind in the lee of Landing Bay that particular morning, as we basked in the warm early-morning Devonshire sunshine, waiting for the right moment to weigh anchor and leave. High water at Avonmouth was a little after seven o'clock that evening, so we'd aimed to take second lock back into the Cumberland Basin at six o'clock, which meant leaving our anchorage at 10am. We were already late leaving, and when a couple of young common Atlantic grey seals popped up alongside and began to gobble up our scraps as we scraped them over the side we were even later leaving. Still, eventually all good things come to an end, as they say in the movies, and immediately after Alan confirmed to me that he'd completed yet another full engine room check, and Nik confirmed that the RIB was securely lashed down onto it's cradle after he and Kev had craned it back aboard long before waking their skipper up, I fired up the engine, carefully positioned the ship's bow directly above the anchor, then gave Nik the order to winch it back aboard.

A little over two hours until slack water at low tide, by which time we should be well on our way towards Ilfracombe, after which the incoming spring tide, by my own precise calculations, should give us a speed over ground at the tide's maximum flow rate, shortly after we'd run between the middle of the Holmes and altered course towards the English & Welsh Grounds Racon Buoy, of somewhere in the region of thirteen knots. Seventy tons travelling at fifteen miles per hour. *Try stopping that ya great white bitch!* I steered the Marovonne out of the lee of Lundy's Landing Bay, pushed our speed through the water up to eight knots, settled us on a new compass heading of 092 degrees, then left Kevin sat at the wheel whilst he steered the ship halfway between Bull Point and the Horseshoe Rocks and onwards towards Ilfracombe. The south-westerly wind was blowing at roughly a force three, however it was blowing over an inflowing spring tide, which meant that everything, including us, was moving in the same direction. This of course made for an entirely flat-calm sea, with virtually nothing in the way of breeze, and as we steadily passed Foreland Point and headed up towards the Breaksea Light I sat peacefully alone up on the coachroof and watched the world go by, whilst Master Bates, Seaman Staines and Roger The Cabin Boy attended to the essentials. We altered course yet again after passing between the Holmes, and once we reached English & Welsh Grounds I decided once again to take control of the ship myself. Nik carried out one final engine room check for me, filling the day tank one last time and tweaking up the stern gland, and I asked Kev and Al well in advance to prepare our mooring lines and fenders for pulling alongside the muddy wall in the Cumberland Lock starboard-side to.

At five thirty we entered the mouth of the River Avon, and as we tracked past Avonmouth Signal Station I slowed our speed to just three knots through the water, which still equated to four knots over ground given the continuing flow of the incoming tide. As we approached Black Rock, shortly before passing under the Clifton Suspension Bridge, I called the Dockmaster on the VHF.

"City Docks Radio, City Docks Radio, this is Marovonne, do you read, over."

"Marovonne, City Docks Radio, reading you loud and clear, welcome home, over."

"City Docks, Marovonne. Thanks Bob. We're currently just east of Black Rock, is there any chance of locking us straight in, over."

"The lock's empty Chris, the gates are open and ready, come straight on in and heave your warps ashore, over."

"Roger that Bob, with you in five, Marovonne out."

I pulled the ship to a dead halt alongside the south wall half-way through the huge lock a little before 6pm, and a little over an hour before high water, whereupon Nik and Kev threw our mooring lines ashore, then Bob passed each of them through the chain rings and handed them back down to us. He then closed the lower gates and opened the top sluices, and after the lock filled, whilst the top gates were gradually dragged open by their mechanical series of iron chains, the traffic sirens began to blare, the road barriers dropped, and the massive Plimsol Bridge which carried the busy dual-carriageway high up above powered itself open and allowed us through into the Cumberland Basin. I thanked Bob the Dockmaster for his ever-helpful assistance as I manoeuvred the Marovonne through into the centre of the basin, and I kept her stationary out in the middle whilst we waited for the Plimsol Bridge to close, and then subsequently for Junction Bridge to open. No sooner had we passed through the permanently-open Junction Lock and entered the harbour itself, pottering along on tick-over at just one knot, than Baywatch Pete, one of the Harbourmaster's assistants, and all-round top geezer, pulled alongside us in a RIB very similar to our own, but with two distinct differences. Firstly it had *HARBOURMASTER* written down both sides, spelt *correctly* in large white letters, and secondly it was significantly faster than ours. Not that there was any particular relevance to that at the time, even though there had been on more than one occasion in the past! Pete pulled alongside my fully-open port-side wheelhouse door and welcomed us back into port with a genuinely warm smile. He then informed me that Roy had left his heavy, sixty-foot, steel river-trip launch, the Anthony, moored against Prince Street Wharf where my own mooring had always been, and he'd left it alongside an old wooden pontoon so that it was currently taking up *two* mooring spaces instead of just one. In all honesty this was probably a blessing in disguise, because the chances were he'd succeeded in stopping anything else from invading my own mooring location, however, as things stood, the bow of the Anthony was completely in our way, thus making it impossible for us to moor against our usual part of the quay unless it was moved. *'Hmmm, typical bloody Roy!'* I immediately thought to myself.

That said, Baywatch Pete courteously offered his assistance, and immediately sprang into action in order to single-handedly save the day. He shot ahead of us in his high-speed RIB and pulled it alongside one of the floating pontoons outside the Waterfront Tavern, just up inside St Augustine's Reach and well out of the way. Armed with both his ingenuity as well as his authority, he nimbly hopped ashore, jogged around to the stretch of Prince Street Wharf that the Anthony was moored alongside, slackened off all four of her well-wound ropes, then heaved his body against them until the Anthony, along with it's firmly attached rotten old wooden pontoon, gradually began to move backwards. He stopped heaving once the Anthony's solid iron stern was about ten feet away from Prince Street wall, leaving just about sufficient room for any little dinghies that might need to access the old flight of stone steps right in the very corner of that section of the dock, and then re-lashed all four of the Anthony's now-lengthened mooring ropes back in precisely the same place that he'd found them. *Just perfect, thank you for your generous assistance young Pete. I would've struggled to find anywhere else suitable to park a sixty-five foot ship in that part of the harbour without your help.* As we sat motionless, blocking the exit from St Augustine's Reach into the main section of the harbour whilst waiting on Pete to move the Anthony some twenty-odd feet back out of our way, Richard came steaming full speed towards us driving one of the Number Seven Ferry Boats, one hand held firmly down on the switch to the boat's exceptionally loud air-horn, the other hand gesticulating wildly out of his cabin window for us to get the hell out of his way. Firstly, that wasn't possible, I had neither the ability nor the intention of moving anywhere until I was able to pull gently alongside my own mooring space; and secondly, I knew full well that he was only trying to wind me up. With his hand still pressed firmly down oh his boat's horn-switch he steamed noisily past our stern at significantly more than the four knot speed limit, missing our tail end by a mere three feet, then continued to run his passengerless ferry out into the open expanse of harbour with a huge grin on his face, and a wicked belly-laugh that was almost as loud as the horn on the roof of his empty boat.

"Welcome home Chris," shouted Pete from the quayside, laughing himself at Richard's little ruse too, as he stood there in front of the bronze statue of John Cabot ready to take our mooring lines. I nudged the Marovonne in and out of gear and pulled her portside-to up against the quay wall, then Nik and Kev threw our bow and stern lines ashore. Pete kindly ran them through the chain rings on the quayside for us and passed them back across, then I secured them both to the fore and aft cleats myself, after which, at roughly quarter past seven that evening, I shut the engine down and asked Kevin to reconnect our shore-power cable. *Finally*, after nearly four months out of town, my beautiful little home was once again back precisely where she belonged.

BACK WHERE SHE BELONGS ON PRINCE STREET WHARF

EPILOGUE

Roughly an hour later, after I'd completed one final check down in the engine room whilst Nik, Kev and Al cleaned up right the way through, and vacuumed half a ton of sand out of the carpets, the four of us stepped ashore together, wandered the one hundred yards around the corner into Prince Street, climbed those familiar steps once again and walked in through the front door of the Shaky. Helen threw her arms around my neck and hugged me the minute I stepped through the door, and moments later Sarah copied her and did something fairly similar to Kevin. Both Nigel and Anna were working together behind the bar, and generously offered the four of us a pint each on the house, accompanied by the heartfelt words; *'Welcome home strangers'*. Brian was the next one to comment; *'Well, well, well, if it ain't them four prodigal pirates, Pugwash, Bates, Staines and the Cabin Boy',* and almost wet himself with the giggles. Guy, sat over in the corner of the Shaky's back bar in his wheelchair, literally did wet himself as he joined in with Brian's cackling and spilt at least half of his pint in his lap. I acknowledged pirates Willy and Barnabus, and affectionately laughed *with* them and not *at* them. Adrian and Alison were sat at the far end of the bar chatting to Sandy and Market Phil, and they paused their conversation long enough to welcome us home, and to ask with genuine interest as to the whereabouts of the other three ships that we'd sailed with. I sidled up to them with my arm draped around Helen's shoulder and gave them the low down as best I knew it.

"Raymondo took the Roehampton straight down to St Mary's with Jean, Jamer, Arthur and Dave aboard, in order to witness the total eclipse, and to the best of my knowledge they're still down there as we speak. Not only that, but from what I've learnt since they would've had a perfect sighting of the eclipse, which is more than I can say for the rest of us. Rick brought the Joseph down to Padstow, and Ronnie brought the Courageous back around from Falmouth, and the three of us got to see bugger-all on account of the dense cloud cover. Anyway, Rick's taken the Joseph off to St Mary's to meet up with the Roehampton, and he's got Lloyd, Derek, Will, Shabby and Little Karen with him, and as far as I know Ron and Johnnie are both still aboard the Courageous moored up down in Padstow. I would imagine Rick and Ray will probably sail back home in a day or two from now, although I suspect Ronnie'll leave the Courageous down in Padstow for a few more weeks yet like he usually does."

Little Kim had listened quietly to everything I'd said, and came over and gave me a big hug afterwards, welcoming all four of us back to normality. Rob wasn't in there with her, not that they were attached to each other in any way, but as I understood it he'd had a radio interview to conduct at the time for BBC Radio Bristol, which was clearly far more important than a Sunday evening in the pub! Long Tom was sat at the bar, and listened to my précis of the current state of play with interest. He shook my hand after I'd finished, informing me that Catriona wasn't with him because she worked behind the bar in the Nova Scotia on Sunday evenings. He also informed me, much to my envy, that him and Cat had witnessed a perfect sighting of the eclipse when they'd driven down to visit Little Dave and Jo, who were both still working down in Falmouth at the time, and had Ronnie managed to ride his luck a little better he would've stayed on a bit longer instead of trekking back around to Padstow. *Hey ho, like I said, shit happens!*

Not long after that Big Mike walked in with little Bogart the terrier, followed not long afterwards by Robnoxious, accompanied as always by Mostin the five-stone Irish Potato Hound. After a brief struggle to keep the two mutts separated from each other, Rob elected to leash Mostin in the back bar whilst Mike elected to leash Bogey around the front, and Nigel served Mike whilst Anna served

Rob. Alan and Kevin wandered around to the front bar to chat with Big Mike, Helen and myself got deeply embroiled in a conversation about the eclipse with Robnoxious, whilst Nik popped outside to Prince Street and wandered back in five minutes later with yet another plastic traffic cone for Mostin to chew up.

"So, how goes it with the crew of the good ship Marovonne?" Anna asked me during a brief lull in the conversation. "I don't suppose anything of interest happened to you during your voyage back home by any chance? I mean, come on now Chris, you've usually got a good story or three to tell, have you not?"

'Haha,' I thought wickedly to myself, *'the perfect opportunity to regale our gathered group of friends with yet more TRUE tales of excitement and horror from the depths of our surrounding oceans.'*

"D'you know, it's funny you should ask that Anna," I began, addressing my captive audience with a voice filled with excitement and enthusiasm, "because something *extremely* dramatic most definitely did happen to us on the way from Padstow to Lundy Island. It all began like this you see. Young Roger The Cabin Boy here went off to the local butcher's shop ..."

I now had the full attention of every single person in the back bar of the Shakespeare Tavern, and I spent the next twenty minutes or so recounting the story of precisely how we'd managed to capture the world's largest-ever great white shark, rendering each and every one of them entirely speechless as I captivated them by leaving not one single detail to their imagination. I'd placed great emphasis on the truth and accuracy of my descriptive tale of danger and excitement, which, as I made blatantly obvious, could so easily have ended in disaster and tragedy.

" ... and that, dear listeners, is sadly the reason why I have no photographs available to prove it."

"I've never heard such a complete and utter load of bullshit in my entire life," laughed Nigel from behind the bar after I'd finished.

"I'll have you know that Captain Pugwash here has a first-class honours degree in bullshit," chirped up Robnoxious, as he spilt a little of his ale over Mostin whilst beginning to laugh uncontrollably, along with everyone else gathered around me in the back bar.

I raised my hand, and held it there until silence returned to the room once again, then in honour of the multi-talented Master Mariner himself, I screwed my eyes up, crossed my fingers, and bravely shouted;

"LETTING GO AFT!"

Christopher John Reason

THE SHAKESPEARE TAVERN, PRINCE STREET, BRISTOL

COMMERCIAL ACKNOWLEDGEMENTS

Bristol City Council Leisure Services *(Richard, Geoff & Pete)*

Port Of Bristol Authority *(Bob)*

Number Seven Ferryboats *(Richard)*

Curtis & Pape of Looe in Cornwall

Gardner Marine Engineering

Swansea Coastguard

Padstow Harbour Commissionaires *(Malcolm & Steve)*

The Old Red Oss & The Blue Ribbon Oss *(Their Mayers, Musicians, MC's, Teasers & Loyal Followers)*

Padstow Passenger Vessels *(Jubilee Queen, Black Tor, Jaws, Thunder, Sea Fury & The Water Taxi)*

Padstow Harbour Seasonal Fairground

St Austell Brewery *(The Custom House, The Shipwright's, The Golden Lion, The Harbour Inn, The Padstow Institute, The Rock Inn, The Ship Inn in Wadebridge)*

Padstow Eateries *(The Prawn On The Lawn, Cally's Oyster Bar, St Petroc's Bistro, The Quayside Café, Padstow Fish & Chip Café, Rick Stein's Seafood Restaurant, Granny's Pasties, The Rest A While Tea Gardens near Lellizzick)*

HMS Dasher *(Lieutenant Sue Moore and her crew)*

HMCC Vigilant *(Her skipper and crew)*

Halfords

Supasnaps

Padstow Fishermen *(Phil Britts & The Blue Fox)*

Printed Publications *(Total Eclipse Of The Sun by Pam Hine)*

The Landmark Trust *(Lundy Island)*

The Marisco Tavern *(Shaun & his staff)*

The National Coastwatch Institution

Bristol Eateries *(The Olive Shed, The Raj in King Street, The Nova Scotia Pub & Hotel)*

And last but by no means least, The RNLI, just for always being there to rely on!

PERSONAL
ACKNOWLEDGEMENTS

Nigel & Anna and their staff and customers at the Shakespeare Tavern *(Lorna, Adrian, Alison, Brian, Guy, Phil, Sandy, Mike & Bogart, Rob & Mostin)*

My own crew aboard the Marovonne *(Nik, Kevin, Alan, Rue & Alf)*

Rick and his crew aboard the Joseph *(Lloyd, Kim, Cathy, Will, Derek, Mel, Nikki, Giles, Karen, Shabby, Dave & Jo, Ben & Karen)*

Ray and his crew aboard the Roehampton *(Jean, Jamer, Dave, Arthur & Shiela)*

Ron & Johnnie aboard the Courageous 2

Tom & Catriona aboard the Kathleen B

Rob & Kim aboard the Clair de Lune

Wylde Green *(Black Jack Davey, Paul & Kate)*

Visitors to the party *(Benny, Helen & Sarah)*

Work colleagues *(Tony & Roland)*

AUTHOR'S NOTE

Thank you for taking the time to read May Day Mayhem, I do hope you enjoyed it. If you did, you might also like to give my first two books a try, both of which contain even more truly-honest and accurately-documented misadventure stories, almost as bad as this one!

The Phoenix and The Lundy Misadventure, both available now from Amazon Bookstore.

Most of all I'd like to thank my wonderful wife Helen for her patience, and my three amazing children, Michelle, Tori & Alex, for their encouragement, without all four of whom none of these books would even have been possible. Mind you, I've got a horrible feeling that my forth book will probably involve even more alcohol than the contents of my third one just has!

IN LOVING MEMORY OF VERY CLOSE FRIENDS SADLY NO LONGER WITH US

Lloyd *'Master Mariner'* Roberts

Nikolas *'Nik'* Payne

John *'Tankman Jamer'* James

Anna Lucas

Thomas *'Will'* Williams

John '*Johnnie*' Fox

Alfred '*Alf*' Smith

'*Little*' Kim Gardner

'*Big*' Mike Smith

Sandra '*Sandy*' Allen

Guy '*Barnabus*' Rogers

Brian '*Willy*' Rees

Robert '*Robnoxious*' Sapsford

Arthur Ellis

Roy Mildon

Mostin the dog

Bogart the dog

TS Roehampton

MV Courageous 2

To each and every one of you, man, woman, beast or ship, I hereby raise my glass.

THE END

Printed in Poland
by Amazon Fulfillment
Poland Sp. z o.o., Wrocław